Ophthalmic Research

Journal for Research in Experimental and Clinical Ophthalmology

Founded 1970 by O. Hockwin, Bonn, G. Naumann, Hamburg and D.F. Cole, London

KARGER

Printed in Switzerland on acid-free paper by Reinhardt Druck, Basel

Appears bimonthly: 1 volume per year (6 issues)

Ophthalmic Research

Guidelines for Authors

Submission

Only original papers written in English are considered and should be sent to:

Dr. Gijs F.J.M. VRENSEN
Department of Morphology
The Netherlands Ophthalmic
Research Institute (NORI)
Meibergdreef 9
1105 AZ Amsterdam
(The Netherlands)
Telephone (020) 566 44 28
Telefax (020) 691 65 21

Manuscripts should be submitted in triplicate (with three sets of illustrations of which one is an original), typewritten double-spaced on one side of the paper, with a wide margin.

Aims and Scope

'Ophthalmic Research' is meant as an international forum for the dissemination of peer-reviewed information on all aspects of basic research in the field of ophthalmology and visual sciences without refraining from publishing clinical research papers. It specifically aims to elucidate the healthy and pathological functioning of the eye and visual system using the full range of biological, physical and epidemiological research methods.

Types of Papers

(1) The main body of papers to be published will be *'Original Papers'* on experimental research. (2) *'Review Papers'* of up to 30 manuscript pages will be published from invited authors and by direct submission. In both cases the manuscripts will be subject to peer reviewing. Review papers will be published free of charge. (3) *'Short Communications'* of up to 3–4 pages dealing with new original concepts or technical approaches will be published on short notice. (4) *'Ophthalmic Research'* has a tradition in publishing *'Supplements'* which can be published under the responsibility of guest editors. Requests for such supplements should be addressed to the managing editor.

Conditions

All manuscripts are subjected to editorial review. Manuscripts are received with the explicit understanding that they are not under simultaneous consideration by any other publication except an abstract. Submission of an article for publication implies the transfer of the copyright from the author to the publisher upon acceptance. Accepted papers become the permanent property of 'Ophthalmic Research' and may not be reproduced by any means, in whole or in part, without the written consent of the publisher. It is the author's responsibility to obtain permission to reproduce illustrations, tables, etc. from other publications.

Arrangement

Title page: The first page of each paper should indicate the title (main title underlined), the authors' names, and the institute where the work was conducted. A short title for use as running head as well as the full address of the author to whom correspondence should be sent are also required.

Full address: The exact postal address complete with postal code must be given at the bottom of the title page. Please also supply phone and fax numbers, as well as your e-mail address.

Key words: For indexing purposes, a list of 3–10 key words in English is essential.

Abstract: Each paper needs an abstract of up to 10 lines.

Small type: Paragraphs which can or must be set in smaller type (case histories, test methods, etc.) should be indicated with a 'p' (petit) in the margin on the left-hand side.

Footnotes: Avoid footnotes. When essential, they are numbered consecutively and typed at the foot of the appropriate page.

Tables and illustrations: Tables and illustrations (both numbered in Arabic numerals) should be prepared on separate sheets. Tables require a heading and figures a legend, also prepared on a separate sheet. For the reproduction of illustrations, only good drawings and original photographs can be accepted; negatives or photocopies cannot be used. Due to technical reasons, figures with a screen background should not be submitted. When possible, group several illustrations on one block for reproduction (max. size 144 × 196 mm) or provide crop marks. On the back of each illustration, indicate its number, the author's name, and 'top' with a soft pencil. Photographs of microscopic preparations should be labeled with the magnification scale, e.g. 1 μm.

Color illustrations: Up to 6 color illustrations per page can be integrated with the text at the reduced price of CHF 660.–/USD 545.00 per page. Color illustrations are reproduced at the author's expense.

References: In the text identify references by Arabic numerals [in square brackets]. Material submitted for publication but not yet accepted should be noted as 'unpublished data' and not be included in the reference list. The list of references should include only those publications which are cited in the text. Do not alphabetize; number references in the order in which they are first mentioned in the text. The surnames of the authors followed by initials should be given. There should be no punctuation other than a comma to separate the authors. Cite all authors, 'et al' is not sufficient. Abbreviate journal names according to the Index Medicus system. (Also see International Committee of Medical Journal Editors: Uniform requirements for manuscripts submitted to biomedical journals. Br Med J 1988;296:401–405.)

Examples

(a) Papers published in periodicals: Sun J, Koto H, Chung KF: Interaction of ozone and allergen challenges on bronchial responsiveness and inflammation in sensitised guinea pigs. Int Arch Allergy Immunol 1997;112:191–195.

(b) Monographs: Matthews DE, Farewell VT: Using and Understanding Medical Statistics, ed 3, revised. Basel, Karger, 1996.

(c) Edited books: Parren PWHI, Burton DR: Antibodies against HIV-1 from phage display libraries: Mapping of an immune response and progress towards antiviral immunotherapy; in Capra JD (ed): Antibody Engineering. Chem Immunol. Basel, Karger, 1997, vol 65, pp 18–56.

Page charges

There is no page charge for papers of 3 or fewer printed pages (including tables, illustrations and references). Each additional complete or partial page is charged to the author at CHF 520.–/USD 433.00/DEM 650.–. The allotted size of a paper is equal to approx. 8 manuscript pages (including tables, illustrations and references). Authors of manuscripts that will exceed this allotted size are requested to submit, together with the manuscript, a written statement of their willingness to accept page charges.

Galley proofs

Unless indicated otherwise, galley proofs are sent to the first-named author and should be returned with the least possible delay. Alterations made in galley proofs, other than the correction of printer's errors, are charged to the author. No page proofs are supplied.

Reprints

Order forms and a price list are sent with the galley proofs. Orders submitted after the issue is printed are subject to considerably higher prices.

KARGER

Fax +41 61 306 12 34
E-Mail karger@karger.ch
www.karger.com

The Guidelines for Authors are available at:
www.karger.com/journals/ore/oreinst.htm

Ophthalmic Research

General Information

Publication data: 'Ophthalmic Research' is published 6 times annually. Volume 30 with 6 issues appears in 1998.

Subscription rates: Subscriptions run for a full calendar year. Prices are given per volume.

Personal subscription:
Subscription + postage and handling
CHF 332.– + CHF 23.50 Europe
CHF 332.– + CHF 35.50 Overseas
USD 261.00 + USD 23.50
(Must be in the name of, billed to, and paid by an individual. Order must be marked 'personal subscription'.)

Institutional subscription:
Subscription + postage and handling
CHF 664.– + CHF 29.40 Europe
CHF 664.– + CHF 44.40 Overseas
USD 522.00 + USD 29.40

Airmail postage: CHF 36.–, USD 30.00.
(Extra per volume.)

Discount subscription prices:
Association for Eye Research;
Association for Research and Vision in Ophthalmology.

Microforms: Please direct all enquiries and orders to: University Microfilms Inc.
300 North Zeeb Road, P.O. Box 1346
Ann Arbor, MI 48106-1346 (USA)

Subscription orders: Orders can be placed at agencies, bookstores, directly with the
Publisher S. Karger AG, P.O. Box,
CH–4009 Basel (Switzerland)
or with any of the following distributors:
Deutschland: S. Karger GmbH, Postfach
D–79095 Freiburg
France: Librairie Luginbühl
36, bd de Latour-Maubourg
F–75007 Paris
Great Britain, Ireland: S. Karger Publishers
58 Grove Hill Road
Tunbridge Wells, Kent TN1 1SP
USA: S. Karger Publishers, Inc.
26 West Avon Road, P.O. Box 529
Farmington, CT 06085
India, Bangladesh, Sri Lanka:
S. Karger India Subscription Agency
B–5/132 Safdarjung Enclave
New Delhi-110029
Japan: Katakura Libri, Inc.
Take 1 Bldg, 2nd Floor
4-5-7 Yushima, Bunkyo-ku
Tokyo 113

Change of address: Both old and new address should be sent to the subscription source.

Single issues and back volumes: Information can be obtained through the Publisher.

Advertising: Correspondence and rate requests should be addressed to the Publisher.

Bibliographic indices: This journal is regularly listed in bibliographic services, including *Current Contents®*.

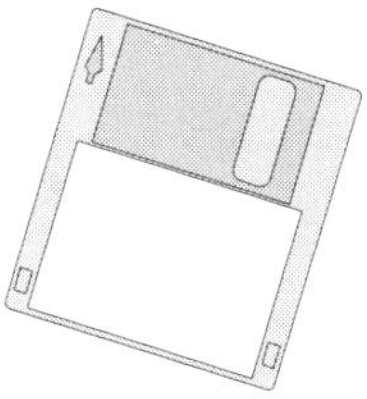

Disk Submission

A **comprehensive version** of these guidelines for the **submission of manuscripts and illustrations on disk** can be accessed online under **www.karger.com/journals/disk_mai.htm** or requested as a leaflet from the editorial department.

Please follow the general rules on style and arrangement in the **"Guidelines for Authors"** of the journal. Submit a **double-spaced printout** of your manuscript matching the file on disk exactly.

Technical Information

Store only data pertinent to this manuscript. Include your fonts (screen and printer fonts for Macintosh).
For a **text only** manuscript, use a 3.5 inch disk. For **text and illustrations,** use 3.5 or 5.25 Magneto Optical Disc; CD-ROM (DOS or hybrid); iomage Zip/DOS (100 MB), or 44 MB, 88 MB or 200 MB SyQuest. Compress extensive data using ZIP format.

Data Description

Label your disk with the **title of the journal or book** for which it is submitted; a **short version** of the paper's title; your **name,** postal and e-mail address, fax and phone number; **hard and software** used, including the version; and the **complete list of the file names.** File names consist of eight characters before the dot identifying the file and three characters after the dot identifying the application.

Text and Format

The **preferred word-processing package is MS-Word.** Other commonly used PC text programs and ASCII formats are accepted.
Update your data when you revise subsequent to the reviewer's or editor's decision and mark revisions clearly. Manuscripts accepted for publication are subject to **copy editing:** changes and/or questions will be marked in the manuscript, which will be returned to you with your disk and the galley proofs for checking.
Enter your text continuously flush left. Do not use any layout functions. Do not split words at the end of a line. **Do not use indentations.** Use a blank line before and a hard return at the end of paragraphs. **Arrange headings flush left.** Insert only **one space after punctuation marks.** Insert Greek letters, mathematical symbols etc. with your word-processing program. Use **boldface and italics** as well as sub- and superscript where appropriate. **Tables are part of the text** and should be placed at the end of the text file. Separate the individual parts of a table by lines. Use the tabulator instead of spaces. Format operation data on one line in the same column. **Legends to illustrations are part of the text** and should also be listed at the end of the text file.

Illustrations

Store illustrations as separate files: do not embed them in your text. Export **line drawings/vector graphics** as TIF, EPS or WMF format. Use Photoshop for processing and retouching **scanned half-tone images.** Save the original scan and the processed version. Export **black and white or color images** as TIF or EPS format in their anticipated size in print.
For detailed information on how to submit illustration data on disk please consult the leaflet or **www.karger.com/journals/disk_mai.htm.**

KARGER

Fax + 41 61 306 12 34
E-Mail karger@karger.ch
www.karger.com

The Journal Home Page is available at:
www.karger.com/journals/ore

KI 98 DISK

KARGER

S. Karger
Medical and Scientific Publishers
Basel · Freiburg · Paris · London
New York · New Delhi · Bangkok
Singapore · Tokyo · Sydney

Drug Dosage
The authors and the publisher have exerted every effort to ensure that drug selection and dosage set forth in this text are in accord with current recommendations and practice at the time of publication. However, in view of ongoing research, changes in government regulations, and the constant flow of information relating to drug therapy and drug reactions, the reader is urged to check the package insert for each drug for any change in indications and dosage and for added warnings and precautions. This is particularly important when the recommended agent is a new and/or infrequently employed drug.

Printed in Belgium by
Drukkerij van der Poorten n.v., Kessel-Lo
ISBN 3–8055–6794–4

Ophthalmic Research

EVER

European Association for Vision and Eye Research

Abstracts

October 7–10, 1998
Palma de Mallorca, Spain

Guest Editor
L. Missotten, Leuven, Belgium

KARGER

Basel · Freiburg · Paris · London · New York · New Delhi · Bangkok · Singapore · Tokyo · Sydney

EVER

European Association for Vision and Eye Research

Joint European Research Meeting in Ophthalmology and Vision

October 7-10, 1998, Palma de Mallorca, Spain

ABSTRACT BOOK

Table of Contents

About EVER

EVER, the EUROPEAN Association for VISION and EYE RESEARCH was formed in the fall of 1997 as a result of collaborative efforts by several European Ophthalmic research associations. It is important to note that the Association for Eye Research (AER), the European Community Ophthalmic Research Association (ECORA), and the Joint European Research Meetings in Ophthalmology and Vision (JERMOV) have given up their own identities and collectively joined EVER. Within a few months the membership of EVER has grown to over 1.000. EVER is a non-profit organisation. The aims of the Association shall be to encourage research and the dissemination of knowledge concerning the eye and vision by means of meetings, publications and exchange activities. Membership of EVER is open to individuals of any nationality engaging in or with an interest in ophthalmic and vision research. Membership forms and a copy of the constitution can be obtained from the secretariat. The association is divided in scientific sections. There are at present eleven Scientific Sections, representing major areas of research. In time the number of sections may grow. Any group within EVER may, in any case, propose and organise Symposia and Workshops or other activities within the meetings of EVER, which will be held every year in the first half of October.
Other Societies such as the European chapter of the International Society of Clinical Electrophysiology of Vision (ISCEV), the Ophthalmic Oncology Group, the European Eye Bank Association (EEBA) and the European Cornea Conference co-operate in this year's joint meeting, continuing the tradition which started at the 1994 JERMOV in Montpellier.
Secretariat EVER: Postbus 74, B-3000 Leuven. Fax ++32 16 33 67 85

The complete schedule of the sessions is available on the **Web site**: www.ever.be

ABSTRACTS

The abstracts are arranged in order of their numbers in the programme book. Abstracts of posters have three-digit numbers. They are grouped according to subject. Abstracts of oral presentations have four-digit numbers and are arranged per session.

The abstracts are photographic reductions of the submitted abstract forms. The authors are sole responsible for their contents.

Outlines new experimental approaches

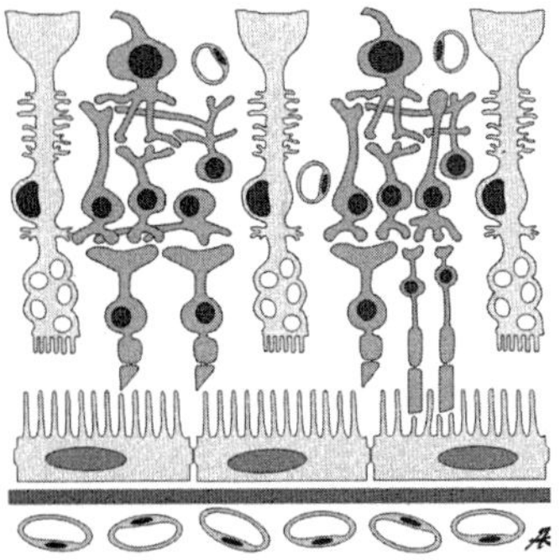

Diseases of the Retina

Editors: Peter Wiedemann, Leon Kohen

This collection of papers presents new experimental approaches in the pathophysiology, diagnosis and treatment of macular and retinal diseases. Two different techniques are described which aim to restore vision in the macular area. Transplantation into the subretinal space is a possibility that is now starting to have clinical applications. For the first time German government funded projects using a prosthesis in the macula are described, including the preliminary experimental results. The role of gene therapy is also discussed by leading international experts and readers will find new knowledge about the biology of Müller cells and choroidal circulation. This publication will be of immense value not only to all academic rcti nologists but also to ophthalmologists with a keen interest in future developments in the field.

Contents

Ophthalmic Research
Editor: Vrensen, G.F.J.M. (Amsterdam)
ISSN 0030–3747
Special issue: Vol. 29, No. 5 (1997)
Included in subscription

Fields of Interest: Ophthalmology; Transplantation, Diabetes, Prosthetics

Diseases of the Retina
New Approaches in the Diagnosis and Therapy of Macular and Retinal Diseases,
Leipzig, November 1996
Editors: Wiedemann, P.; Kohen, L. (Leipzig)
124 p., 55 fig., 4 in color, 5 tab., soft cover, 1997
CHF 58.– / DEM 69.– / USD 50.50
Prices subject to change
DEM price for Germany, USD price for USA only
ISBN 3–8055–6577–1

KI 97474

KARGER

Posters

101

PROJECTIONS FROM THE MESENCEPHALIC TRIGEMINAL NUCLEUS TO THE VESTIBULAR NUCLEI AND THE CEREBELLUM : AN ANATOMICAL SUBSTRATE THAT MAY BE INVOLVED IN THE VESTIBULO-OCULAR REFLEX ADAPTATION

BOURCIER F, [1,3] PINGANAUD G, [2] BUISSERET-DELMAS C,[2] and BUISSERET P [3]
1. Dept of Ophthalmology, CHU de Tours, France. 2. JE 2159, Neuroanatomie Fonctionnelle des Systèmes Sensorimoteurs, Université Paris VII 3. Laboratoire d'Anatomie Comparée, Museum National d'Histoire Naturelle, Paris, France.

Purpose The mesencephalic trigeminal nucleus (Me5) contains somata of first order neurons associated with the proprioceptors of extraocular muscles (EOM). Projections from the Me5 to the medial vestibular nucleus and to the vestibulo-cerebellum have been demonstrated. However it is important to determine 1) if a single Me5 neuron project to vestibular nuclei (VN) and vestibulo-cerebellum, 2) if Me5 neurons project to other VN, 3) and vestibular nuclei project to the Me5.
Methods VN were injected with retrograde and/or anterograde transported tracers (HRP, HRP-gold complex, fluorochromes and biotinylated dextran amine) in 11 rats and both in VN and cerebellum in 4 rats.
Results Some neurons of the caudal Me5 send simultaneously the same information to the VN and the vestibulo-cerebellum. Me5 neurons project to medial VN but also to the inferior vestibular nucleus (IVN). In turn, these neurons receive afferences from medial VN and IVN.
Conclusion The vestibulo-ocular reflex could thus be generated through VN and regulated by the vestibulo-cerebellum. Therefore, the present anatomical connections could be the pathways of an involvement of EOM proprioceptors in vestibulo-ocular reflex.

102

The Amilorid Sodium Sensitive Channel in Retina

Golestaneh N., Nicolas C. Ferrari P., Agarwal M.K., Mirshahi M.
INSERM U 86, 15 rue de l'Ecole de Médecine 75006 Paris

Purpose: Ion and fluid transport regulation mechanisms play a prominent role in the maintenance of several physiological processes in the eye that include aqueus humor secretion and intraocular pressure, hydratation, transparency of cornea and the lens and photoreceptor function. We studied the presence of the Amilorid Sodium Sensitive Channel (ASSC) in sequential development of rat retina at days 2 and 15.
Methods: Western blot and immunohistochemistry analysis were performed using a polyclonal antiserum raised against the 14 amino acid peptide corresponding to the region 44-58 of the α subunit of this protein cloned from rat colon. RT-PCR analysis of retina mRNA followed by sequence analysis was assessed using the specific MCR primers.
Results: *Immunoblotting with the polyclonal anti-ASSC serum,* revealed a major band of 82-86 kDa in extracts prepared from whole rat. retina. Immunohistochemistry, using the ASSC-specific antiserum, revealed strong fluorescence in pigmented epithelium *and ganglion layers at days 2 and in photoreceptor layer and* inner nuclear layers at days 4. At days 13 and adult rat retina, specific areas in the inner and outer segments of photoreceptor were stained. The expression of the ASSC in the rat retina in sequential events of development were confirmed with a predicted 520 bp having 100% homology with rat kidney ASSC.
Conclusion: This widespread distribution of the ASSC generally colocalizes with the mineralocorticoid receptor, such that steroid hormone-mediated ion regulation would appear to add a new parameter in the functional expression of ocular tissues. Aided in part by financial assistance of AFRP.

103

Mitochondrial Abnormalities is Diseased Human Retinas

FEHER J., PAPALE A., SARKOZY A., BALACCO GABRIELI C.
Program for Ophthalmic Neuroscience, Institute of Ophthalmology, University of Rome "La Sapienza", Rome, Italy.

Pupose: Mitochondrial alterations play a crucial role in the pathogenesis of several diseases. The aim of these studies was to describe basic ultrastructural changes of retinal mitochondria in various eye diseases and correlate these abnormalities with the clinical pictures.
Methods: Fifty-two human retinas were studies with transmission electron microscopy. The eyes were enucleated in the early eightieth due to intraocular tumor, absolute glaucome of various origin or severe injuries.
Results: Three main types of mitochondrial alterations were observed: (1) proliferation of the mitochondrial cristae, which was usually associated with enlargement of the mitochondria and with the appearence of intramitochondrial proteinous crystals or lipofuscine granules; (2) normal size or slightly swollen mitochondria with highly damaged cristae, and finally (3) large mitochondria with poor cristae and electronlucent matrix.
Conclusions: Mitochondrial changes were found in the RPE-photoreceptor complex and in the inner retinal layers.These abnormalities may be correlated either with the metabolic burnst or with the cell damage due to proliferative or degenerative retinal disease, respectively.This is the first ultrastructural presentation of the retinal mitochondriopathy.

104

SPATIAL RELATIONSHIPS BETWEEN MOSAICS OF NEURONS IN TURTLE RETINA.

Cuenca N,[1] Solessio E,[2] Anastasopoulos G,[2] and Kolb H.[2]
1. Biotechnology Dept., Univ. Alicante, Alicante, Spain.
2. Moran Eye Center, Univ. Utah, Salt Lake City, USA.

Purpose: To understand the organization of neural populations that might have circuitry relationships in the vertebrate retina.
Methods: We have studied mosaics of colocalizing immunoreactive (IR) neurons in turtle retinal wholemounts by laser confocal microscopy. Flourescently labeled antibodies to calcium binding proteins, γ-aminobutyric acid (GABA) and choline acetyltransferase (CHAT) have been used. The resulting immunostained mosaics are quantitated by nearest neighbor and cross correlation statistics.
Results: Two mosaics of amacrine cells are calbindin-IR, colocalize CHAT and are strongly cross correlated. Two populations of horizontal cells and a normally placed and a displaced amacrine population are calretinin-IR. The H1 cells and the displaced amacrine cells are highly cross correlated. Calbindin bipolar cell populations and a normally placed and a displaced population of CHAT-IR amacrine cells are also in a close mosaic relationship.
Conclusions: A relationship between two or more mosaics of neurons containing calcium binding proteins seems to exist in turtle retina and may indicate a common developmental ancestry and a related neural circuitry. We suspect the same is true in other vertebrate retinas.
Supported by EY04355, EY05972, Research to Prevent Blindness and DGICYT PB94-1501.

105

LOCALIZATION OF AMPA-TYPE GLUTAMATE RECEPTOR SUBUNITS IN THE GOLDFISH RETINA

Kamphuis W., Vandenbranden C., and Kamermans M.
Netherlands Ophthalmic Research Institute and Graduate School for the Neurosciences Amsterdam (Amsterdam, The Netherlands)

Purpose Excitatory synaptic communication in the retina is mainly driven by the neurotransmitter glutamate through activation of different classes of glutamate receptors (GluR) with distinct properties regarding desensitization and calcium conductance. The distribution of the AMPA-type ionotropic GluR subunits in the goldfish retina was investigated using in situ hybridization and immunohistochemistry.
Methods Goldfish retinas were immersion fixed for 10 min in 4% PFA. Cryosections were incubated with antibodies specific for subunits of the AMPA- (GluR-1, -2/3 ,-4). The distribution of the AMPA-class subunit encoding transcripts was investigated using riboprobes from rat and goldfish cDNAs.
Results GluR1 was detected in some ganglion and amacrine cellbodies and was present in fine filaments in the outer nuclear layer. GluR2/3 was found in the outer plexiform layer. GluR4 was present in Müller cells and in a punctate pattern in the outer plexiform layer. The in situ hybridizations confirmed the differential expression in the retina.
Conclusions These results show that the GluR-subunits are differentially expressed in the goldfish retina indicating a functional diversity of AMPA-type GluR mediated synaptic communication in the retina.

106

ISOLATED RABBIT CONE PHOTORECEPTORS LABELED WITH OPSIN SPECIFIC ANTIBODIES

FIGARO A, HUEMER K-H and GLÖSMANN M.
Dept. of General & Comparative Physiology,
University of Vienna Medical School (Austria)

Purpose: Mammalian photoreceptor cells have been well characterized both in wholemounts and slices. Among isolated cells only rods have been described. We have developed a dissociation procedure that allows a distinction between isolated rod and cone photoreceptors. The classification of these cell types was also confirmed by immunolabeling.
Methods: Rabbit retinal cells were dissociated by enzymatic treatment of isolated retinae and subsequent trituration. Cells were kept in modified culture medium for further characterization. Cell viability was verified by Trypan blue exclusion. Isolated cells were fixated for labeling with antibodies against cone opsins.
Results: The majority (about 90%) of the photoreceptors showed typical rodlike features like cylindrical inner segment and small cell body. This allowed classification of rods even when outer segments or synaptic spherules were damaged by the dissociation. Some photoreceptors displayed distinctive attributes like large inner segments with discrete ellipsoid and myoid regions and large somata and nuclei.
All the cone opsin positive photoreceptors displayed the same features as this small population of the viable photoreceptors.
Conclusions: Both morphological features and immunolabeling data confirm that the small population represents the cone photoreceptors in rabbit retina.

107

PLASTICITY OF SYNAPTIC RIBBON AND SYNAPTIC VESICLE DENSITY IN PHOTORECEPTOR TERMINAL AFTER SHORT-TERM DARK-ADAPTATION

(GARCÍA M, GUARDIOLA J.V., and DE JUAN J.) Departamento de Biotecnología, Universidad de Alicante, Alicante, Spain.

Purpose. Cone pedicles and rod spherules contain electron-dense ribbons perpendicular to the synaptic cleft. It has been reported that rods contain one or two synaptic ribbon (S.R.) whereas the number varies greatly in cones depending of the spectral cone type. Also it has been reported that they show dynamic changes according to the environmental lighting conditions. The aim of this work is double. First, to determine changes in number and length of synaptic ribbon and synaptic vesicle density after short-term light and dark adaptation. Second, to study if there are differences between different species of teleost. **Methods.** *Dicentrarchus labrax* and *Sparus auratus* were dark- and light-adapted for 1h at noon. The retinas were processed by transmission electron microscopy and the number and length of S.R. per pedicle and synaptic vesicle density were measured. **Results.** In both species, about 70% of spherules contain one S.R. whereas the 30% lack of them in all lighting conditions. No differences were observed in length. In *S. auratus*, the number and length of pedicle S.R. were unaffected by the lighting conditions. In *D. Labrax,* number and length of pedicle S.R. in dark-adapted fish showed a strikingly decrease to about 50% and 40%, respectively compared to light-adapted animals. In both species, the density of synaptic vesicles in two types of terminals showed a significative increase after dark-adaptation: to about 50% in *S. auratus*, and to about 25% in *D. labrax.* **Conclusions.** The observation of two types of spherules, with zero or one ribbon, suggests the possible existence of two types of rods. In *S. auratus*, the number and length of pedicle S.R. seems to be independent of lighting conditions, whereas *D. labrax* exhibits a marked plasticity dependent of exogenous stimuli. Finally, the densities of synaptic vesicles show identical increase in cone pedicles and rod spherules in the dark-adapted state. Supported by GV-2521/94 and DGICYT PB 96 0414.

108

EFFECT OF THE OPTIC NERVE SECTION ON THE INNER PLEXIFORM LAYER OF THE RETINA

GERMAIN F, CALVO M & DE LA VILLA P.
Dept. of Physiology, Universidad de Alcalá, Madrid (Spain)

Purpose To study the structural changes of the inner plexiform layer (IPL) following axotomy of the retinal ganglion cells (RGCs).
Methods The experiments were performed in control and axotomized retinas (7, 14, 21 days after the optic nerve section (ONS)). Immunocytochemistry against the α and γ subunits of the $GABA_A$ receptors was performed and the organization of the IPL was studied. Further ultrastructural details on RGCs and IPL were analized by scanning electron microscope (SEM).
Results Axotomized RGCs showed blebs on its surface. Both, the transverse sections at the SEM and the inmunocytochemistry showed a decrease of the cells in the ganglion cell layer and a significant reduction of the thickness of the IPL with a remarcable disorganization of its typical stratification. A decrease in the cellular contain of the inner nuclear layer was also observed.
Conclusion After ONS, the surviving RGCs have quantitative and qualitative changes in their dendritic processes determining a disorganization of the IPL and possibly a new functional organization.

109

IDENTIFICATION AND COMPARISON OF ASTROCYTOSIS IN THE TRAUMATISED AND GLAUCOMATOUS HUMAN OPTIC NERVE HEAD

NEEDHAM AD, BROTCHIE D, WARDROP DRA and GRIERSON I.
Unit of Ophthalmology, University of Liverpool (U.K.)

Purpose To identify tectonic and immunological markers suitable for demonstrating reactive astrocytosis. To utilise these markers to compare the distribution, morphology and number of activated astrocytes in traumatised and glaucomatous human optic nerve heads (ONHs).
Methods Longitudinal sections of frozen and fixed human ONHs were processed with either a modified haematoxylin stain or immunological markers to known components of the astrocyte cytoskeleton, particularly GFAP.
Results In contrast to the normals, the modified haematoxylin stain localised cell processes within the traumatised and glaucomatous ONHs. Analysis of adjacent sections labelled for GFAP suggested these processes belonged to activated, hypertrophic astrocytes with increased GFAP expression.
Conclusions Modified haematoxylin staining in conjunction with immunolocalisation of GFAP provides a more accurate technique for identifying astrocytosis than localisation of GFAP alone. The combined use of these procedures will increase our understanding of the maximal site and role of astrocytosis in glaucoma.

110

QUANTITATIVE ESTIMATIONS OF FOVEAL AND NONFOVEAL RETINAL CIRCUITY IN HUMANS

SJÖSTRAND J[1], POPOVIC Z[1] and CONRADI N[2].
1. Institute of Clinical Neuroscience, Departement of Ophthalmology, Göteborg University (Sweden)
2. Institute of Laboratory Medicine, Department of Pathology, Göteborg University, (Sweden)

Purpose. In agreement with data in monkeys we have previously reported ganglion cell to cone ratios of approximately 3 in the human foveal retina, thereby offering quantitative support for the on-off retinal ganglion cell systems. In the present study we have attempted to analyse where and how this ratio is reduced towards the periphery.
Methods. A stereologic analysis of retinal ganglion cells (RGC) and cone (C) density was performed using the disector method. Three normal human retinae, removed in the course of cancer surgery, were examined. Displaced amacrine cells were identified by immunohistochemistry and the extension of Henle fibers were measured.
Results. RGC and cone densities were in good agreement with our previously reported data, reaching 45-55.000 cells/mm^2 at approximately 0.6-0.7 mm ecc. RGC:C ratios were calculated from numbers in annuli allowing compensation for lateral displacement. The ratio was around 2.0 at an ecc. of 1.6 mm, 1.0 at an ecc. of 3.0 mm and 0.5 at 9 mm ecc.
Conclusion. Our findings suggest that visual acuity is determined by the cone mosaic within approximately the central 5 degrees and by the ganglion cells outside this zone.

111

THE COURCE OF OXYGEN SATURATION ALONG THE RETINAL VESSELS IN NORMALS

SCIBOR. M (1), MICHELSON. G (1),
SCHWEITZER. D (2), HAMMER. M (2), THAMM. E (2)
1) Dept. Ophthalmology, University Erlangen- Nürnberg, (Germany)
2) Dept. Ophthalmology, University Jena,. (Germany)

Purpose: The measurement of oxygen saturation in retinal arterioles and venoles at variable distances from the optic disc in normals.
Methods: The determination of oxygen saturation was performed using a fundus reflectometer that enables simultaneous acquisition of spectra arranged in a horizontal line across the fundus. The basis for the non-invasive estimation of the oxygen saturation is different extinction spectra of hemoglobin and oxyhemoglobin.The measu rements of the reflectance spectra were perfomed in a wavelength range from 400 nm to 700 nm. We measured 6 healthy eyes at 5 variable distances from optic disc corresponding in retinal arterioles and venoles.
Results: In retinal venoles we observed a reduction of retinal oxygen saturation by 9 % with the extensive distance from the optic disc. In retinal arterioles the oxygen saturation shows in average the same values 91%+-5%.
Conclusions: The retinal oxygen saturation in arterioles shows no significant differences at variable distances from the optic disc. In venoles we observed a recognizable reduction of oxygen saturation with extensive distance from the optic disc.

112

MORPHOLOGICAL EXAMINATION OF ENDOTHELIAL CELLS IN LONG TERM CULTURES

SAHM M. and SEIFERT P.
Alfried-Krupp Laboratory, Dept. of Ophthalmology, University of Bonn (Germany)

Purpose Endothelial cells in culture, are of the dedifferentiated phenotype. For physiological examinations they were used up to the seventh passage. The aim of the present work was to investigate the ultrastructure of bovine retinal capillary endothelial cells (BRCEC) in vitro after several passages.
Methods BRCEC were isolated and cultured in MCDB-medium with 20% platelet poor horse serum in a humidified atmosphere of 5% CO_2 and 3% O_2 at 37°C. To evidence their original characteristics a standard two-stage indirect immunohistochemical technique was applied using an anti-CD31/PeCam antibody. Cell suspensions of several passages were prepared for transmission electron microscopy (TEM).
Results Immunohistochemical staining revealed specific labeling of BRCEC with anti-CD31/PeCam antibody. Compared to the initial cells, which show only few organels, the number of mitochondria and the amount of rough endoplasmic reticulum (ER) increased considerably upon second passage. Additionally at passage eight, a prominent smooth ER has developed. Control cells from other tissues did not show corresponding changes.
Conclusions Endothelial cells in culture gradually modify their ultrastructure, especially the organisation of their organelles. After several passages, according to morphological criteria (TEM) they demonstrate high metabolic activity.

113

RETINAL VASCULAR PATTERN IN LONG FINE PILOT WHALE (*Globicephala melas*).

(MENGUAL R, GARCIA M, GUARDIOLA J.V and DE JUAN J.)
Departamento de Biotecnología, Universidad de Alicante, Alicante, Spain

Purpose: A characteristic of vascular pattern of retina is the great variability in the vertebrate. Whereas the ramification of retinal arteries of human and domestic animals have been described in detail, the features concerning the vascularization of Cetacea is practically unknown. The aim of this work is to provide information about the retinal angyoarchitecture of the *Globicephala melas*. **Methods**: 20 eyes of *Globicephala melas* were fixed in 10% formalin. In 10 eyecups, the retinal vascular pattern was described and draw "in situ" and the retinas were photographed. In the other 10 eyecups, the retinas were dissected and they were flat mounted in a slide, described and draw to study the possible differences between the vascular pattern "in situ" and flat mounted ones. Measurements were taken from bifurcation's vessel in the central area of the retina. **Results**: The pattern of vessels is essentially radial and uniform, in accordance with the holangeotic retinas, although the dorsal retina shows an increase in the vascular density. Measurements of the angles indicate that the bifurcations undergoes a dichotomous pattern, that is, form Y-shaped branches with arms of similar diameter in central and periphery of the retina. We have not observed any differences between the bifurcation's value "in situ" and flat retinas. **Conclusions**: The uniform vascular distribution and pattern's geometry with dichotomous branching of similar diameter suggests an equal blood supply, and level of pressure and temperature in whole retina.

Supported by GV-2521/94 and DGICYT PB 96 0414.

114

CHANGES OF THE TRABECULAR COLLAGEN FIBRES WITH AGE

POTAU JM, CANALS M, COSTA J, MERINDANO MD and RUANO D.
Ocular Morphology Unit, Dept. Human Anatomy, Faculty of Medicine, University of Barcelona (Spain)

Purpose

To analyze the evolution of the central collagen fibres of the trabecular beams with age and to relate it with the aqueous humour outflow resistance increase observed in aged patients.

Methods

20 non glaucomatous trabecular meshworks, ages 23 to 99 years, were observed by transmission electron microscopy, and the morphological aspects of their collagen were compared qualitatively.

Results

There was an increase of the area occupied by plates of compacted collagen embedded in an amorphous granular material derived from the elastin-like fibres sheaths in the central core of the uveal and sclerocorneal trabecular beams with age.

Conclusions

The progressive compactation of the collagen fibres of the trabecular beams around the elastin-like fibres with age, could increase the rigidity of the trabecular meshwork and alter the control of the ciliary muscle on the aqueous humour drainage.

115

THICKENING OF THE TRABECULAR BEAMS IN PRIMARY OPEN ANGLE GLAUCOMA

POTAU JM, CANALS M, COSTA J, MERINDANO MD and RUANO D.
Ocular Morphology Unit, Dept. Human Anatomy, Faculty of Medicine, University of Barcelona (Spain)

Purpose

To identify the morphological changes of the trabecular meshork beams in primary open angle glaucoma and their relationship with the disorders of the aqueous humour outflow.

Methods

The ultrastructure of 15 glaucomatous and 20 non glaucomatous trabecular meshworks was compared by using scanning electron microscopy and transmission electron microscopy.

Results

A thickening of the uveal and sclerocorneal trabecular beams was observed in the glaucomatous trabecular meshworks by scanning electron microscopy. Transmission electron microscopy revealed that this thickening was due to the enlargement of the basal membrane of the beam, that showed an important accumulation of clusters of long spacing collagen. Other disorders were also described.

Conclusions

The thickening of the trabecular beams can reduce the area of the trabecular orifices, altering the aqueous humour drainage.

116

COMPARATIVE ANATOMY OF INTRINSIC CHOROIDAL NEURONS IN DUCK AND HUMAN

SCHRÖDL F[1], BERGUA A[2], MAY CA[3], BREHMER A[1], LÜTJEN-DRECOLL E[3], NEUHUBER WL[1]
[1] Dept. of Anatomy I[1] and II[3], Univ. of Erlangen, Germany
[2] Dept. of Ophthalmology, Univ. of Erlangen, Germany

Purpose: The choroid of duck (*Cairina moschata*) and human contains up to 2000 intrinsic neurons costaining for nitric oxide (NOS) and vasoactive intestinal polypeptide (VIP; Bergua et al 1996, Flügel et al 1994). The aim of this study was to compare structure and chemical coding of choroidal neurons in these two species. **Methods:** Aldehyde fixed duck and human choroids were cryosectioned (20 µm) and processed for demonstration of galanin (GAL), VIP, NOS, tyrosine hydroxilase (TH), smooth muscle actin (SMA) and NADPH-diaphorase. Conventional, fluorescence and confocal laserscanning microscopy were used. **Results:** In both species most of the NOS/VIP choroidal neurons co-stained for GAL as did fibers of the perivascular plexus. They recieved a dense TH+ sympathetic input. Some perikarya and numerous varicose nerve fibres closely apposed to smooth muscle cells in the duck choroid. **Conclusion:** Despite morphological differences between avian and human choroids their innervation is similar. Besides choroidal blood vessels, smooth muscle cells are a main target forming a "lymphatic sponge" in duck, while they are concentrated in the anterior parts of the human choroid. The sympathetic innervation of choroidal neurons may be inhibitory. Since choroidal neurons are lacking in non-primate mammals, our results suggest the duck as a suitable model for glaucoma research.

Supported by DFG/SFB 539 BII.2 and 3

117

TROCHLEAR NERVE BY MICRODISSECTION

VILLAIN M[1], CANDON E[2], CANOVAS F[2], BONNEL F, ARNAUD B[1]
1. Service d'Ophtalmologie - Hôpital Gui de Chauliac, Montpellier (France)
2. Laboratoire d'anatomie de la faculté de médecine, Monpellier (France)

Purpose: To study the anatomical course of trochlear nerve in head, in cavernous sinus and in orbit, with the main surrounding relations.

Methods: This anatomical study rests on thirty trochlear nerves (IV) , and only on the trunk. We used the microscope for the dissection and so better it respected.

Results: In 56,6% the trunk born by 2 bundles. His total length is 86 mm in mean, for the three portions infratentorial, intracavernous, intraorbital. The infratentorial portion is so called, because 100% of nerves are under the plane of incisura tentori. For 27 nerves we found one contact with cerebellar artery superior. Ten ramus tentorii for thirty nerves are in the lateral wall of cavernous sinus. 23 trochlear nerves ended on the medial face of obliquus superior muscle. The 7 remaining on the superior rim of muscle.

Conclusion: The nervous trunk can be seen in trochlear paralysis with radiologic study according to pathologic elements. The study in normal subject by magnetic resonance imaging is restricted by the very small diameter of nervous trunk and the limits of actual machines.

118

RETROBULBAR CELLULAR TISSUE (RBCT): EMBRIOGENESIS AND ITS ROLE IN SOME EYE DISEASES

G.A.SHILKIN-1, V.V.GEMONOV-1, N.S.YARTSEVA-1, Z.G.IVANOVA-1, A.G.SHILKIN-2, M.KOLEDINTSEV-2

1.Moscow Medical Stomatological Institute
2.Eye Microsurgery Complex. Moscow, Russia

Purpose. To study the RBCT influence on eyeball normal development and on eye diseases. **Methods**. 120 cadaver RBCT of embrions & peoples were examined histologically. 250 myopia, hyperopia, retinal distrophy, glaucoma patients were investigated by plethismography, echography, and on the operation table. **Results**. RBCT has origin from paraaxial neuromesenchima and closely related with chorioidea, sclera, eye and fascial muscles in embriogenesis. RBCT conteins a lot of blood vessels, undifferented cells and scleral growth zona in fruits. RBCT conteins of main part of orbita vascular system, APUD-system cells and specific lipids in people. Ishemia and various types of cell disturbans were discovered in the pathology. Worked out conservative and surgical procedures give positive results. Besides RBCT is an adequate place for different curative cell-cultural transplantations (B-cells in diabetis, hepatocites, sclera). **Conclusion**. RBCT is an eye growth regulator (in children) and trophic matrix for eyeball. RBCT has importance in some eye diseases.

119

THE LACRIMAL ARTERIES

A. DUCASSE, J.F DELATTRE, C. AVISSE
Service d'Ophtalmologie - Pr A. DUCASSE Laboratoire d'Anatomie Pr J.B FLAMENT
REIMS France

The authors present the two types of lacrimal arteries : classical lacrimal artery arising from the ophthalmic artery and meningolacrimal artery arising from the middle meningeal artery.

METHODS : One hundred orbital dissections after arterial injection with latex Néoprène.

RESULTS : The classical lacrimal arteries have been found in 83 orbits ; these arteries are calibred from 0.3 to 1.8 with an average of 0,99mm. They give collateral branches to muscles : lateral rectus in 81%, superior rectus in 69%, palpebral levator in 41%. The meningolacrimal arteries, branches of the middle meningeal arteries have been found in 27 orbits. Their caliber are less important : 0.3 to 1.5mm with an average of 0.73. They give few branches for the muscles : lateral rectus 4/27, superior rectus 2/27, palpebral levator 8/27.

CONCLUSION : Lacrimal gland must be supply by a classical lacrimal artery arising from the ophthalmic artery, branche of the internal carotid or by a meningolacrimal artery arising from the middle meningeal artery branche of the external carotid. In 73% of the orbits there is only one classical lacrimal artery ; in 17% there is only a meningolacrimal artery and in 10 percents there are 2 lacrimal arteries, one classical and one meningolacrimal.

120

THE ETHMOIDAL ARTERIES

A. DUCASSE*, C. AVISSE**, J.B FLAMENT**
Laboratoire d'anatomie Pr J.B FLAMENT **
Service d'Ophtalmologie Pr DUCASSE *
REIMS FRANCE

The authors report the aspects of the ethmoidal arteries.

METHODS : 100 orbits have been dissected by superior approach after arterial injection.

RESULTS : The posterior ethmoidal artery is not constant. In 23% of the orbits there is no posterior ethmoïdal artery. When it is present, this caliber is 0.4mm on average. It arises from the ophthalmic artery in 75 percent, from the supraorbital artery in 17 percent, from the anterior ethmoidal artery in 7%. The artery crosses the trochlear nerve in 94% of the orbits. It gives branches for the superior obliquus muscle in 59%, for the palpebral levator in 37%.

The anterior ethmoidal artery is most frequent. It is absent in only 2 orbits. This caliber is more important ; on average 0.73mm (from 0.2 to 1.5). It arises from the ophthalmic artery in the most cases and usually the ophtalmic artery gives it in the anterior ethmoïdal foramen. It gives branches for the superior obliquus muscle in 49%,rarely for the medial rectus or the palpebral levator.

CONCLUSIONS : The ethmoïdal arteries are different ; the anterior is more frequent, more important in caliber. The posterior usually gives more branches.

121

MECHANOCHEMICAL PECULIARITIES OF SCLERA

SAULGOZIS J. and PONTAGA I.
Latvian Center of Biomechanics, Riga, Latvia

Purpose Mechanochemical properties of sclera are important in formation of myopia, staphyloma and eye form changes.
Methods Relations between elasticity modulus E (tested on normal, glaucomatic and myopic sclera strips by load equal to IOP= 2.67, 13.33, 26.66 kPa) and content of total collagen,Q, soluble fraction of Q,elastin and glycosaminoglycans, GG, were studied by multivariate linear (L) and nonlinear (NL) analyses.
Results Rise of Q in norm caused minute E gain, but rise of Q soluble fraction lowered E at IOP=2.67 and 13.33 kPa (specific influence for L=27.38 and 16.51%, for NL= 17.45 and 13.29%, respectively).Rise of GG caused L gain of E by 7.01%. At 26.66 kPa increase of Q rose E (L=33.27 % and NL=16.37%). In glaucoma rise of Q at 2.67 kPa lowered E (L=7.55% and NL= 6.42%). At 13.33 and 26.66 kPa E rose (L=14.43 and 34.05%; NL=11.79 and 19.32%, resp.). Effect of Q soluble fraction was minute. Rise of GG caused L and NL gain of E. In myopia rise of Q leaded to small E gain at 2.67 and 13.33 kPa. At 26.66 kPa the relation was significant (L=9.81% and NL=7.11%). Rise of Q soluble fraction didn't effect E at 2.67kPa, but at 13.33 and 26.66 kPa E reduced (L=9.92 and 13.80%; NL=8.47 and 10.04%, resp.). An increase of GG caused rise of E at all levels of IOP (L=17.20, 13.43, 10.98%; NL=9.46, 10.76, 12.67%, resp.).
Conclusions Generally the sclera stiffness is effected by glycosaminoglycans, total collagen and elastin (norm), total collagen (glaucoma) and collagen soluble fraction (myopia).

122

INVESTIGATION OF EYE MECHANICAL STABILITY

SAULGOZIS J.and PONTAGA I.
Latvian Centre of Biomechanics, Riga, Latvia

Purpose The mechanical stability of sclera has basic role in eye normal functions and recovery after trauma, illnesses and surgery.
Methods The tests were done on 25 enucleated human eyes in modeled physiological conditions and on 135 patients (age 25 - 45 years) in clinic by loading the eye by 1.5 N force. A special measuring device (corneo - scleral pressure cup, broad band ultrasound transducer, loading mechanism) was used considering the experience of D.G.Shiengelia (1978). The length of eye anterior-posterior axis (L) was measured by ultrasound biometry just before and after the load application. Changes of the sclera stiffness in vitro were modeled using thin rubber truss on the eye equatorial region. The eye anterior and posterior pole was not undergoing deformation (influence of corneo - scleral cup and post bulbar tissue) so the strain was calculated only for eye equatorial part ($\varepsilon = (\Delta Le/Le)\ 100$, %; Le = L-11,mm).
Results At normal IOP = 2.15 - 2.87 kPa for emmetropic eyes in vitro the strain ε = 1.53±0.33 %. In vivo for glaucomatic, emmetropic, middle (6 D) and highly (10 D) myopic eyes ε = 1.88±0.51 %, 2.70±0.47 %, 3.68±1.04 % and 3.09±0.87 %, respectively.
Conclusions The sclera of glaucomatic eyes is stiffer than of normal eyes. The method allows to monitor the eye coat deformability changes in myopia and to determine the effect of scleroplastics. The strain decrease in high myopia is due to eye form and stress distribution changes in the equatorial sclera.

123

THE INFLUENCE OF NEAR-FOCUS X-RAY RADIATION OF THE THYMUS ON THE DEVELOPMENT OF CONNECTIVE TISSUE OF THE SCLERA

Bushueva N.N., Dumbrova N.E.
The Filatov Institute of Eye Diseases and Tissue Therapy, Odessa, Ukraine

Method: We have elaborated an experimental model of suppression of the thymus function in 35 newborn rats by means of a near-focal X-ray radiation, with a dose of 0.6Gr. The control group included 30 newborn rats. Histologic and electronmicroscopic examinations of the thymus and sclera were conducted within 1.5 months after birth of experimental and control animals.
Results: In most rats after radiation of the thymus gland there developed a picture of the Wasting's syndrome.In electronmicroscopic preparations it was found that the sclera of intact rats, aged 48 days, is represented by a formed connective tissue with a distinctly organized lamellar structure rich of actively functioning fibroblasts. In rats, 48 days after X-ray radiation, tissue of the sclera showed desorganization of collagenic laminae with cellular polymorphism, destruction of a part of cells in a form of lysis, and the presence of transparent areas free from fibrils.
Conclusion: The action of X-ray radiation on the thymus causes disorders in regulatory mechanisms of the development and destruction of connective tissue in the sclera of the growing organism.

124

A MANAGEMENT ALGORITHM FOR INHERITED EYE DISEASES

CHURCHILL AJ.
Dept. Ophthalmology and Molecular Medicine, St.James's University Hospital (UK)

Purpose: In recent years there has been an explosion of genetic information for the Ophthalmologist to try to remember when faced with familial eye conditions. We have attempted to construct an algorithm to guide the general Ophthalmologist through this minefield using aniridia as an example.
Method: Ten British Paediatric Ophthalmologists were contacted either by questionnaire or personal interview and asked for their management of a newly diagnosed aniridic. In particular attention was focused on history taking, clinical examination and follow up.
Results: All 10 specialists replied detailing their management. This information has been combined with our own local experience to provide a step by step guide to inherited eye disease, including what questions to ask, advice to the parents and when to screen blood for genetic mutations.
Conclusions: Public awareness of genetic research is reaching new heights with increasing media interest. Many Ophthalmologists have not received specific training in genetics and may feel disadvantaged when faced with familial ocular conditions in the clinic. This study suggests one method of approach so that the Ophthalmologist may feel more confident in such a situation.

125

GENETIC STUDY OF CHOROIDEREMIA (CHM) DISEASE IN SPANISH POPULATION

MJ Trujillo*, I Lorda*, M Rodriguez de Alba*, R Sanz*, C Ramos*, A Ibañez, A Gimenez*, B Gª-Sandoval, G Antiñolo, M Baiget, M Beneyto, M Carballo, C Ayuso*& Spanish Multicentric and Multidisciplinary Group of Research on Retinitis Pigmentosa
Dept of Genetics. Fundación.Jiménez.Díaz.Madrid (SPAIN)

Purpose:- To characterize at a cytogenetic and molecular level a sample of 7 Spanish families affected with CHM.
Methods:- Molecular studies: SSCP analysis of REP-1 gene to search for mutations (exons: 1,3,5,6,7,8,11,12,13,14,15). Linkage analysis with 3 intragenic markers in 4 families.
Results:
1.A new balanced translocation between chromosomes X and 4 in a women affected with choroideremia.
2.A new nonsense mutation in exon 8 identified as Ser340X.
3.A previously identified polymorphism in exon 5 (Ala117Ala)
4.Two families present a low positive lod-score
5.Two families present exclusion of linkage to CHM gene
Conclusions:
1.Karyotype allows detection of cytogenetic anomalies at CHM locus.
2.Mutations in REP-1 gene are not always detected in CHM cases.
3.Genetic heterogeneity is probably present in choroideremia disease like in other many different retinal disorders.

126

CLINICAL AND MOLECULAR GENETIC STUDY OF BARDET-BIEDL SYNDROME IN SPAIN

BAIGET M[1], VALVERDE D[2], LORDA I[3], CALAF M[3] BRICHETTE I[2], VAZQUEZ-GUNDIN F [2], , TRUJILLO MJ [3] AND SPANISH MULTICENTRIC GROUP OF RP
1- Hospital Sant Pau, Barcelona, Spain
2-Oncological Center of Galicia , La Coruña, Spain.
3-Department of Genetics; Fundacion Jimenez-Diaz, Madrid.

Purpose: To characterize the clinical and molecular aspects of Bardet-Biedl syndrome in Spain.
Methods: Affected patients were identified through the Spanish RP Register. We made clinical investigations in 13 patients out of 9 families and molecular analysis throughout 11 microsatellite markers on chromosomes 3,11,15 and 16 corresponding to the four identified BBS loci in 13 families.
Results. Clinical analysis showed that all patients presented retinal dystrophy and obesity. The type of retinal dystrophy is variable, with an age of onset between 1st and 2nd decade. Polydactyly, hypogonadism and renal abnormalities were present in 50% of the patients. Mental retardation was present only in 3 cases. The patients share a characteristic face. Intrafamilial variation was observed, specially affecting polydactyly and age of onset of retinal dystrophy. Molecular analysis showed that at least 30% of the studied families are linked to chromosome 16. A fifth locus is suggested.
Conclusions: Interfamilial, but also intrafamilial clinical variation affecting the cardinal features of the BBS have been observed and can hardly be explained only by the genetic heterogeneity.

127

SPANISH AUTOSOMAL RECESSIVE RETINITIS PIGMENTOSA PATIENTS: INVOLVEMENT OF B-SUBUNIT OF ROD PHOSPHODIESTERASE (PDE-B)

BAIGET M[1], VALVERDE D[2], CALAF M[1], BENEYTO M, CARBALLO M, AYUSO C, ANTIÑOLO G, MILLAN JM, TRUJILLO MJ & SPANISH MULTICENTRIC and MULTIDISCIPLINARY GROUP OF RESEARCH ON RETINITIS PIGMENTOSA.
1.- Dept Genetics. Hospital San Pablo, Barcelona (SPAIN)
2.- Oncological center of Galicia, La Coruña (SPAIN)

Purpose: To stablish the involvement of PDE-B gene in the pathogenesis of ARRP in Spanish families.
Patients and Methods: Ophthalmological and molecular studies were done in 48 Spanish ARRP pedigrees, comprising 31 consanguineous and 17 non consanguineous families.
The promoter region and all exons of PDEB were amplified by PCR and analyzed SSCP. Abnormal migrating bands were sequenced.
Results: We found 26 variant bands by SSCP analysis. DNA sequencing and cosegregation analysis led to the identification of five disease-causing mutations in the PDE-B gene. Three mutations (71bp duplication in exon1, Leu699Arg and Arg552Gln) were present in homozygosis in the affected members of 3 consanguineous families. Two mutations (Gln298X and Asp600Asn) were found as compound heterozygotes in two affected of a non consanguineous family. The remaining abnormal bands correspond to polymorphisms or rare variants that are not associated with the disease.
Conclusions:
Mutations in the B-PDE gene accounts for less than 10% of ARRP families in Spain.

128

ANALYSIS OF RHODOPSIN GENE AMONG SPANISH RP PATIENTS

AYUSO C[1], ANTIÑOLO G, BAIGET M, BENEYTO M, CARBALLO M, VALVERDE D, MILLAN JM, SANCHEZ A, REIG C, TRUJILLO MJ[1] and SPANISH MULTICENTRIC and MULTIDISCIPLINARY GROUP OF RESEARCH ON RETINITIS PIGMENTOSA.
1.- Dept Genetics FUNDACION JIMENEZ DIAZ, Madrid (SPAIN)

Purpose: To stablish the involvement of rhodopsin (RHO) gene in the pathogenesis of Retinitis Pigmentosa (RP) in Spanish affected patients.

Patients and Methods: Ophthalmological and molecular studies were done in Spanish patients, belonging to 91 ADRP, 154 ARRP, and 111 SRP unrelated families.
We performed DNA analyses by PCR amplification of promoter region and 5 exons of RHO gene, including intron-exon boundaries followed by SSCP analyses and sequencing.

Results: 15 ADRP families showed 14 different dominant mutations and in 2 additional families there were linkage between RHO locus and disease. No Pro23His mutation was detected and only Pro347Leu was found twice in Spanish RP patients.
None mutation was observed in ARRP but one mutation was present in 1 SRP case (0.9%).
There were no differences in heterozigosity for previously described polymorphisms between RP and general Spanish population.

Conclusions:
RHO gene mutations are responsible for 18% of ADRP families in Spain and less than 1% of ARRP or SRP cases could be due to RHO mutations.

129

SCREENING OF MUTATIONS IN PERIPHERIN /RDS AND ROM1 GENE IN SPANISH FAMILIES WITH RETINITIS PIGMENTOSA

M.CARBALLO, C.REIG , P. OLIVE.
Servei Labotaratori. Hospital de Terrassa (Spain) .Grupo Multicéntrico Español de Investigación de Retinosis Pigmentario.

Purpose
Mutations in human peripherin/RDS and ROM1 gene, which code for proteins found in the outer segment disc membrane of the photoreceptor cells of the retina, have been implicated as a cause of autosomal dominant and digenic retinitis pigmentosa. Unlike rhodopsin, in which all the mutaions reported are associated to retinitis pigmentosa (RP) some mutations in the human peripherin/RDS gene cause other retinal degeneration different of RP. Except for ROM1 null alleles that cause RP when associated with a peripherin/RDS mutation (digenic mechanism) a definite relationship between retinal degeneration and ROM1 mutations cannot yet be stablished.

Methods
We have screened autosomal dominant, autosomal recesive and simplex case of spanish RP patients, previously excluded for mutations in the rhodopsin gene for futher sequence alterations in peripherin/RDS and ROM1 gene by DGGE and SSPE.

Results
Two punctual mutations in exon 2 (173, 208 codon) of the peripherin/RDS gene was detected in patients with a RP phenotype. Three additionaly mutations in exon 2 of peripherin/RDS gene was detected in spanish families with macular dystrophy phenotype. Any mutation in ROM1 gene detected in the spanish families seems to be the cause of RP by itself.

Conclusions
Mutations in peripherin/RDS is cause in 2 % of autosomal dominant retinitis pigmentosa in spanish families. Some mutations in peripherin/RDS also produce dominant macular dystrophy different from RP. No direct correlation between mutation in ROM1 gene a RP was obteined.

130

GENETICS AND EPIDEMIOLOGY OF RETINITIS PIGMENTOSA IN SPAIN

AYUSO C[1], ANTIÑOLO G, BAIGET M, BENEYTO M, CARBALLO M, VALVERDE D, NAJERA C, SANCHEZ A, REIG C, TRUJILLO MJ[1] and SPANISH MULTICENTRIC and MULTIDISCIPLINARY GROUP OF RESEARCH ON RETINITIS PIGMENTOSA.
1.- Dept Genetics FUNDACION JIMENEZ DIAZ, Madrid (SPAIN)

Purpose: To delineate the epidemiological aspects of Retinitis Pigmentosa (RP) in Spain: distribution of genetic types and clinical evolution of them.

Patients and Methods: Ophthalmological and familial studies were done in a sample of RP 1556 Spanish patients, belonging to 886 unrelated families. We performed genetic classification and segregation analyses, following previously described criteria.

Results: We found 111 syndromic (13%) and 775 non-syndromic RP families. Genetic types were: 13% of ADRP, 39% ARRP, 6% XLRP , 40% SRP and 2% of unclassified families. Segregation ratio in ADRP was 0.424 and penetrance 85%. In ARRP, we observed 48% of consanguinity.
XLRP group showed the earliest age of onset of symptoms and the most severe evolution, followed by ARRP and SRP patients. Among ADRP cases, the worse clinical course was observed in type I/diffuse.

Conclusions: There is a low frequency of Spanish XLRP families and a high frequency of ARRP (39%) with a high consanguinity rate
XLRP patients underwent the worse clinical evolution whereas ADRP and SRP presented mild symptoms and evolution.

131

ROD-CONE DYSTROPHY IN TWO BROTHERS WITH FRAGILE X SYNDROME

JENSEN H[1], HJALGRIM H[2] and SJÖ O[1].
1. Div of pediatric ophthalmology and handicap, Copenhagen University, (Denmark)
2. John F. Kennedy Institute , Copenhagen (Denmark)

Purpose: Fragile x syndrome is the most commen form of heritable mental retardation, caused by a dynamic mutation on Xq27.3. Phenotypic the males have large ears and macro-testes. A high prevalence of strabismus and refractive errors is seen. Rod-cone dystrophy has not previously been reported.

Method: Two brothers with fragile x-syndrome, both verified by cytogenetic examination to have the karyo-type: 46,Y,fra(X), and by Southern blot to have a full mutation. The oldest brother (25y11mo) complained a-bout night blindness starting 1-2 years earlier, while the youngest brother (14y9mo) had no complains. An ophthalmological examination, including full field electroretinogram (ERG) was performed.

Results: Visual acuity was 20/20 in both, fundus examination showed arteriolar attenuation and ERG showed rod-cone dystrophy in both.

Conclusion: Progressive retinal dystrophy is seen in a wide variety of genetic disorders, but this is the first time seen in patients with fragile x syndrome.

132

THE *CACNA1F* GENE IS MUTATED IN PATIENTS WITH INCOMPLETE CSNB

Bech-Hansen NT,[1] Naylor M,[1] Maybaum T,[1] Bergen AB,[2] Rosenberg T,[3] Weleber RG,[4] , Miyake Y,[5] Boycott, KM[1]

[1]Dept. Medical Genetics, University of Calgary (Canada), [2]The Netherlands Ophthalmic Research Institute (The Netherlands), [3]National Eye Clinic (Denmark), [4]Oregon Health Sciences University (USA), [5]Nagoya University School of Medicine (Japan)

X-linked congenital stationary night blindness (CSNB) exists as two distinct clinical entities. The gene for complete CSNB (CSNB1) maps to Xp11.4, while the gene for incomplete CSNB (CSNB2) maps to Xp11.23. Mutation analysis of the *CACNA1F* gene, which codes for a retina-specific voltage-gated L-type calcium channel α_1-subunit protein (α_1F), originally revealed six loss-of-function mutations in families with incomplete CSNB (Bech-Hansen et al. Nature Genet. 19:264-267, 1998). Analysis of additional patients with incomplete CSNB has revealed several new mutations in *CACNA1F*. Each of the *CACNA1F* mutations observed in patients with incomplete CSNB appears to result in either total loss-of-function or in domain-specific defects in the L-type calcium channels of the retina containing the α_1F polypeptide. Our studies continue to support the observation that incomplete CSNB represents an example of a human channelopathy.

133

CLUSTERING OF MUTATIONS IN THE GENE FOR BEST MACULAR DYSTROPHY

Wadelius C[1], Koisti M J[1],Bakall B[1],Marknell T[1],Ingvast S[1], Sandgren O[2],Li W[3],Xie G[3],McGarty-Dugan V[3],Figueroa D[3],Austin C P[3],Metzker M L[3],Caskey C T[3],Petrukhin K[3]
1.Dpt of Genet and Pathol/Clin Genet, Uppsala Univ, Sweden
2. Dpt of Ophthalmology, Univ Hosp, Umeå, Sweden
3.Merck Research Laboratories, West Point, PA, USA

Best macular dystrophy (BMD) is an autosomal dominant disease with variable expressivity, causing reduced central vision. In later stages of BMD as well as in age-related macular degeneration, an accumulation of lipofuscin is found, in and beneath the retinal pigment epithelium (RPE). A very large Swedish pedigree, founded in the 17th century was studied in the attempts to identify the BMD gene. Analysis of the haplotypes in over 250 people allowed the mapping of the gene to 800 kb. By sequence analysis and biocomputing a novel gene was identified with expression specifically in RPE. It is part of a family with 14 members in *C. elegans* and a couple in man. The cDNA of 2.2 kb encodes a 585 residue protein, now named bestrophin, with unknown function. From the analysis of twentythree independent Best families fourteen different mutations were detected in eighteen families, many affecting residues conserved in *C. elegans*. Only missence mutations, clustered in certain regions, were detected. The 3' UTR is complementary to the 3' UTR of the ferritin heavy chain 1 gene providing a possibility of antisence interaction. The bestrophin gene may now be analysed for possible contribution to AMD.

134

MYOSIN VIIA GENE MUTATIONS IN SIX USHER TYPE 1B FAMILIES

BENEYTO M[1], ESPINOS C[2] and Spanish Research Group in Retinitis Pigmentosa
1. U. Genética y D. Prenatal. Hospital La Fe. Valencia, Spain.
2. Dpto. Genética. Fac. Cienc. Biológicas. Valencia. Spain.

Purpose: Mutations in the myosin VIIa gene (MYO7A) are associated with Usher syndrome type 1B (USH1B), a disorder characterized by congenital profound hearing loss, vestibular areflexia and prepuberal onset of retinitis pigmentosa (RP). We describe here on the MYO7A mutations detected in six Spanish USH1B families.
Methods: Mutation screening by SSCP and DNA sequencing.
Results: Screening covering 27 of the gene's 49 exons detected five different mutations in six unrelated families. A nonsense mutation and a single base pair deletion were found in the homozygous state in four patients from two families. Seven patients from four families were found to be compound heterozygotes for different mutant alleles or simple heterozygotes. The onset of RP symptoms usually occurs at childhood, although two important exceptions have been noted. All of our patients showed a severe impairment of visual function during the third or fourth decade of life.
Conclusion: The exact mechanism of the retinal degeneration in USH1B patients with MYO7A mutations remains unclear, however, clinical description of patients with known mutations in this gene could help to know the basis of this condition.

135

CHARACTERIZING ESTs OF GENES ASSIGNED TO BIOLOGICAL ROLES IN THE RPE

PARAOAN L[1,2], GRIERSON I[2] and MADEN BEH[1].
1. School of Biological Sciences, and 2. Unit of Ophthalmology, Department of Medicine, University of Liverpool (UK)

Purpose To examine the nature of transcripts in the RPE, as a starting point in defining expression patterns of active genes in this tissue.
Methods Clones from various RPE cDNA libraries were randomly isolated and subjected to partial sequencing with the view to generate ESTs.
Results More than 300 RPE clones were analyzed by single-pass sequencing. ESTs of 250-450 nucleotides were generated and compared with sequences in nucleotide and peptide sequence databases. The emphasis of the analysis was put on identification of transcripts identical or highly similar to database sequences encoding proteins of known function or localization thus revealing active molecular components responsible for performing functions of the RPE cells. The putatively identified ESTs were tentatively classified with respect to the biological roles of proteins encoded by the matched genes.
Conclusions A prominent feature that resulted from the sorting of the RPE ESTs according to their possible cellular roles is that approximately a third of the total number of assigned ESTs represent genes with involvement in gene/protein expression, with a major subcategory concerned with protein turnover.

We acknowledge the gift of an aliquot of a human foetal RPE cDNA library from Dr. Dean Bok, UCLA, USA.
Suported by The Wellcome Trust.

136

PERIPHERAL CORNEAL OEDEMA, SENSORINEURAL DEAFNESS AND ROD CONE DYSTROPHY

JACKSON AJ, LOTERY AJ, FRAZER DG, DONNELLY U, COLLINS A, NEVEU M
Dept of Ophth., Royal Victoria Hospital, Queens University Belfast, N.Ireland

Purpose: This case of a 38 year old male, with gradual onset visual and hearing loss, illustrates an unusual association between peripheral corneal endothelial decompensation, sensorineural deafness and rod cone dystrophy. **Methods:** Assessments included, refraction, electrophysiology, specular microscopy, fundus photography, fluorescein angiography, colour vision, visual acuity and audiometry. **Results:** Visual acuities were 6/6 right and 6/9 left. Refractive findings were regular and there was no previous ophthalmic history, or family history, of ocular problems or deafness. Bilateral symmetrical sensorineural deafness was noted. Electrophysiological findings, consistent with rod cone dystrophy, were noted in either eye (subnormal pattern, flicker and rod electro-retinograms). Bilateral macular pigment epithelial atrophy and a tritan colour vision defect were noted. Mid peripheral corneal endothelial cell counts were reduced to <1000 cells per mm2. With the exception of bilateral punctate cortical lens opacities, all other ophthalmic findings were normal. **Conclusions:** We believe that this association between peripheral corneal endothelial cell loss and accompanying corneal oedema, progressive sensorineural deafness and rod cone dystrophy has not previously been demonstrated. In the most closely related condition, Harboyan Syndrome, electrophysiology findings are normal and corneal oedema is diffuse and associated with stromal scarring. This may be a new syndrome.

137

βig-h3 GENE ANALYSIS IN A FAMILY WITH CORNEAL LATTICE DYSTROPHY TYPE I (CLD1) NEGATIVE FOR R124C MUTATION

SCHMITT-BERNARD C.F.[1,2,3], TUFFERY S.[2], GOUIN-CHARNET A.[3], ARNAUD B.[1],CLAUSTRES M.[2], ARGILES. A.[3]
1. department of ophthalmology, C.M.C. Gui de Chauliac, C.H.U. Montpellier (France)
2. Laboratoire de biochimie-génétique, Institut de biologie, Montpellier (France)
3. Institut de Génétique humaine, CNRS, Montpellier (France)

Purpose : The authors report the screening of the βig-h3 gene in a family negative for exon 4 - R124C mutation of this gene.
Methods : Lattice corneal dystrophy of type I in this family was set on clinical and histological criteria showing onset of the disease at age 20 in affected members, typical sub-epithelial haze and linear branching deposits in stomal layers, recurrent corneal erosions, red-green dichroism under polarised light with congo red staining on corneal buttons. Screening of the βig-h3 gene was performed by RT-PCR on mRNA extracted from blood samples using primers designed for the study, and by PCR on DNA extracted from blood samples by using previous reported primers (Munier et al., 1997).
Results : Screening of the βig-h3 gene in this family with CLD1 and controls revealed various as yet undescribed polymorphisms and one potential mutation in exon 14.
Conclusions : R124C (Munier et al., 1997) and A556D + P551Q (Sommer et al., 1998) have been implicated in CLD1. Afshari et al., 1998, and Wang et al., 1998 revealed misdiagnosis of CLD1 after re-examination of families negative for R124C mutation of the βig-h3 gene. The R124C-negative family we screened for mutation in the βig-h3 gene showed typical clinical features of CLD1 and a potential mutation in exon 14 for which further studies are in progress.

138

CONSTITUTIONAL MUTATIONS DETECTED IN BOTH RB1 ALLELES IN AN ISOLATED UNILATERAL RETINOBLASTOMA PATIENT

BENEYTO M[1], SANCHEZ F[2], MATEU. E[1], NAJERA C[2], PRIETO F[1]
1. U. Genética y D. Prenatal. Hospital La Fe. Valencia Spain.
2. Dpto. Genética. Fac. C. Biológicas. Valencia. Spain

Purpose: Patients with isolated unilateral retinoblastoma (Rb) are traditionally considered to be carriers of a germ-line mutation in ~12% of cases. However, recent data related to the high incidence of somatic and germline mosaicism in these affected individuals provide that patients with unilateral Rb and no family history of retinoblastoma may be either homogeneous carriers or mosaics at a probability much higher than previously reported. Therefore, mutation analysis is important for genetic counselling in these cases.
Methods: Haplotype analysis and mutation detection by SSCP and sequencing of DNA and RNA from peripheral blood and tumoural cells.
Results: Sequencing of peripheral blood DNA identified an heterozygous mutation of a splice donor sequence inducing exon 5 skipping in the patient and his unaffected father. Deletion of the maternal RB1 alelle was also detected in a high proportion of leukocyte DNA from the patient. Both mutations were detected in DNA and RNA from all tumour cells.
Conclusion: These findings have important implications for genetic counselling and genetic analysis in patients with isolated unilateral retinoblastoma.

139

DNA MITOCHONDRIAL STUDY IN KEARNS-SAYRE SYNDROME.

GONZALVO F[1], IZAGUIRRE L[1], PLAYAN A[2], MARCUELLO B[1], FERNANDEZ J[1], MONTOYA J[2], HONRUBIA FM[1].
1. Dept. Ophthalmology. Miguel Servet Hospital. Zaragoza. Spain.
2. Dept. Biochemistry. Zaragoza University. Spain.

Purpose: To detect the presence of mitochondrial DNA (mtDNA) deletions in two patients and relatives with features of Kearns-Sayre syndrome (SKS). To describe the ophthalmological findings of SKS.
Methods: Opthalmological and sistemic study of two symptomatic patients with SKS. Orbicular muscle and venous blood samples were taken for the mtDNA analysis. Southern blot and polimerase chain reaction techniques were used to screen for mtDNA deletions.
Results: A 4,977 base pair deletion in the muscle sample in a proportion of 72% was detected in one patient. The deletion extended from nucleotids 8,483 to 13,459. No deletions were found in the venous blood samples of the two patients and relatives. The study of mtDNA mutations asociated with MELAS, MERRF and Leigh disease was negative in the other patient.
Conclusions: The study of mtDNA deletions in SKS must be made muscle, since we may obtain negative results of venous blood samples in patiens with mtDNA deletions.

140

MUTATION SCREENING IN JUVENILE GLAUCOMA

BOOTH A,[1,2] CHEN H,[2] ANWAR R,[1] DO T,[2] NOBLE B,[3] NGUYEN T [2] and MARKHAM A.[1]
1. Molecular Medicine Unit, University of Leeds, (England)
2. Department of Ophthalmology, University of California San Francisco, (USA)
3. Department of Ophthalmology, Leeds General Infirmary, (England)

Purpose The *TIGR* gene is the only gene to date to have been identified as a cause of primary open-angle glaucoma. The aim of this study was to identify families with juvenile-onset primary open-angle glaucoma (J-POAG) and perform mutation screening of the *TIGR* gene.
Methods Mutation screening was performed using the techniques of SSCP, BESS and direct sequencing.
Results A three generation family was identified with J-POAG. Mutation screening revealed a missense mutation which resulted in an amino acid change from proline to leucine at codon 370 (Pro370Leu) in exon 3 of the *TIGR* gene.
Conclusion This is the first description of the Pro370Leu mutation in a British family. It has been suggested that mutations in this region of the *TIGR* gene could lead to accumulation of the *TIGR* protein and obstruction of aqueous outflow.

141

ABCR GENE AND FAMILIAL EXUDATIVE AGE-RELATED MACULAR DEGENERATION

SOUIED EH[1,2], DUCROQ D[1], GERBER S[1], ROZET JM[1], PERRAULT I[1], MUNNICH A[1], COSCAS G[2], SOUBRANE G[2] and KAPLAN J[1].
1. INSERM U393, Hôpital des Enfants-Malades, Paris
2. Clinique Ophtalmologique Universitaire de Créteil; France

Purpose: To screen mutations in the ABCR gene in patients affected with familial cases of exudative age-related macular degeneration (AMD) and to establish phenotype-genotype correlations.
Methods: Visual acuity measurement, fundus examination and fluorescein angiography were performed for each unrelated patient (n=45). The coding sequence of the gene was analyzed using a combination of single-strand conformation polymorphism (SSCP) and direct sequence analysis of the fifty exons of the ABCR gene.
Results: Clinical features were ascertained in all AMD patients. After a first screening using PCR-SSCP, many abnormal pattern of migration of the ABCR gene have been found in several patients, compared to healthy controls. Direct sequencing was performed for each abnormal profile.
Conclusions: Retinal characteristics, compound heterozygous missense mutations and sequence variants will be presented. Several lines of evidence support the idea that the base substitutions are disease-causing mutations.

142

CELL DEATH IN THE CORNEAL EPITHELIUM.

GAGNA CE, KUO HR, and LAMBERT WC.
Dept. Pathology, UMDNJ-Med. Sch., Newark, NJ (USA)

Purpose To immunohistochemically examine cell death in the epithelium of the normal adult dog cornea.
Methods We employed an anti-B-DNA monoclonal antibody (mAb) and an anti-Z-DNA mAb specific for double-stranded (ds-)DNA. A anti-single-stranded (ss-) DNA polyclonal antibody was also used to detect denatured ss-DNA. Data was quantified using the Vickers M86 microspectrophotometer.
Results The limbal stem cell epithelium and peripheral corneal epithelium contain ds-DNA. The basal layers of the limbus contained the highest levels of B-and Z-DNA immunoreactivity, and the suprabasal layers revealed a gradual decrease in B-and Z-DNA. The peripheral corneal cells revealed the next highest B- and Z-DNA immunoreactivity, followed by the mid-peripheral, and central epithelial cells. All corneal zones exhibited the same gradual decrease in B- and Z-DNA as these cells proliferated from the deepest epithelium to the surface cells. The midperipheral and central cornea revealed the highest ss-DNA content.
Conclusions These results suggest that limbal and peripheral cells contain intact ds-DNA and as cells move to the central zone basal layer and proliferate to the corneal surface, we observe production of ss-DNA. Our data suggest that the limbus acts as a source of stem cells. The production of ss-DNA may prevent the formation of Z-DNA, therefore, negatively affecting transcription and normal cellular processes. We believe that the decrease in B- and Z-DNA, and increase in ss-DNA represents an increase in terminal differentiation.

143

EXPRESSION OF CD40, CD40 LIGAND, FAS, FAS LIGAND, HLA DR IN THE HUMAN CONJUNCTIVAL EPITHELIUM

BOURCIER T,[1] BRIGNOLE F,[2] DE SAINT-JEAN M,[1] GOLDSCHILD M,[1] GOGUEL A,[2] and BAUDOUIN C[1].
Depts. of Ophthalmology 1 and Immunohematology 2, Ambroise Paré Hospital, University of Paris-V, (France).

Purpose To investigate by flow cytometry in normal and pathological conjunctival epithelium the expressions of CD40, CD40 ligand, HLA DR class II antigen as inflammatory markers and of the apoptotic markers Fas (CD95), Fas ligand.
Methods Impression cytology specimens were collected in 95 patients: 40 normal eyes from 25 patients, 60 eyes from 35 patients with chronic conjunctivitis of various origin, including 15 with soft contact lens. 60 eyes from 35 patients with moderate to severe keratoconjunctivitis sicca. Cells were processed for flow cytometry. Percentages of positive cells were recorded and levels of fluorescence quantified by using a calibration curve established with fluorescent beads at standardized intensities.
Results Fas and CD40 were found in all eyes, but at significantly higher levels in pathological eyes than in normal ones, without difference between the different pathologies. Fas ligand and CD40 ligand were variably expressed by conjunctival cells, but in significantly higher percentages of cells in pathological eyes than in normal eyes. In those eyes a strong expression of HLA DR was observed. Highly significant correlations were found between Fas, Fas ligand, HLA DR and CD40 levels.
Conclusions This study confirms that conjunctival epithelial cells normally express Fas antigen and Fas ligand, but apoptosis-related markers are significantly enhanced in inflammatory eyes and correlated to HLA DR and CD40. These results suggest strong relationships between apoptosis and inflammatory pathways in the ocular surface.

144

DISTRIBUTION OF ALDEHYDE DEHYDROGENASES IN THE RAT EYE

Pinazo-Duran MD, Azorín I., Iborra FJ y Renau-Piqueras J.
Centro de Investigación Hospital Universitario La Fé (Valencia, España)

Purpose: Genetic variants have been found for several **aldehyde dehydrogenases (ALDHs)** in vertebrates and their roles are suggested to be manifold, from the conversion of retinal to *retinoic acid* (which regulates gene expression and development) to the removal of *acetaldehyde* (primary oxidation product of ethanol). We postulate that the ethanol-induced neuro-retinal defects, as previously reported (*Pinazo-Durán et al.*; Teratology 1993;48:302; *Strömland and Pinazo-Durán*; Teratology 1994; 50:100), may be due to ethanol-toxic-metabolites, as well as changes in retinoic acid disponibility.

Methods: We have investigated the distribution of cytosolic ALDH (class 1) and mitochondrial ALDH (class 2) in the 21-day- fetuses (21G), 10-day-newborns (10P) and mature rat eyes (AD), b2y means of biochemical, histochemical and cytochemical techniques, using specific antisera anti-ALDH 1 and anti-ALDH 2.

Results: Our results showed that the enzymatic activitities for these isoenzymes were significantly higher in the cornea, retina-choroid and optic nerve than in the lens. Strong immunofluorescence for ALDH 1 was detected in the 21G, 10P and AD rats in the retina-choroid, with the most intense reaction in the cytolosic compartment of neurons and glial cells. Positive immunoreaction for ALDH 2 was noted in the 21G and 10P eyes with a maximum in the AD retina and choroid and co-localizing with the lipid peroxidation sites occuring in these tissues. Immunocytochemical studies demonstrated the subcellular distribution of ALDHs in the rat eyes, in an age-related fashion .

Conclusions: All data suggest that a) the high ALDH1 levels found in the immature retina as compared to the adult eyes may be modulators of retinoic acid synthesis and crucially involved in the normal and altered neuro-retinogenesis and b) the co-localization of ALDH2 with the lipid peroxidation sites, may indicate that it plays a crucial role in the detoxication of peroxidic aldehydes from the eyes.

145

MOLECULAR CHARACTERIZATION OF K CHANNELS IN THE MAMMALIAN LENS.

ALBERTI G, BALLABENI A and MARAINI G.

Institute of Ophthalmology, University of Parma, Parma (Italy)

Purpose To molecularly characterize some of the K channels present in the mammalian lens.
Methods cDNA was obtained from rat, pig and human lenses total RNA by reverse transcription and tested by PCR using 6 different sets of primers for the following K-channels: KCN, IRK, ROMK, HiGIRK2 (U24660), KCNA3, and HUMKCH. Transparent human lenses were obtained from eye bank donors aged 13-75 years. Human β-B2-crystallin specific primers were used as a positive control for testing the cDNA. The PCR amplification products were identified on the basis of the expected size and sequenced.
Results Out of the six different sets of primers, only the IRK primer set allowed the identification of a PCR product of the expected size (245 bp) both in rat, pig and human lenses.
Conclusions. The IRK channel, first cloned and functionally characterized in man in brain tissue, is an inward rectifier potassium channel. Firstly reported to be present in cultured human lens epithelium, has now been identified in freshly dissected human lenses.

Supported by BioMed grant BMH4-CT96-1593

146

PRESENCE OF 90K PROTEIN IN PATIENTS UNDERGOING CATARACT SURGERY

PE GALLENGA[1], L LOBEFALO[1], C CRUDELI[1], G DELLA LOGGIA[1], B FORNARINI[2], O FUSCO[2], L MASTROPASQUA[1]
[1] Institute of Ophthalmology and Legal Medicine
[2] Chair of Medical Oncology
"G.d'Annunzio" University Chieti - Italy

Purpose: To determine whether 90K is present in human aqueous humor in patients undergoing cataracts extraction and to establish if there is a relationship between 90K aqueous and serum/tear levels.
Methods: tear, aqueous and serum samples (≈100μl) were obtained after informed consent from 10 healthy subjects. 90K was quantitatively determined using an enzyme-linked immunosorbent assay (ELISA). The concentration of 90K was then calculated in μg/ml with the reference standard curve
Results: Mean 90K value was 3160 μg/ml in the serum, 35.75 μg/ml in the aqueous and 617.38 μg/ml in the tears. A significant relationship was found between serum and tear 90K levels ($p<0.05$), while no relationship was found between serum and aqueous 90K levels and between sex and age and 90K values.
Conclusions: 90K is present in aqueous of subjects undergoing cataract surgery. Because of its immunomodulatory properties, 90K may play a role in the intraocular response to states of immune activation.

147

THE ROLE OF PROTEOLYTIC ACTIVITY OF CATHEPSIN A IN THE PATHOGENESIS OF CATARACT IN HUMAN LENS

STANKIEWICZ A. and OBUCHOWSKA I.
Dept. Ophthalmology, Med. Academy, Białystok (Poland)

Purpose
To evaluate cathepsin A activity in the aqueous humour in patients with cataract, absolute glaucoma and malignant melanoma of choroid.
Methods
Cathepsin A activity was determined by the ninhydrin colorimetric method with synthetic substrate (N-Cbz-Phe-Ala) at its optimum pH 5.0.
Results
In the human aqueous humour of the eyes with cataract cathepsin A activity was more than three times higher than in the eyes with melanoma and absolute glaucoma.
Conclusions
Higher cathepsin A activity in the aqueous humour in cataract points to its importance in cataract pathogenesis. It is well known that occurrence of proteolytic enzymes is associated with formation of vacuoles and opacities and dissolution of lens cortex in hypermature cataract. Because cathepsin A is the only enzyme in the eye, which can cleave carboxyl bonds in proteins, it is probably involved in the proteolytic process in cataractous lens.

148

MATURE CATARACT DEVELOPMENT AFTER PROTON BEAM IRRADIATION FOR CHOROIDAL MELANOMA.

RAPOPORT P, MOREL X, DHERMIES F, MEYER A, RENARD G.
Dpt. Ophthalmology, Hôtel-Dieu, Paris.

Purpose : We studied a group of patient who underwent proton beam irradiation for choroidal melanoma, in order to estimate incidence and risk factors of radiation-induced mature cataract

Methods : 125 patients have been irradiated for choroidal melanoma between 1992 and 1997. 98 of them have been included in retrospective analysis including age, gender, tumoral characteristics, dosimetry data, lens description and associated complications.

Results : Significant lens opacifications developed in 33 patients (33.7%) : cataract was mature at time of diagnosis in 12 (36.3%) cases. All these patients have suffered total lens irradiation for important tumoral volume (median 1.4 cm3) of anterior localisation. Incidence of anterior segment complications was maximal in association with mature cataract development.

Conclusion : Leading risks factors of proton beam induced mature cataract development are volume of lens irradiated as well as amount of irradiation received by the lens. Association between mature cataract, uveitis, rubeosis and glaucoma appears to be frequent after proton beam irradiation. Adequate dosimetry data may be useful in the follow-up of irradiated patients.

149

LOSS OF ACCOMMODATION IN TERMS OF MOLECULAR RELAXATION PROCESSES

C. Meyer[1], F. Soergel[2,3], B. Abele[2,3], W. Pechhold[2,3], H. Laqua[1]
1. Dept. of Ophthalmology, University of Luebeck, Germany
2. Dept of Applied Physics 2 & 3. Institute for Dynamic Materials Testing, University of Ulm, Germany.

Purpose. To quantify the parameters of the relaxation time which are relevant for the accommodative process by means of dynamic mechanical analysis (DMA).
Methods. In our wide range viscoelasticity spectrometer (frequency 1 mHz - 1 kHz), the complex shear compliance spectra J(f) = J´(f) - i * J´´(f) (reciprocal shear modulus G) of lenses from explanted donor eyes of different ages were measured. The relevant parameters (i.e. relaxation frequency f_m, relaxation strength, width parameter) were analysed. f_m corresponds to a relaxation time t (2p * f_m * t = 1) which can be determined from in vivo experiments with human experimentees.
Results. From the lens´ 3 relaxation processes at lower (f_{m1}, medium (f_{m2}) and higher frequencies (f_{m3}), the processes f_{m1} and f_{m2} are relevant for the accommodative process.
Conclusions. With increasing stiffness (decreasing accommodation), the relaxation frequency f_{m2} was found to be nearly constant (corresponding to a relaxation time in the order of 100ms) - whereas f_{m1} was shifted to lower frequencies with increasing stiffness. Moreover the distributions of all relaxation times (frequencies) became broader with increasing stiffness.
Comm. Rel.ships: None

150

IN VITRO EFFECT OF MINOXIDIL ON LENS EPITHELIAL CELLS PROLIFERATION VERSUS CORNEAL ENDOTHELIAL CYTOTOXICITY.

HERNANDEZ-GALILEA E [1], BARAHONA JM [1], VAZQUEZ R[2], URRUTIA M[1], CASTRO R[1], SANCHEZ F[2].
1.Dep. of Ophthalmology, 2.Dep. of Anatomy, Faculty of Medicine, University of Salamanca Salamanca (Spain).

Purpose: To evaluate the inhibitory effect of minoxidil on cultured proliferating Lens Epithelial Cells (LECs) versus cytotoxic effect on corneal endothelial cells in culture, because minimun side effects over anterior chamber and corneal endthelium are required to succesful therapy of posterior capsular opacification (PCO). **Methods:** Rabbit lens epithelial cells and corneal edothelium were cultured in DMEM at 35ºC in 5% CO2 in multiwells during 7 days. Both types of cells were exposed to minoxidil (1, 2 and 4 mM) for 1 hour. Control group and Balanced Salt Solution group were included. After seven days multiwells were procesed to Light microscopy study. Morphometric study of cellular population of LECs and corneal endothelium cells were done, using a computed planimetry system **Results:** Dose-dependent effect on LECs proliferation was noted and non confluent colonies of cells were observed on all treated groups. Morphologic changes in normal aparence of corneal endothelial cells after 1 hour of minoxidil treatment has been observed and evidence for different intracellular alterations included the minimal dose exposure, was confirmed **Conclusion:** The effectiveness of minoxidil suppresing LECs proliferation appears to be conditioned by toxicity on corneal endothelial cells, suggesting a limited use as a safety therapeutic agent to prevent PCO.

Supported by grant of *Junta de Castilla y Leon* (SA 59/97)

151

EXPERIMENTAL STUDY ON THE PROTECTIVE EFFECT OF APRACLONIDINE 0,5% IN BLOOD - AQUEOUS BARRIER BREAKDOWN AFTER CATARACT SURGERY

Arguedas F.A[1],Ruiz Lapuente C. [2],Martínez Giralt O[2], Martínez Palmer A. [2]

1. Hospital Santa Tecla, Tarragona.Universidad de Reus
2. Hospital del Mar. Universidad Autónoma de Barcelona

Purpose: Apraclonidine 1% has shown to reduce protein content in anterior chamber after laser surgery. To evaluate the efficacy of apraclonidine 0,5% as a protective agent for Blood-Aqueous Barrier (BAB) breakdown occurring after cataract surgery.

Methods: Seventy eyes of White New Zealand rabbits were allocated to seven groups: Group A: Extracapsular surgery. Group B: same as group A with IOL implant. Group C: Same as group B with previous treatment with apraclonidine. Group D: IOL implant with previous treatment with apraclonidine. Group E: Same as grup C with postsurgical treatment with apraclonidine. Group F: same as froup D with postsurgical apraclonidine. Group G IOL implant alone. Aqueous protein content was determined 24 hours postsurgically. Results were compared with ANOVA and t-tests.

Results: Aqueous proteins where in a mean rank from 527,3± 343 (mean ± SD) to 2002 ± 376,9 (mean ± SD). Protein content was significantly lower in groups undergoing IOL implantation alone without extracapsular surgery (p = 0,01). In groups operated on with extracapsular cataract extraction apraclonidine failed to reduce protein content in aqueous. In eyes with intraocular lens implant treatment demonstrated to reduce protein content significantly.

Conclusion: Protein measurement in eyes treated with cataract extraction showed no benefit of the inclusion of apraclonidine in them. Lower degrees of agression such as IOL implant alone resulted on a decreased protein level when compared to other surgeries or absence of treatment.

* Supported by FISS - 94 Grant.

152

CHOLESTEROL OXIDES MAY INDUCE LENS OPACITY IN ORGAN CULTURE

GIRÃO H, MOTA M AND PEREIRA P
Dept. Ophthalmology, Biomedical Institute for research in Light and Image, Coimbra (Portugal).

Purpose: To establish the cytotoxicity and effect on transparency of cholesterol oxides, hydrogen peroxide and linoleic acid hydroperoxide (HPOE) in human lens in organ culture. Methods: Human lenses were obtained from healthy volunteers and transferred immediately to Dulbecco's modified Eagle's medium (DMEM supplemented with 10% fetal calf serum and antibiotics. Lenses were incubated (37°C, 5% CO_2) with 1 mM H_2O_2, 1μM 7-ketocholesterol, 1μM 7β-cholesterol and 1μM HPOE in the presence of copper. Cytotoxicity was evaluated by protein leakage to the medium and changes in lens transparency were registered by photography. Results: Human lenses in culture were shown to be resistant to H_2O_2 (1mM) and HPOE (1μM) with minimal changes in transparency and no detectable release of protein to the medium. 7β–OH-cholesterol and 7-keto-cholesterol induced a marked oppacification of the lens and a significant cytotoxicity as evaluated by the release of protein to the medium. Conclusions: Products of cholesterol oxidation are more toxic to the lens in culture then products of fatty acid oxidation or H_2O_2. Accumulation of such products in vivo may contribute to lens oppacification and cataract formation.

153

THE ANTIOXIDANT EFFECT OF CHOLESTEROL IN LENS MEMBRANES

PEREIRA P, GIRÃO H, AND MOTA M

Dept. Ophthalmology, Biomedical Institute for research in Light and Image, Coimbra (Portugal)

Purpose To establish whether cholesterol may act as an antioxidant in the lens, increasing membrane resistance to oxidation. Methods Lens membranes were obtained from human donors and from bovine eyes. Liposomes of dipalmitoylphosphatidylcholine containing different molar ratios of cholesterol and vitamin E were also used. Oxidation was stimulated by thermal decomposition of AAPH. Lipid hydroperoxides were measured by the FOX assay. Cholesterol oxidation was evaluated by GC and consumption of vitamin E by HPLC. Membrane resistance to oxidation was evaluated by fluorescence quenching of the probe parinaric acid. Results. Production of lipid hydroperoxides is only initiated after total consumption of endogenous vitamin E. The oxidation pattern for vitamin E and cholesterol in the lens are very similar as are their effects on lens membrane resistance to oxidation.. The products of cholesterol oxidation (7α and 7β diols and 5α,6α-epoxy) do not initiate peroxidative chain-reaction in lens membranes whereas linoleic acid hydroperoxides can stimulate lipid peroxidation. The incorporation of cholesterol to 35% and vitamin E (3 μm) in PC liposomes increases its resistance to oxidation by 68% and 64% respectively. Conclusions. It is suggested that cholesterol may act as an antioxidant in lens membranes intercepting the peroxyl radicals formed during lipid peroxidation, being converted to more stable alcohols or epoxides.

154

ORAL ANTI-OXIDANT MICRONUTRIENTS SLOW PROGRESSION OF AGE-RELATED CATARACT: RESULTS OF THE ROCHE-EUROPEAN-AMERICAN-CATARACT-TRIAL (REACT)

SCHALCH W[1], KÖPCKE W[2], CHYLACK LT Jr[3], BRON AJ[4], BROWN N[4], HURST M[5], MITCHEL S[5], THIEN U[6], and the REACT group.

1. F. Hoffmann-La Roche Ltd., Basel, (Switzerland)
2. University Münster (Germany)
3. Brigham and Women's Hospital, Boston (USA)
4. University of Oxford, (UK) 5. University of Bradford (UK)
6. Biometric Center, Munich (Germany)

Purpose: To determine if oral supplementation with a mixture (mg/day) of vitamin E (600) vitamin C (750) and β-carotene (18) can influence the progression of early age-related cataract.

Methods: Patients from out-patient clinics in Boston, Bradford, and Oxford with early cataract of predefined grade were recruited for this double-masked, placebo-controlled, multi-center trial. Starting with 297 subjects, 231 concluded 2 and 158 3 yrs of treatment. The extent of cataract was measured quarterly using digital images of the lens recorded by a retroillumination CCD camera and expressed as change in the "% of pixels opaque" (Δ%PO). Prognostic factors were modeled using a recursive partition procedure (CART).

Results: After three years, Δ%PO was 1.73 in the vitamin group vs. 3.3 in the placebo group (p=0.022). While the effect was stronger in the US subjects, it was not significant in the UK. An analysis of prognostic factors suggests that vitamin E serum levels may contribute more to the effect than the other micronutrients.

Conclusions: Oral supplementation with these micronutrients slightly decelerates early age-related cataract progression. The center effect may be due to the more advanced cataract in the UK.

155

AN IMMUNOPEROXYDASE (PAP), INDIRECT IMMUNOFLUORESCENCE (IFI) AND TRANS IMMUNO-ELECTRON MICROSCOPY (TEM) STUDY OF THE AGED HUMAN LENS CAPSULE

((F. MAJO[1], M. MONTARD[1], B. DELBOSC[1], S. WANNEBROUCQ[1], B. KANTELIP[2])).

Dept. Ophthalmology [1], Dept. Pathology [2], J. MINJOZ Hospital, BESANCON (FRANCE).

Purpose To locate collagen types I (I), III (III) and IV (IV), laminin and fibronectin in the aged human lens capsule. Results of three different immunostaining techniques were compared. **Methods** Twenty two successive phaco were performed on twenty two patients from the age of 40 to 100 years (mean age 74,2). Four anterior lens capsules were processed for immunoperoxydase (PAP) and fifteen for indirect immunofluorescence (IFI) and trans immunoelectron microscopy (TEM) study. Primary antibodies were specific for types I, III (Institut Pasteur de Lyon, France), type IV, laminin and fibronectin (DAKO Corp., Denmark). Secondary antibodies were bound to peroxydase for PAP, to fluorescein and rhodamine for IFI, and to ten nanometer gold particles for TEM. All the capsules were stained by all the specific antibodies. **Results** Collagens I and III were observed in all the capsules' thickness, with the strongest labeling under the lens epithelial layer with PAP and IFI technique. Labeling of the collagen IV was located in all the capsules'thickness with TEM and only under the lens epithelial layer with PAP and IFI. Whatever technique used, laminin was detected in the inner layer of capsules. No labeling of fibronectin was observed. **Conclusion** We report that collagens I and III seem to be the most important components of the aged human lens capsule, even though other authors state it is the IV. Collagen and laminin have a particular distribution throughout the capsule's thickness : this could mean that they each have a specific function. Collagen types' distribution (I and III > IV) in the aged lens capsule could be an indirect sign of lens epithelial metabolism modification. NONE

156

THE ORIGIN OF ELSCHNIG'S PEARLS

WILLEKENS B AND VRENSEN GFJM. Dept. Morphology, The Netherlands Ophthalmic Research Institute, Amsterdam

Purpose: Posterior capsule opacification (PCO) is a major complication of extracapsular cataract extraction (ECCE) (20-40% of cases) due to aberrant proliferation and differentiation of lens epithelial cells (LEC's) left in the bag after ECCE. Two types of PCO are distinguished: the fibrosis-type and the pearl-type (1). This study aimed to unravel the cellular origin of Elschnig's pearls.

Methods: Capsular bags with immature PCO and exhibiting pearls were obtained from donor eyes (Cornea Bank, Amsterdam) and were routinely prepared for light and electron microscopy (transmission and scanning).

Results: Accumulation of globular elements was observed on the anterior and posterior surface of the anterior capsule and the anterior surface of the posterior capsule. At the same locations monolayers of LEC's were found some of which exhibit ballooning of their surface.

Conclusion: The presence of ballooning cells is evidence that Elschnig's pearls originate from undifferentiated LEC's. This further suggests that proliferated LEC's, left after ECCE, differentiate along two routes.

(1) Apple DJ et al., Survey Ophthalmol, 1992; 37: 73-116.

157

HISTOMORPHOMETRY OF THE LENS CAPSULE AND EPITHELIUM

MARTÍNEZ A[1], ABREU J A[1], LOSADA M[1], MENDEZ R[2], AGUILAR J[1].

1-Dept. Ophthalmology. Hospital Universitario Canarias. Spain.
2-Dept. Pathology. Hospital Universitario Canarias. Spain.

Purpose: To analyse the epithelial cell size and the lens capsule by automatic histomorphometry with a VIDS V system.

Methods: During routine cataract surgery cases after performing a capsulorhexis (CCC) and diathermic capsulotomy (DC) we saved the extracted anterior capsular fragment and sent it to the pathologist . The histopathological study consisted in a histomorphometric analysis of semithin sections stained with toluidine blue and an automatic images analyser (computer with the VIDS program).

Results: Histomorphometry showed an average epithelial cell size of 15.12 microns. The measure is accomplished over the computer . All the cells presented the same length.

Conclusions: the longitude of the epithelial cells is 12.70 – 17.54 microns, with an average of 15.12. This cell size is independent of the CCC or DC diameter.

158

A COMPARATIVE PATHOLOGIC STUDY OF CAPSULORHEXIS VERSUS DIATHERMIC CAPSULOTOMY

ABREU J A[1], MARTÍNEZ A[1], CORDOVES L[1], MENDEZ R[2], GONZALEZ DE LA ROSA M[1].
1-Dept. Ophthalmology. Hospital Universitario Canarias. Spain.
2-Dept. Pathology. Hospital Universitario Canarias. Spain.

Purpose: To compare the structural effects produced on the lens capsule and epithelium by capsulorhexis (CCC) and diathermic capsulotomy (DC) of different diameters.

Methods: During routine cataract surgery cases after performing a CCC or a DC of 4.5, 5.5, or 6.5 mm in diameter, we saved the extracted anterior capsular fragment and sent it to the pathologist. The histopathological study consisted in hematoxylin-eosin and PAS stains together with the histomorphometric analysis of semithin sections stained with toluidine blue. The pathologist was blinded to the tecnique used.

Results: Histomorphometry showed an average epithelial cell size of 12-15 microns. CCC capsules had a clean and sharp margin with undisrupted epithelial cells reaching it. On the other hand, the DC capsules showed a swollen, slightly retracted and more intensely stained margin, with the closest 6 to 10 cells undergoing a necrobiotic process.

Conclusions: In CCC, the capsular epithelium does not seem to be affected. We detect a physical damage with DC of 90-150 microns in extension, that could be an added factor in capsular opacification prevention in capsulotomies of 6.5 mm or larger, due to its proximity to the germinative area of the epithelium. In 4.5 and 5.5 capsulotomies the intensity of the trauma does not seem to influence the later capsular fibrosis or opacification.

159

CRISTALLIN SELF-ORGANISATION AFTER EXPERIMENTAL DISSOCIATION INTO POLYPEPTIDES

AHREND M, BOURS J, WEGENER A, BREIPOHL W
Department of experimental Ophthalmology, RFW-University, Bonn; Germany

__Purpose:__ Lens ageing is associated with protein aggregation to high molecular weight complexes in the nuclear region, a relative decrease of water-soluble (WS) and an increase of water-insoluble (WI) cristallins. This study was to investigate experimental lens polypeptide aggregation as a model for protein ageing and the importance of α-cristallin in this context. __Methods:__ Homogenates of calf lens equatorial and nuclear sections were dialysed at various exchange rates. __Results:__ Both, rapid and slow dialysis provoked extensive recombination of native proteins from polypeptides in equatorial and nuclear samples. However, only dialysis of nuclear cristallins resulted in WI-protein formation. WI-cristallin recombination proved to be especially high with slow dialysis. Reintegration into α-cristallins and WS high molecular weight complex of polypeptides „lost" during the course of denaturation was supported by the addition of urea during the following IEF. The relative amounts of α-cristallin and WI-Protein fractions were increased all other WS-protein fractions decreased during this process. __Conclusion:__ The experimentally provoked lens cristallin dissociation into polypeptides and especially their recombination to a „native" cristallin pattern under different rates of dialysis can be considered a model for naturally occuring lens cristallin ageing in the nucleus but not equator. This ageing process is apparently linked to α-cristallins.

160

Macromolecular study of the chaperone function of bovine α-crystallin.

ABGAR S., AERTS T., CLAUWAERT J.
Department of Biochemistry, University of Antwerp (Belgium).

__Purpose:__ α-crystallin, a member of the small heat shock protein family, is the predominant structural protein of the vertebrate eye lens cytoplasm. It probably plays an important role in preventing the uncontrolled aggregation of the other lens proteins crystallins and keeping the lens cytoplasm devoid of light scattering. We have used stressed conalbumin (by reducing the -S-S-bonds) as a model for studying the α-crystallin-stressed protein interaction.

__Methods__: We studied the α-crystallin-conalbumin complex in temperature range 26 °C to 37 °C using gel filtration chromatography, SDS-PAGE electrophoresis, equilibrium sedimentation and photon correlation spectroscopy. α-crystallin prevented the the formation of large conalbumin aggregates by binding the stressed proteins.

__Results__: α-crystallin was operating as a chaperone in the temperature range 20 to 37°C and its activity was only limited by the (non)availabilty of stressed proteins. This could be concluded from the kinetics of the aggregation of the stressed conalbumin in the absence and the formation of the α-crystallin-conalbumin complex in the presence of α-crystallin. This complex was formed at a 1 to 1 ratio of the α-crystallin aggregate (molar mass 650,000 g/mol) and conalbumin.

161

EFFECT OF TOPICAL KETOROLAC IN THE ARACHIDONIC ACID METABOLISM IN EXPERIMENTAL ANTERIOR UVEITIS.

CUEVAS R, RUIZ O, FERRER E, TORRON C, ROJO A, PABLO L, POLO V, HONRUBIA FM.

Dept Ophthalmology. Hospital "Miguel Servet". Zaragoza. Spain.

Purpose: To studied the effect of topical ketorolac-tromethamine in the arachidonic acid metabolism on a model of endotoxin induced uveitis (EIU) in albino rabbits.

Methods: EIU was produced by intravitreal injection in the right eye with 10 ng LPS A Salmonella typhimurium endotoxin in 5 l saline solution. We have used 60 animals (5 groups of 12 animals each). Control group (G-I) was injected with saline (5 ul); endotoxin group (G-II) was injected with 10 ng of ET; group III, IV and V were injected with the same amount of ET and treated with topical ketorolac-tromethamine every 6, 4 and 2 hours respectively. The animals were sacrificed 24 hours after the ET administration and we determined E2 prostaglandin and B4 leukotriene concentration in the aqueous humor.

Results: In all treated groups with ketorolac-tromethamine we observed a significant reduction ($p < 0,05$) in aqueous humor concentration of E2 prostaglandin without increase of the B4 leukotriene concentration comparing with endotoxin group.

Conclusion: Ketorolac tromethamine produced an inhibition of ciclooxigenase metabolism of arachidonic acid without increase of lipooxigenase pathway.

162

RELATION BETWEEN LASER FLARE PHOTOMETRY AND CLINICAL OUTCOMES IN HLA-B27 RELATED ANTERIOR UVEITIS

BERNASCONI O[1], AUER C[1,3], LADAS JG[2], GUEX-CROSIER Y[1], TRAN VT[1], HOLLAND GN[2], HERBORT CP[1,3]

1. Hôpital Ophtalmique, UNIL, Lausanne (Switzerland)
2. Jules Stein Eye Institute, UCLA, Los Angeles (USA)
3. La Source Eye Center, Lausanne (Switzerland)

Purpose: to correlate laser flare photometry (LFP) with slit-lamp evaluation of aqueous cells and flare in HLA-B27 uveitis in a prospective multicenter trial.

Methods: slit-lamp parameters were correlated to laser flare photometry in a masked fashion in HLA-B27 uveitis patients with a standard topical therapy on days D0, D1, D2-4, D7, D14, D21, D28, and months 2 and 6.

Results: fifty episodes (41 patients) of acute anterior HLA-B27 related uveitis were included. Restoration of blood-aqueous barrier was monitored with much more sensitivity by laser flare photometry than by cells evaluated by slit-lamp examination. There was a time lag between the 50 % reduction of aqueous cells measured by slit-lamp (14 days) as compared to the 50 % reduction of laser flare photometry (3.9 days): $p<0.001$ (sign test).

Conclusions: laser flare photometry is significantly superior to slit-lamp cell evaluation to monitor anterior chamber inflammation in acute HLA-B27 uveitis.

163

INTERLEUKIN-13 INHIBITS ENDOTOXIN-INDUCED UVEITIS

MARIE O., THILLAYE-GOLDENBERG-B., NAUD M.C., de KOZAK Y.

INSERM U450/XR86 , PARIS , FRANCE

PURPOSE: The goal of the present experiments is to inves tigate the effects of recombinant human interleukin-13 (IL-13) in endotoxin-induced uveitis (EIU) in rat. This cytokine, recently described, is produced by Th2 cells and shares many of the properties of IL-4, such as suppression of production of proinflammatory cytokines (TNF-α, IL-1, IL-6) and inhibits cytotoxic functions of monocytes/macro phages. **METHODS:** Male Lewis rats, 8 weeks old, were subcutaneously pretreated with 50 µg/kg of IL-13 in 0,2ml of saline. Thirty mn later, rats were injected in one footpad with 350µg/kg of lipopolysaccharide (LPS) from *Salmonella typhimurium* in 0,1ml of saline to induce uveitis. Two other subcutaneous IL-13 injections were performed (6 and 10 hours later). The intraocular inflammation was evaluated at slit-lamp 23 hours after LPS injection, then rats were killed for immunohistological examination. **RESULTS:** Clinical evaluation showed a significant inhibition of EIU in IL-13 treated rats. This result was confirmed by the significant decrease of the number of OX-42+ cells (mainly polymorphonuclears) and of ED-1+ cells (monocytes macrophages), in the different eye tissues, without any effect on ED2+ celis (resident tissue macrophages). **CONCLUSION:** IL-13 may be considered as a promising mediator in ocular inflammation regulation.

164

CHURG-STRAUSS SYNDROME – A CASE REPORT

STUEBIGER N, SCHLOTE T AND ZIERHUT M.

Department of General Ophthalmology, University Eye-Clinic Tuebingen, Germany

Purpose The Churg-Strauss syndrome, also known as allergic granulomatosis with angiitis, is a necrotizing vasculitis with unknown pathogenesis. The necrotizing granulomatous vasculitis involved small and medium-sized arteries, kapillaries and veins, characteristic changes are intra- and extravascular, eosiniphilic granulomas, accompanied by clinically symptoms: bronchial asthma, hypereosinophilia and fever. Ocular manifestations are rare.

Case report A 53 year old woman suffered from bronchial asthma, relapsing lung infiltrates and sinusites since 1994. In august 1997 she suddenly discovered vasculitic skin manifestations on both legs and a mononeuritis of the left nervus peroneus. At the same time visual acuity of the right eye decreased, before she had had some attacks of amaurosis fugax. The funduscopy showed a central retinal artery occlusion. Laboratory findings: blood eosinophilia of 20%, increased IgE value (396 kU/l), and negative parameters for anticytoplasmatic antibodys in granulocytes (p- and c-ANCA).

Conclusion The clinical and laboratory findings are characteristic signs for a Churg-Strauss-syndrome. In cases without such typical disorder-manifestations the histologic examination leads to the diagnosis and helps to differentiate from other necrotizing vasculitides, e.g. polarteriitis nodosa or Wegener´s granulomatosis. This case report discloses the necessity of including the Churg-Strauss syndrome in the differential diagnosis of ocular ischemia.

165

INFLUENCE OF PSYCHOEMOTIONAL FAKTORS ON THE STATE IMMUNE SYSTEM IN PATIENTS WITH RETINA DYSTROPHY

CHAURA A., DEGTJARENKO T ,BUSCHUEVA N.
FILATOV INSTITUTE OF EYE DISEASES (UKRAINE)

Purpose Immunodisfunction plays an importaint role in pathogenesis retina dystrophy.The influences psychoemotional factors on immune system (IS) are not cleared up yet. The aim of this investigation is to study psychoemotional faktors on the state of IS in patients with retina dystrophy.
Methods The specific and non-specific immunity, psychoemotional peculiarities was investigated in 27 patients of 12-22 years old with complicated form of myopia. The control group consists of 20 healthy people of the same age.
Results The patients with retina dystrophy experience a high level of uneasiness and autism, an increase of psychosomatic complaints The decrease of the content of B-lymphocytes and of phagocytic activity of the neutrophyles as well as the increase of the sensitivity T-cells to the eye antigens (retina, uvea) are observed. The negative and statistically correlative relation between the level of uneasiness and the content of B-lymphocytes, T-helpers and phagocytic activity of the neutrophyles was established.
Conclusions The research conducted proves the influence of psychoemotional factors on IS and the necessity of the correction of these disorders in patients with retina dystrophy.

166

EXPRESSION OF CELLULAR AND VIRAL INTERLEUKIN-10 IN A RABBIT MODEL OF PVR

WILLERMAIN F.,[1,2] COOL V,[2] BAUDSON N,[2] LIBERT J.,[1] VELU T.,[2] BRUYNS C.,[2] and CASPERS-VELU LE[1].

1. Dept Ophthalmology, CHU Saint-Pierre (Belgium).
2. I.R.I.B.H.N, Erasme Hospital, ULB (Belgium).

Introduction: Proliferative vitreoretinopathy (PVR) is a common complication of retinal surgery. The pathogeny of PVR involves both inflammatory and proliferative components.

Aim of the work: We evaluate the therapeutic potential of interleukin-10 in a rabbit model of PVR. Both the cellular (cIL-10) and the viral (vIL-10 from EBV) IL-10 possess anti-inflammatory and immunosuppressive properties. cIL-10 seems to possess also some pro-inflammatory properties.

Methods : Rabbit dermal fibroblast (RDF)-neo, RDF-cIL-10, RDF-vIL-10 cells were obtained by transduction of RDF with retroviral particles carrying the *neo* gene alone or with the cIL-10 or vIL-10 gene, respectively, and by Geneticin selection. PVR were induced by intravitreous injection of 2.10^6 cells.

Results: At 28 days, according to Fastenberg's classification, mean grades were 2.0 for RDF-vIL-10 (n=6), 3.4 for RDF-cIL-10 (n=5), and 2.75 for control RDF-neo (n=4). No anterior segment inflammation was observed in all groups.

Conclusions: vIL-10 and cIL-10 may have opposite activities on the generation of PVR and of anterior segment inflammation, which may have therapeutic implications.

167

INDOCYANINE GREEN ANGIOGRAPHIC FEATURES OF TUBERCULOUS CHORIORETINITIS

TJ Wolfensberger[1], B Piguet[1], CP Herbort[1,2] [1]Hôpital Ophtalmique Jules Gonin, Lausanne, [2]La Source Eye Center, Lausanne, Switzerland.

Purpose: To determine indocyanine-green angiographic features of tuberculous chorioretinitis. **Methods**: 15 eyes of 8 patients (5 female, 3 male; 52±6 years) with tuberculous chorioretinitis were studied with indocyanine green angiography (ICGA) performed according to a standard uveitis protocol. Diagnosis was made if caseating granulomas and acid-fast bacilli were present in a biopsy in combination with a positive Mantoux test (2 cases). The diagnosis of presumptive tuberculous origin was established in the presence of a strongly positive Mantoux test (6 cases, average diameter 15±2 mm), and if striking clinical improvement occured after institution of antituberculous treatment. Average follow-up was 11±3 months. **Results**: The features on ICGA could be classified into four main categories: First, irregularly distributed, hypofluorescent dark choroidal lesions in the early and intermediate phases, invisible or not on funduscopy or fluorescein angiography and localised in the midperiphery (40% of eyes), in the macula (13 %), in both regions (20 %), in the macular and peripapillary region (13 %) or in all three regions (13 %). The dot diameter ranged from 0.3-3.0 disk diameter. These lesions either became isofluorescent in the late phase of the angiogram (Type 1), present in all eyes, or remained hypofluorescent (Type 2), present in 66 % of eyes. Second, focal hyperfluorescence in the form of multiple small spots (on average 42±15 per fundus) appearing in the mid and late phases (47% of eyes). Third, fuzzy choroidal vessels with leakage at around 10 minutes of the angiogram, and fourth, late diffuse choroidal hyperfluorescence with staining at around 40 minutes of the angiogram. The latter two changes were present in 66 % of eyes. Type 1 lesions, fuzzy choroidal vessels and diffuse choroidal hyper-fluorescence tended to regress with anti-Tbc and steroid treatment. **Conclusions**: ICGA allowed to assess and quantify the hitherto unknown extent of choroidal involvement in tuberculous chorioretinitis, and its characteristic appearance might represent an additional valuable tool for diagnosis and monitoring.

168

INCIDENCE AND EVOLUTION OF PAPILLITIS IN OCULAR TOXOPLASMOSIS

DURIG J,[1] BERNASCONI O[1] and GUEX-CROSIER Y[1].
1.Jules Gonin Hospital, University of Lausanne,Switzerland.

Purpose: To define the incidence and clinical features of papillitis in acute ocular toxoplasmosis.
Methods: The data chart of patients followed at the uveitis clinic of Jules Gonin Eyes Hospital presenting a clinical feature compatible with an ocular toxoplasmosis were retrospectively reviewed. Diagnosis of toxoplasmosis was defined on a clinical basis and all patients had a positive ELISA test against *T. Gondii*. Optic nerve papillitis was documented either by fundus photography and/or fluorescein anagiography. The following criteria were analyzed: incidence, visual outcome, slit lamp examination and when available Octopus visual field testing.
Results: 16/48 (33%) patients (mean age of 39,65 ± 12.50 years; range 14 - 54) with acute ocular toxoplasmosis had a papillitis. All patients were treated with a standard regiment consisting of pyrimethamine 25-50 mg/day, sulfadiazine 6-8 mg/day, folinic acid 15 mg/day associated two days later with systemic oral steroid therapy 1mg/kg/day. Mean initial visual acuity improved from 0.87±0.13 to 1.17±0.09 ($p \leq 0.020$; t-test) after a mean time therapy of 70 ± 10 days. Only 7/16 patients had a satellite scar signing a previous toxoplasmic focus.
Conclusions: The optic nerve involvement in ocular toxoplasmosis is frequently associated with a decrease of visual acuity that resolve after therapy in most of the cases.

169

OCULAR PROBLEMS AND TOXOPLASMA INFECTION IN INDIGENOUS PEOPLE FROM UPPER RIO NEGRO, AMAZONAS, BRASIL

FIGUEIREDO, J.F.C.[1], RODRIGUES, M.L.V.[1], CRUZ, A.A.V.[1], CARVALHO, R.A.C.[2], MARTINEZ, R.[1], SANTOMAURO-VAZ, M.A.J.[3] and PASSOS, A.D.C.[1]

[1] – Medical School of Ribeirão Preto, University of São Paulo, Brazil; [2] – Instituto de Olhos de Manaus, Amazonas and Medical School of Ribeirão Preto; [3] – Centro de Saúde Escola "Dom Walter Ivan", São Gabriel da Cachoeira.

Purpose: to investigate the association between ocular diseases and antecedents of *Toxoplasma gondii* infection.
Methods: Blood samples were collected from 10 indigenous with ocular problems (chorioretinitis and corneal alterations) and from 15 indigenous and descendents, without ocular diseases. It was performed the detection of class IgG and IgM antibodies against *Toxoplasma gondii* (indirect immunofluorescence reaction), considering positive titters ≥ 1/16.
Results: The indirect immunofluorescence reaction was positive in all of the subjects with ocular problems and in 4 controls, with significant difference between the groups (p=0.0005).
Conclusion: There was a positive association between antecedents of *Toxoplasma gondii* infection and the ocular diseases studied.

170

ANTI-LIPOPOLISACCHARIDE ANTIBODIES IN PATIENTS WITH UVEITIS

MISIUK-HOJLO M.[1], LUGOWSKI C.[2], NIEDZIELA T.[2], PORYCKA D.[1], SZYMANIEC S.[2]

1. Dept. Ophthalmology, Wroclaw University of Medicine, Wroclaw, Poland
2. Inst. of Immunology and Experimental Therapy, Wroclaw, Poland

Purpose: To investigate whether the patients with uveitis have abnormal serum level of anti-LPS antibodies.
Methods: We studied 80 patients with anterior and posterior uveitis and 25 without any signs of uveitis, examined during the years 1996-97. In every patient, intraocular inflammation was investigated according to standard diagnostic criteria. Serum levels were determined in ELISA test. Endotoxins isolated from Escherichia coli 01, 010, 0111, J5 and from Klebsiella pneumoniae 03 were used as the antigens.
Results: The highest level of antibodies was found against LPS E. coli 01 of R1 core type, wich is present in 70% of E. coli clinical isolates; the lowest level of antibodies was observed against LPS E. coli J5, the rough mutant of Rc type.
Conclusion: In our material we didn't find significative higher level of anti-endotoxin antibodies against Escherichia coli 01, 010, 0111, J5 and Klebsiella pneumoniae 03 lipopolisaccharides in comparison with control group.

171

DEVIC-LIKE DISEASE IN SYSTEMIC LUPUS ERYTHEMATOSUS (SLE)

GIORGI D,[1] GIORGI A,[2] PACE F,[2] BALACCO GABRIELI C.[1]
1. Institute of Ophthalmology, "La Sapienza" University, Rome, Italy. 2. Department of Clinical Medicine, "La Sapienza" University, Rome, Italy.

Purpose: To review the literature of clinical and laboratory characteristics of SLE patients suffering from neuromyelopathy optica (Devic-like disease) reported since 1973-1997. In addition, aim of this study was to evaluate the presence of spinal cord disease in 7 SLE patients with optic neuropathy.
Methods: The 1982 revised American Rheumatism Associations' criteria were employed to diagnose SLE. One patient was also considered as suffering from antiphospholipid syndrome in association with SLE. All patients here reported had a full clinical and ophthalmological examination.
Results: By review of the literature it appears to be clear that transverse myelopathy is the more neurological disease seen in SLE patients suffering from optic neuropathy. Particularly, on 51 SLE patients with optic neuropathy, the 41.1% presented signs of myelopathy. In our 7 SLE patients, only a 23-year-old woman had clinical signs of acute and transient myelopathy.
Conclusions: It is note that patients with nervous system Lupus suffering from Devic-like disease have been well documented by several authors. The entity of Devic-like disease is defined by the concurrence of visual loss due to optic neuropathy and acute transverse myelopathy. By results of our review, optic neuropathy and myelopathy appear to be strongly associated in SLE. The latter prompted us to performe a full ophthalmological evaluation in SLE patients suffering from myelopathy.

172

HAMMAPATHIES IN CHILDREN WITH DIFFERENT EYE PATHOLOGY.

L.E.Teplinskaya, E.V.Mazanova, A.F.Kaliberdina
Helmholtz Institute of Eye Diseases, Moscow, Russia

Purpose. Study of disorders of humoral immunity, correlation with character of the process in children with uveitis and congenital glaucoma.
Methods. Immunodiffusion (Mancini et al, 1965)
Results. 149 children were examined. Hammapathies were detected in 57% cases of uveitis and 62,9% cases of glaucoma. Hypoimmunoglobulinemia G, A, M established in 35,9% of uveitis and in 60% of cases with glaucoma. Selective or combining deficiency of IgA (D-IgA) prevailed. D-IgA was revealed in 24,6% of children with panuveitis, toxoplasmic and idiopathic chorioretinitis and in 51,4%- of glaucoma, mainly in advanced and far advanced stages. Low levels of IgM and IgG were detected in uveitis in 5,3% and 6,1%, in glaucoma -5,7% and 2,9% accordingly. Hyperimmunoglobulinemia was found in 21,1% of patients with uveitis, mainly anterior and neurochorioretinitis and in 8,6% of children with glaucoma, and was presented by high levels of IgM and IgG. Hammapathies were accompanied by chronic recurrent infections in 44% of cases. Disorders of immunity were detected in 70% of mothers of children with congenital glaucoma.
Conclusions. Humoral immunodeficiency mainly presented by D-IgA and prevailed in children with congenital glaucoma over uveitis patients, and was accompanied by various somatic pathology.

173

CONDITIONS OF AIDS PATIENT WITH CYTOMEGALOVIRUS RETINITIS IN A BRAZILIAN UNIVERSITY HOSPITAL

RODRIGUES, M.L.V., FIGUEIREDO, J.F.C., MABTUM, E.A., CASTRO, G. and SOUZA, N.V.
Faculty of Medicine of Ribeirão Preto, University of São Paulo – Ribeirão Preto, SP, Brazil

Purpose: to study the systemic conditions, mainly the presence of other opportunistic infections, in AIDS patients, with cytomegalovirus retinitis.
Methods: Twenty patients, in follow-up in the Uveitis/AIDS out-patient clinic – Hospital das Clínicas, Faculty of Medicine of Ribeirão Preto, were studied.
Results: The mean number of opportunistic infections was 4/patient, and the most frequent infections were: oral moniliasis, tuberculosis, toxoplasmosis and *P.carinii* pneumoniae. All of the patients have high viral load and CD_4^+ count < 106 cells/mm^3.
Conclusion: Despite the local conditions and the number of opportunistic infections associated, the profile of cytomegalovirus in Ribeirão Preto is similar to this disaese´s profile in developed countries.

174

RACE AND ETHNICITY AS RISK FACTOR TO OPHTHALMOSCOPIC ALTERATIONS IN CHILDREN WITH AIDS

FIGUEIREDO RS AND RODRIGUES MLV
Dept. ophthalmology and Otolaringology, Faculty of Medicine of Ribeirao Preto, University of Sao Paulo, Ribeirao Preto, SP Brasil

Purpose: To report the ophthalmologic findings and the race of 3 1 cases of AIDS pediatric from a reference Hospital of the Northeast of Brazil.

Methods: Between july I996 and may 1998, 31 cases of ambulatory AIDS pediatric underwent indirect ophthalmoscopy every 6 months and patients with ocular abnormalities were examined every two weeks. A questionnaire which include a initial characterization of the patient was elaborated. The questionnaire include information about sex, age, race and type of transmission.

Results: All the ophthalmoscopic abnormalities finding were present in the children black "mulatto". Cotton - wool spots were observed in 03 patients. Perivasculitis was observed in 02 patients. Corrioretinitis was observed in 01 patient.

Conclusion: The race black "mulatto" seems to be a important risk factor associated to presence of abnormalities ophthalmologic finding.

175

INSUFFICIENCY OF ACCOMMODATION IN PATIENTS WITH AIDS

BUENO-GIMENO I (1), ESPAÑA-GREGORI E (1)(2), DÍAZ-LLOPIS M (2), MONTÉS-MICÓ R (1), MENEZO-ROZALÉN JL (2).
(1) Dept. Òptica. Universitat de València. SPAIN.
(2) Hospital Universitari LA FE. València. SPAIN.

Purpose: To evaluate the accommodative power in patients with advanced AIDS.

Methods: Amplitude of accommodation was measured in 21 patients, aged 17 to 44, by the push-up method and the concave lens method. The patients were classified by age and we compared their accommodation's values with normal Hoffstteter's values. T-Student test was employed for statistical analysis.

Results: Significant statistical differences were observed in every group if we compared with mean normal amplitude. Values below minimal normal amplitude were observed in every group, but only in young groups with significant statistical difference.

Conclusion: In patients with avanced AIDS accommodative power is below the lower limit of what might be accepted as normal for the patients age.

176

RETINAL INVOLVEMENT IN AIDS PATIENTS : COMPARISON BEFORE AND AFTER USE OF HIV PROTEASE INHIBITORS (PI)

DOAN S, COCHEREAU I, GUVENISIK N, DIRAISON MC, REN L, MOUSALLATI M, KOROBELNIK JF, HOANG-XUAN T.
Bichat Claude-Bernard Hospital, Paris (France).

Purpose : To assess the effect of Highly Active Antiretroviral Therapy (HAART) on the epidemiology of opportunistic retinal infections in HIV-infected patients.
Methods : We compared prospective data about fundus examination collected in 1995 (without HAART) *vs* 1997 (with HAART).
Results : The number of examined patients decreased from 952 in 1995 to 726 in 1997. The incidence of CMV retinitis (CMV-R) decreased from 6.1% (1995) to 1.2% (1997). In patients with CMV-R, CD4 cell counts increased (15/µL *vs* 169/µL), and mortality was reduced (30% *vs* 4%). Relapses of CMV-R decreased (36% *vs* 17 %). In 1997, mean CD4 cell counts were lower in patients with active CMV-R (37/µL) than in patients with inactive retinitis (197/µL), but 37% of active CMV-R occurred in patients with CD4 cell counts > 50/µL (*vs* 1.5% in 1995). The incidence of other opportunistic retinal infections also decreased.
Conclusion : On HAART, the incidence of CMV-R and other opportunistic retinal infections, as well as the relapses of CMV-R decreased, probably related to the restoration of immunity.

177

QUANTIFICATION OF THE CMV RETINITIS PROGRESSION BY IMAGES ANALYSIS OF ANGIOGRAPHY IN AIDS PATIENTS TREATED WITH PROTEASE INHIBITORS.

CASSOUX N[1], BRAHMI D[2], GIRON A[2], LEHOANG P[1], FERTIL B[2]
1. Dpt Oph., 2. INSERM U494 - CHU Pitié Salpêtrière (France)

Purpose: To assess the progression of area of CMV retinitis on a series of numerized angiograms in AIDS patients based on the comparison of hand-outlined segmentation.
Methods: Five AIDS patients with CMV retinitis treated with protease inhibitors were evaluated every 3 months with numerized fluorescein angiography. The lesion borders have been repeatedly outlined in double blind by two ophthalmologists. This approach was designed to get intra and inter-expert variability of distances between outlines. The local variation of lesion boundaries over a series of angiographies was subsequently analyzed and given a statistical label.
Results: In 4 patients (CD4+ cell counts over 100 /µl and viral load indetectable) the variation of the outlines of lesions in registered images was comparable to expert variability. This result signed a stabilization of the retinitis border. In contrast, a statistically significant local deviation between outlines was observed for one patient who has presented a clinical relapse of CMV retinitis.
Conclusions: Our method has confirmed and quantified the stabilization of the CMV retinitis scar in 4 patients and the progression of the CMV retinitis in one. This method is objective, reproductible and more accurate than funduscopy.

178

HEMATOGENOUS CANDIDAL ENDOPHTHALMITIS: RANDOM AMPLIFIED POLYMORPHIC DNA ANALYSIS IN AN HIV-INFECTED PATIENT

LABETOULLE M[1], MIAILHES P[2], NAAS T[3,5], FRAU E[1], GUIBERT M[3], BOURREE P[4], NORDMANN P[3,5], GALANAUD P[2], OFFRET H[1].
Departments of Ophthalmology[1], Parasitology[4] and Bacteriology[5],
Hôpital de Bicêtre, Le Kremlin-Bicêtre, France.
Departments of Internal Medicine[2] and Bacteriology[3],
Hôpital Antoine Béclère, Clamart, France

Purpose: Hematogenous candidal endophthalmitis is a sight-threatening disease infrequent in non-drugs addicts. We report the results of Random Amplified Polymorphic DNA (RAPD) analysis showing that the isolates of *Candida albicans* from a cutaneous abscess and from the vitreous body were identical in a non-drug addict HIV-infected patient suffering from a presumed hematogenous candidal endophthalmitis. **Methods:** A 31-year-old HIV infected patient (11 CD4-cells/µl), non-drug addict, reported a sudden vision loss in the left eye a few days after a cutaneous abscess at the site of a peripheral catheter. An ophthalmological examination showed a presumed candidal endophthalmitis. The cutaneous abscess and the vitreous biopsy were cultured, and the fungus isolates analysed with molecular biology methods. **Results:** RAPD analysis of the two isolates of *Candida albicans* from both the cutaneous abscess and the vitreous body showed the same banding pattern, whereas an unrelated control strain exhibited a different pattern. **Conclusions:** Such methods of molecular biology applied to *Candida albicans* showed that the hematogenous spread of fungus from a cutaneous abscess to the eye possibly occurred in our patient. Therefore, these results suggest the need of a preventing therapy in deeply immunocompromised patients presenting a fungal cutaneous abscess .

179

CMV RETINITIS AND HIV-PROTEASE INHIBITORS: AN 18-MONTHS SURVEY

LABETOULLE M[1], GOUJARD C[2], ROGIER H[1], FRAU E[1], LANTZ O[3], LECOINTE D[4], FURLAN V[5], DELFRAISSY JF[2], OFFRET H[1]
Departments of Ophthalmology[1], Internal Medicine[2], Haematology[3], Virology[4] and Pharmacology[5]
Hôpital de Bicêtre, Université Paris-Sud, Kremlin-Bicêtre, France.

Purpose: Since the beginning of the use of HIV-Protease Inhibitors (PI), the incidence of opportunistic infections in HIV-infected patients has been described to be reduced. We studied the incidence of CMV retinitis in patients treated with PI for 18 months. **Methods:** 93 HIV-infected patients with a mean initial CD4-cell level at 54/µl (less than 50/µl in 66 patients) were treated with one or two PI with a mean follow-up of 549 days (median follow-up: 609 days). Fundus examination was performed every month in case of a previously treated CMV retinitis (7 patients) or if initial CD4-cell level was below 50/µL, and every 3 months in other cases. **Results:** One of the 7 patients with a previously treated CMV retinitis experienced a progression of the retinitis. Among the 59 patients with less than 50 CD4/µl and without previous CMV retinitis before the beginning of PI, 5 experienced a primary event of CMV retinitis. Three of them experienced at least one release despite anti-CMV drugs. Except for one patient (147 CD4/µl), CD4-cell counts at time of CMV retinitis diagnosis were below 50/µl. **Conclusions:** With a follow-up of 18 months, these results confirmed the increase of the time to progression of previously treated and controlled CMV-retinitis in patients receiving PI treatment (at least 226 days). The risk of developing a first event of CMV retinitis for patients with CD4-cell count below 50/µl was 8.5% at 18 months in our study.

180

SECRETION OF IL-1β, IL-6 AND IL-8 BY PORCINE PIGMENTED CILIARY EPITHELIAL CELLS IN VITRO

KERSTIN WUNDERLICH[1], C. ERB[2] AND M. KNORR[1]
1. University Eye Clinic,Tübingen (Germany)
2. University Eye Clinic, Basel (Switzerland)

Purpose. Interleukin-1β (IL-1β), IL-6 and IL-8 could be detected in aqueous humor of inflamed and non-inflamed eyes and have been implicated as mediators of uveitis. Since pigmented ciliary epithelial cells (PCEC) produce m-RNA for IL-6 the purpose of this investigation was to determine the active synthesis and secretion of IL-1β, IL-6 and IL-8 in porcine PCEC. **Methods.** Monolayers of porcine PCEC were cultured under serum-free conditions during 3 days. The formation of tight junctions was determinded by immunofluorescence-staining using ZO1-antibodies. The content of IL-1β, IL-6 and IL-8 in the conditioned medium was determinded by ELISA. **Results.** Under serum-free conditiones porcine PCEC produced and secreted the inflammatory cytokines IL-1β (0,003+0,001 ng/ml), IL-6 (3,0±1,5 ng/ml) and IL-8 (105±25 ng/ml). **Conclusion.** Although, it has been demonstrated immunochemical that various cytokines are located in the ciliary body, no informations are available concerning the synthesis and secretion about those molecules in this tissue. Our results indicate that PCEC synthesize and secrete inflammatory cytokines like IL-1β, IL-6 and IL-8 in an active manner.

181

LIDOCAINE INTRACAMERAL CONCENTRATION REVISITED BY GAS CHROMATOGRAPHY

RIGAL-SASTOURNÉ J.C, HUARD B, BIDAUX F, MAY F, PARISELLE J, RENARD J-P, MAURIN J-F.
H.I.A Val de Grâce, Paris, France.

Purpose: Topical anesthesia with Lidocaine intracameral injection has become an acceptable method for cataract surgery, but Lidocaine retinal toxicity has been reported in vitro and in vivo in rats. To determine the Lidocaine diffusion space, we evaluated Lidocaine concentration in aqueous humor in topical anesthesia with 1% Lidocaine intracameral injection and compared this result with theorical result of intracameral diffusion space and eyeball diffusion space.
Methods: A gas chromatography technique of analyzing aqueous humor was used to detect the presence of Lidocaine prior to phacoemulsification cataract surgery in 10 patients 1 minute after 0.4 ml preservative free1% Lidocaine intracameral injection. Lidocaine concentrations in the aqueous humor were analysed and plotted.Intracameral and eyeball spaces were explored with B-scan ultrasonography .
Results: Lidocaine was detected in aqueous humor with a good recovery(95%) and linearity($r^2 > 0.95$). The mean concentration after intracameral injection is 550 μg/ml.This concentration is lower than theorical intracameral rate, suggesting that diffusion space is larger than aqueous humor.
Conclusion: Intracameral injection of Lidocaine is an effective technique to anesthetize intracameral structure and can diffuse in posterior segment prior to phacoemulsification. It should not be repeated during cataract surgery, specially with capsular break and zonular disruption.

182

COULOMB CONTROLLED IONTOPHORESIS (CCI) FOR ANTISENSE OLIGONUCLEOTIDE DELIVERY INTO THE RABBIT AND THE RAT EYE

VOIGT M[1,2], PAREL JM[3], POULIQUEN Y[4], COURTOIS Y [1], BEHAR-COHEN F [4,1]
[1]INSERM U450, Paris, [2]Department of Ophthalmology , Charité Campus Virchow, Humbold University, Berlin,
[3]Bascom Palmer Eye Institute, University of Miami,
[4] Department of Ophthalmology of Hôtel-Dieu of Paris.

Purpose: To determine if CCI could allow the penetration of antisense oligonucleotides (ODN) into the rat and the rabbit eye. **Material and methods:** A 21bp ODN, NH2 protected and labelled either with fluorescein or with IR41-9-dATP (0.3μM -3μM) were used for CCI. A transscleral CCI probe was used on the rabbit eye and a transcorneal probe on the rat eye. Eyes that received CCI of a fluorescent ODN were cryosectioned for histochemistry and those which received CCI of IR41-9-dATP ODN or ^{33}P labbelled ODN were extracted from the tissues and visualized on acrylamide gels using a Li-COR 4000 sequencer. **Results:** CCI allows the penetration of intact ODN into the eye. ODN are oberved in all oculat tissues but are mainly concentrated in the iris, ciliary body and in the choroid and, to a lesser extent into the retina. Increased current intensity improves the retinal penetration. **Conclusion:** CCI enhances the penetration of intact ODN into the eye compared to passive transfer. However, whether achieved concentrations could inhibit a biological effect remains to be demonstrated.

183

^{14}C-DICLOFENAC CONCENTRATIONS IN RABBIT OCULAR TISSUES AND PLASMA AFTER INSTILLATION OF 0.1% ^{14}C-DICLOFENAC SODIUM - 0.3% TOBRAMYCIN OPHTHALMIC SOLUTION.

MARTÍNEZ C[1], COSTA J[1], GUASCH J[1] and BERGAMINI M.V.W[2]
1. Alcon Cusí R&D, El Masnou (Spain)
2. Alcon R&D, Fort Worth, (USA).

Purpose. To determine if the bioavailability of ^{14}C-diclofenac (^{14}C-D), in ocular tissues and plasma, is improved when it is administered as a combination of 0.1% ^{14}C-diclofenac sodium - 0.3% tobramycin (^{14}C-DT) compared to sequential administration of single preparations of 0.1% ^{14}C-diclofenac sodium (^{14}C-D) and then 0.3% tobramycin (Tobrex®, T) or of T and then ^{14}C-D.
Methods. NZW rabbits were dosed bilaterally with: 50 μL of ^{14}C-DT; or 50 μL of ^{14}C-D followed by 50 μL of T (30 second interval; ^{14}C-D+T), or 50 μL of T followed by 50 μL of ^{14}C-D (30 second interval, T+^{14}C-D). The concentration of ^{14}C-D [^{14}C-D] at 1 hr. post dosing was measured by liquid scintillation.
Results. [^{14}C-D] (μg/g or ng/mL) in ocular tissues (n= 34-40) and plasma (n= 19-20) are shown in the next table.

Treatment	Conjunctiva	Cornea	Aq. Humor	Plasma
^{14}C-DT	6.1 ± 3.4	7.9 ± 4.5	360 ± 270	47 ± 11
^{14}C-D+T	4.5 ± 2.2	5.8 ± 3.2	280 ± 160	34 ± 11
T+^{14}C-D	5.9 ± 3.9	6.3 ± 3.0	300 ± 170	39 ± 13

Conclusions. [^{14}C-D] is significantly higher ($p<0.05$) in cornea and plasma 1 hr. after dosing with ^{14}C-DT, compared with [^{14}C-D] following sequential administration of ^{14}C-D and T in any order. [^{14}C-D] in conjunctiva and aqueous humor show a clear trend in the same direction. With a clinically utilized dosing interval (30 seconds), the combination provides greater ocular bioavailability than sequential dosing with single entity preparations.

Supported in part by CDTI 950052. E.

184

CYCLOSPORIN A AS A TREATMENT FOR MOOREN´S ULCER

Garat Chifflet M, Güell Vilanueva Jl, Martñinez Castillo V, Freixes Puig S, Cavero Roig LL, Alforja Castiella S.
Department of Ophthalmology. Vall d´Hebron Hospital. Barcelona. Spain.

Purpose: To abow the efficiency of sistemic inmunosupression by cyclosporin (CyA) in the treatment of Mooren´s ulcer, a peripheric ulcerative kerathopathy secondary to inespecific vasculitis of the limbic vessels.

Methods: Four cases refractary to the conventional topic treatment were treated, 2 bilateral and 2 unilateral, during a period of 6 to 36 months. We administred CyA at doses of 5 mgr/Kg/day, keeping the plasmatic levels between 100 and 150 ngr/Kg. After the stabilization phase of the discare the dose was reduced progressively to 1.5-2.5mgr/Kg/day. We added metilprednisolone at an initial dose of 0.25 mgr/Kg/day with a progressive reduction of the dose to 0.1 mgr/Kg/day.

Results: In the four cases stabilization with complete remission of all signs and symptoms of activity was achieved. In all of them a 20 to 30% reduction of the glomerular filtration was observed, not clinically significative. One patient with chronic obstructive pulmonary disease and chronic hepatitis, presented 6 months after the inmunosupressive treatment a respiratory infection that caused the treatment to be suspended. At present the ocular disease remains stable.

Conclusions: The systemic inmunosupression with CyA is an efficient treatment for Mooren´s ulcer, in those cases with aggressive evolution, and no response to conventional topical treatment.

185

Safety of Cyclosporine Ophthalmic Emulsion (Restasis)

Angelov, O., Reis, B., Acheampong, A., Wiese, A., Tang-Liu, D., Brar, B., Allergan, Irvine, Ca. USA

Purpose: 0.1% Cyclosporine Ophthalmic Emulsion (Restasis) was developed by Allergan and has shown great promise in the treatment of Keratoconjunctivitis sicca and in Sjögren's dry eye syndrome. A number of pre-clinical and clinical studies were conducted to evaluate the safety of this new formulation.

Concentrations up to 0.4% of Restasis were administered topically 6x daily for one year in dogs and for 6 months in rabbits without any topical or systemic adverse reactions. The blood drug levels (C max) analyzed in these studies were approximately 15 times higher compared to the blood drug levels in humans treated with the clinical concentration of 0.1% BID of Restasis. The cyclosporine blood levels of dogs treated orally for one year and rats for two years with doses which did not produce any nephrotoxicity or any other toxic effects were approximately 1000 times higher when compared to the drug levels in humans after topical administration of 0.1% Restasis. In a clinical trial of dry eye patients no serious treatment related adverse events and no ocular infections were reported. Trough blood levels as well as peak blood levels were below 0.2 ng/mL.

Conclusion: Restasis is absorbed minimally in the system and has a very large margin of safety, therefore it is safe for topical long term administration in humans.

186

INSTILLATION OF 0.03% MITOMYCIN-C IN ANTERIOR SEGMENT SURGERY

CANO-PARRA J[1,2], BUENO I[2], MONTÉS R[2], ILLUECA I[2], MAURICI J[1]

1. Dept Ophthalmology, Municipal Hospital of Badalona
2. Dept. Optics, University of Valencia.

Purpose: We conducted a prospective study of instillation of 0.03% mitomycin-C as adjunctive treatment of recurrent pterygium, conjunctival granuloma and corneal intraepithelial neoplasia. **Methods:** A total of twenty eyes with recurrent pterygium (13 eyes), conjunctival granuloma (6) and corneal intraepithelial neoplasia (1) were treated with 0.03% mitomicyn-C. Pterygium were treated with excision with postoperative instillation of dexametasone and mitomycin-C (0.3 mg/ml three times a day for three weeks). Conjunctival granuloma and corneal intraepithelial neoplasia were treated only with instillation of dexametasone and mitomycin-C (0.3 mg/ml three times a day for three weeks). **Results:** We evaluate the efficacy and toxicity of this protocol treatment. The mean follow-up was 6 months (range 3 to 16 months). Of the 13 eyes that underwent excision of pterygium none exhibited recurrence, whereas conjunctival granuloma and corneal intraepithelial neoplasia also did not show any recurrence. **Conclusions:** Instillation of 0.03% mitomycin-C appears to be an effective and safe adjunctive treatment of recurrent pterygium, conjunctival granuloma and corneal intraepithelial neoplasia.

187

MODIFICATION OF CHOROIDAL BLOOD FLOW INDUCED BY CERVICAL SPINAL CORD STIMULATION.

SANCHEZ-LEDESMA MJ[2], HERNANDEZ-GALILEA E[1], PINTO JC[1], GONÇALVEZ J[2], BROSETA J[2], BARAHONA JM[1].

1.Dep. of Ophthalmology, 2.Dep. of Neurosurgery, , Dep. of Surgery, Faculty of Medicine, University of Salamanca Salamanca (Spain).

Purpose: Spinal cord stimulation (SCS) has a beneficial vasomotor reponse in peripheral vascular diseases. Experimental and clinical studies have noted increased levels of cerebral blood flow after SCS in animals and in humans. This study evaluate the influence of cervical SCS on chBF in basal conditions, recording the choroidal perfusion changes by means of laser doppler flowmetry. **Methods:** In forthteen New Zealand albino rabbits general anesthesia was done and ecutorial scleral region was presented. ChBF was recorded transclerally using laser doppler flowmetry (PF 2b Periflux). On SCS group a C4 laminectomy was carried out and 0.2 isolated platinium lead introduced in the epidural space and manipulated till the right C1-C2 segments. cSCS started a period of 60 min. using as a electrical parameters 0.1 msec. of pulse width, 85 to 120 cps **Results:** A increase more than 50% on chBF was achieved after cervical SCS compared with basal conditions. **Conclusion:** These results confirm that cervical SCS induce a vasomotor response at the choroid level and significant increase of chBF recorded suggest possible therapeutic applications on different ocular ischemic conditions.

Supported by a grant of *Junta de Castilla y Leon* (SA 32/97)

188

USEFULNESS OF TYPE A BOTULINIC TOXIN IN ENDOCRINE OPHTHALMOPATHY

L COLANGELO, L CROVETTO[1], L LOBEFALO, A GOMEZ MORALES, A AVERSANO, MA D'INCICCO,PE GALLENGA

Institute of Ophthalmology and Legal Medicine, "G.d'Annunzio" University Chieti - Italy / [1]Orbital and Neuroph Dept. S.Lucia Hosp, Buenos Aires Argentina

Purpose: to evaluate the efficacy of type A botulinic toxin in reducing diplopia in patients affected with endocrine ophthalmopathy.

Methods: Fifty-five patients (42 females and 13 males: 91 eyes) were enrolled in the study. The total number of applications of botulinic toxin was 195. In all patients presence of ophthalmoplegia, exophtalmos, edema or lagophtalmos was evaluated at the beginning of the study and 30 days after treatment. Furthermore, palpebral retraction, palpebral rim and ocular deviation were measured. In all patients orbital CT was performed. Botulinic toxin was applied in variable doses from 2.5 UI to 15 UI under electromyographic control.

Results: Mean vertical deviation at the beginning and at the end of the study was respectively 13.58±4.35 and 7.86±1.84 prismatic diopters. Mean horizontal deviation at the beginning and at the end of the study was respectively 24.75±7.41 and 16.66±5.08. Palpebral rim and palpebral retraction decreased respectively of 4.7 mm and 2.25 mm. In 69.7% of patients a subjective improvement of diplopia was found.

Conclusions: Type A Botulinic Toxin seems useful in the treatment of diplopia in patients affected with endocrine ophthalmopathy, particularly in the evolving period of the disease. It can be an useful alternative in patients that don't tolerate the prismatic correction.

189

SECONDARY ACUTE HYPERTENSION AFTER ANABOLIC ABUSE

HETTESHEIMER H.
Dept. Ophthalmology II, University of Tuebingen, Germany

Purpose: Hypertension may be defined as a pathologic elevation of blood pressure. Hypertension is not a clear-cut entity of singular origin. Marked elevation of systolic pressure with little or no elevation of diastolic pressure has etiologic and prognostic significance. Elevation of the systolic pressure depends primarily on cardiac output, elevation of diastolic pressure is a manifestation of increased peripheral resistance after systole. This peripheral resistance is due to several factors: pressure loss or blood flow through the vascular bed, blood viscosity, elasticity of the vessels. Malignant hypertension usually occurs in younger persons, often in the third decade. It may be the result of progressive benign hypertension, or it may bypass such changes when there is a rapid rise in pressure. Secondary acute hypertension may occur in many internal disorders, but also in anabolic abuse. There is general and focal narrowing of the arterioles, retinopathy, possibly neuroretinal edema, and the absence of chronic retinal arteriolosclerosis.
Case report: A 33-year-old man (professional bodybuilder) was seen in the clinic, complaining about reduction of vision on one eye and a progression of strabismus. Best corrected visual acuity was 20/60 on the right eye and light perception on the left eye. The eye movement was normal, there was a strabismus of the left eye, 15° convergence. In the fundus there was a generalized narrowing of the arterioles, hemorrhages in the nerve fiber layer, cotton-wool patches and papilledema (L > R). Blood fusion was 220 : 120 mm Hg. A anabolic abuse for many years was known.
Conclusion: Bodybuilder often use drugs to produce more muscles. Anabolic drugs lead to a growing of all kinds of muscles in the body, also the muscles in the blood vessels. The result is a loss of elasticity of the vessels. Anabolic abuse can cause a secondary malignant hypertension.

190

INFLUENCE OF ICP ON THE BLOOD FLOW PARAMETERS IN THE OPHTHALMIC ARTERY

BARZDZIUKAS V , GVAZDAITIS R , JASINSKAS V , DAUBARIS G , RAGAUSKAS A .
1. Kaunas Medical Academy (Lithuania)
2. Kaunas University of Technology (Lithuania)

Purpose To investigate the influence of ICP changes during orthostatic tests on the blood flow in the ophthalmic artery (OA).
Methods A color TCD pulsed wave (2 MHz) system has been used for measurements in extracranial and intracranial segments of OA. The body tilting tests were applied: lying in +20 degree and -30 degree angles from horizontal position. The group of 19 healthy volunteers (23 - 26 years old) was studied.
Results The peak systolic and mean blood flow velocities in the intracranial and extracranial segments of OA are statistically significantly different in two body positions. The character of Gosling pulsatility index changes is also different in the intracranial and extracranial segments.
Conclusion Our results suggest that the intracranial processes caused by orthostatic tests influence the blood flow dynamic characteristics differently in intracranial and extracranial segments of OA. It could be explained by difference of elastic properties of surrounding tissue in the extracranial and intracranial segments of OA and on the hypervolemia or hypovolemia caused by orthostatic test.

191

CANNABINOID RECEPTORS IN BOVINE IRIDIAL CIRCULAR MUSCLE

LOGRANO MD, PIERRI F
Dept. Farmacobiologico, Università di Bari, Bari (Italy)

Purpose. Because anandamide, a recently discovered endogenous ligand of cannabinoid receptors, reportedly shows cannabimimetic pharmacological activity, we examined its effect on bovine iridial circular muscle.
Methods. To investigate the mechanical properties, bovine eyes were open and iridial muscle was removed and used for functional experiments. The smooth muscle strips were set up under a tension of 1 g in a 30 ml organ bath, containing carbooxygenated Krebs solution at 37°C. Contractile responses were mesured isometrically by means of force displacement transducer (DY0, U. Basile, Italy), and recorded on a linear recorder coupled to a Glass-polygraph.
Results. Anandamide showed a contracturant effect on iridial circular muscle. Contraction induced by it ($ED_{50}=1.1x10^{-7}$ M) was more powerful than carbachol ($ED_{50}=2.1x10^{-7}$ M). The effect was antagonized by forskolin, a specific stimulator of adenylyl-cyclase, in dose-dependent manner. SR 141716A, a specific antagonist of CB1 raceptors, did not showed effect on anandamide induced contraction, neither modified basal tone.
Conclusions. The receptors involved are not CB1 subtype, in fact contraction was not influenced by SR 141716A. CB2 receptors could reduce intracellular cAMP concentration as showed by effects of forskolin. Very little is know about localization and function of CB2 receptors in the eye, but they could constitute a new target of therapeutic agents in the future.

192

CILIARY BODY STUDY BY UBM IN GLAUCOMATOUS PATIENTS AFTER TOPICAL APPLICATION OF LATANOPROST

S. DI STASO, G. GENITTI, L. SABETTI, D. D'ANDREA, A. RENZETTI, E. BALESTRAZZI

Department of Ophthalmology, University of L'Aquila-Italy

Purpose To examine the changes in ciliary body thickness in patients with primary open angle glaucoma (POAG) after application of Latanoprost

Methods 10 patients with POAG treated with 0.50% Timolol were enrolled for this study. Ciliary body of all patients with a 3 week Timolol washout were examined by UBM Humphrey before and after local application of 0.005% Latanoprost

Results Latanoprost decreased the mean ciliary body thickness from 0.80+-0.08 mm. to 0.71+-0.06 mm. ($p<0.05$). No significant changes were noted before and after washout period

Conclusions Latanoprost decreased ciliary body thickness in patients with POAG

193

RHEOLOGY OF VISCOELASTIC OPHTHALMIC SOLUTIONS

LEPORE D[1], BORZACCHIELLO A[2], MINICUCCI G[1], PAGLIARA MM[1], MOLLE F[1], D'AMICO G[1], AMBROSIO L[2], NICOLAIS L[2], SCULLICA L[1]
Dpt Ophthalmology, Catholic University - Rome, Italy[1];
Dpt Materials & Production Engineering, University "Federico II" - Naples, Italy [2].

Purpose: rheological behaviour of viscoelastic solutions is intermediate between ideal elastic solid and a pure viscous fluid. Their linear flow properties can be expressed by shear stress $\tau = G'(\omega)g_0 \sin(\omega t) + G''(\omega)g_0 \cos(\omega t)$, where G' (shear storage modulus) describe material elasticity and G" (shear loss modulus) describe its viscosity. Non-linear flow properties can be determined through viscosity η as function of shear rate γ. Rheological analysis have been applied to various hyaluronic acid (HA) solutions used in ophthalmic surgery, evaluating effects of temperature use. **Materials and Methods:** Viscoat, Ial, Provisc, Biolon, Healon, HealonGV were tested using a BohlinVOR Rheometer at 23° and 37°C, with a cone and plate system (CP5/30cell). Strain sweep test at fixed oscillation frequency followed by small amplitude oscillatory shear test with a sinusoidal shear strain $\gamma = \gamma_0 \sin(\omega t)$ were performed to study viscoelastic linear flow properties. Viscoelastic non-linear flow properties were studied by steady shear test. **Results:** HA solutions rheologically range from liquid-like polymeric solution (Ial-23°), where G">G', to transient-network polymeric solution (Healon-23°, Provisc-37°), with viscous character (G">G') at low frequencies and elastic (G'>G") at high frequencies. HealonGV has an elastic response (G'>G") over the frequency range. Viscoat is thermostable, while Provisc shows a significant G'/G"-crossover frequency modification by temperature. **Conclusions:** space maintenance, tissue separation and protection are related to composition and temperature use of the solution and, above all, to their rheological properties.

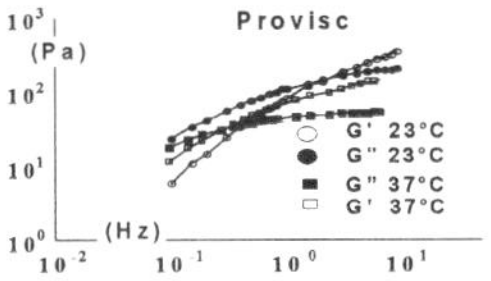

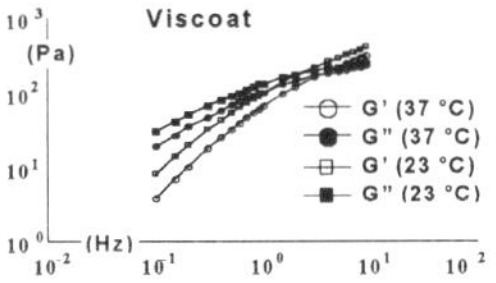

194

EFFICACY AND TOLERANCE OF 0, I % INDOMETHACIN AND 0, I % DEXAMETHASONE OPHTHALMIC SOLUTIONS IN CONTROLLING INFLAMMATION AFTER CATARACT SURGERY

L. MISSOTTEN[1], M.C. RICHARD[2] and C. TRINQUAND[2] and STUDY GROUP
Katholieke Universiteit Leuven, Belgium [1]; Laboratoire Chauvin, Montpellier, France[2].

Purpose: To evaluate the safety and efficacy of 0, I% indomethacin eyedrops compared to 0, I% dexamethasone solution in cataract surgery.
Methods : After obtaining written consent, 145 patients undergoing extra capsular cataract extraction or phacoemulsification with posterior chamber-IOL, were involved in a randomised, double -masked and comparative trial. Patients were instructed to instil 1 drop QID in the eye operated on, for one month starting the day before surgery . During the 2 hours preceding the surgery, one drop was given every 30 minutes. The main efficacy evaluation was based on the assessment of anterior chamber cells and flare. Subjective symptoms, other objective signs and intra ocular pressure were also recorded.
Results : Cellular and protein flare in the aqueous humour decreased with time in both groups. At D30 a statistical significant difference in favour of indomethacin was observed for cellular flare ($p<0{,}05$). Conjunctival hyperaemia was less pronounced in dexamethasone group at D30 ($p<0{,}03$). Although not significant, IOP was lower in indomethacin group at D30. Tolerance of both eyedrops was satisfactory. **Conclusion** : 0,1% indomethacin ophthalmic solution appears as safe and efficient as 0,1% dexamethasone eyedrops in the management of post operative inflammation.

195

EFFECT OF DEXAMETHASONE PHOSPHATE and CYCLOSPORIN ON EXPERIMENTAL AUTOIMMUNE ANTERIOR UVEITIS

SECHOY O, CESSES P, and LATOUR E.
Laboratoire Chauvin, Montpellier (France)

Purpose: To evaluate the antiinflammatory activity of topical Cebedex® (0.1% dexamethasone sodium phosphate eye drops) and cyclosporin (15 mg/kg i.m) on the experimental autoimmune anterior uveitis induced by bovine melanin-associated antigen (MAA) in Lewis rats.
Methods: MAA was extracted from bovine iris by the method described by Broekhuyse et al. (Exp.Eye Res.1993; 56:575). Lewis rats were immunised with a stable emulsion containing 50µg of the antigen and complete Freund's adjuvant in the hind foot pad and with 1µg Bordetella pertussis toxin mixed with 50µg MAA injected intraperitoneally. Cebedex® was topically administered 4 times daily and cyclosporine daily injected, from the day of immunisation until completion of the study on the day 29. The rats were clinically examined using slit lamp and uveitis was graded on a scale of 0 to 4. Histopathological assessment was performed using standard techniques.
Results and conclusions:The inflammation started 9-10 days after injections and consisted mainly of severe iridocyclitis accompanied by dense flare and cells in the anterior chamber. The development of the uveitis was totally inhibited by cyclosporine or Cebedex® administration. This model may be a valuable model to screen drugs potentially interesting for the treatment of human acute anterior uveitis.

196

CLASSIFICATION OF ELECTROPHORETIC TEAR PROTEIN PATTERNS FROM DRY EYES BY A NEURAL NETWORK

Grus FH and Augustin AJ.
Department of Ophthalmology, University of Bonn (Germany)

Purpose. To analyze the electrophoretic patterns of tears from patients with dry eye disease (DRY) and from healthy subjects (CTRL). The patterns were analyzed by means of an artificial neural network (ANN).
Methods. Sixty eyes were examined in this study (DRY: n=43; CTRL: n=17). The tear proteins were separated by SDS-PAGE (sodium-dodecyl-sulfate poly-acrylamide gel electrophoresis). Digital image analysis was performed by ScanPacK (Biometra, Goettingen, Germany). From each electrophoretic pattern a data set was created. The data set was randomly divided into test and training patterns. The ANN was trained by one of these sets. After training, the performance of the ANN was checked by presenting the test data set to the ANN. Furthermore, the data was classified using multivariate analysis of discriminance.
Results. The groups were significantly different from each other ($P<0.05$). The statistical procedure yielded to 97% (known samples) and 71% (unknown samples) correct classifications. The ANN revealed 80% of correct classifications using the test set (unknown samples).
Conclusion. The results reveal significant differences between the two groups. Using the ANN we were able to classify electrophoretic tear protein pattern for diagnostic purposes. This method overwhelmes the results obtained by conventional statistical procedures. Our new approach appears to be a fast and useful method for the detection of dry eyes.

197

OCULAR PHYSIOLOGY AND CONTACT LENS SOLUTIONS

Authors: García-Valldecabres M., López-Alemany A., Montés-Micó R.
Dept. Òptica. Universitat de València. SPAIN

Purpose: The solutions' pH is very important in the contact lens fitting and use. In this work we have measured the pH of five and three hydrogen peroxide systems one-step and two-step recpectively available in the Spanish market, and determined their pH time course/evolution.

Methods: The study were carried out over a 32 days period to investigate the pH fluctuations. The solutions tested were one-step systems [Novoxy, Arion Plus, Oxysept (with B12 vitamine), Biosept and Oxysept] and two-step systems [Arion Oxysept and Peroxizor]. The pH of the solutions was measured using a micropH 2002 Crison pH-meter.

Results: For the one-step systems the initial pH of the disinfection solutions ranged from 3.17 to 3.99 pH units and the final pH after the combined disinfection/neutralization cycle ranged from 6.88 to 7.38 pH units. For the two-step the values obtained ranged from 3.22 to 3.90 pH units for the disinfection solutions and from 7.01 to 7.32 pH units for the neutralization solutions.

Conclusions: All the solutions tested presented pH values, after the neutralization cycle, within the ocular comfort range during the testing period but these values were not close to the tear's pH (7.45 pH units)

198

PRESERVATIVES INDUCE FREE RADICAL PRODUCTION IN CONJUNCTIVAL CELLS *IN VITRO*

DEBBASCH C[1], DE SAINT JEAN M[2], PISELLA PJ[1], RAT P[1], WARNET JM[1], BAUDOUIN C[2].
1. Dept. of cellular pharmacotoxicology and ophthalmology, XV-XX hospital, Paris, France
2. Dept. of ophthalmology, Ambroise Paré hospital, Boulogne, France

Purpose. The aim of this study was to evaluate the effects of benzalkonium chloride (BAK), timolol BAK+ and timolol BAK– on a continuous human conjunctival cell line (Wong Kilbourne derived human conjunctiva). **Methods**. Cytotoxicity tests were assessed according to ECVAM recommendations using microplate cold light cytofluorimetry. Membrane integrity (neutral red test), mitochondrial activity (rhodamine 123 test), and free radical production (dichlorofluoresceine diacetate test) were evaluated. Cells were treated by different concentrations of BAK (0.0001-0.1%), timolol BAK+ and timolol BAK- (0.1-0.4%). **Results**. Using the neutral red fluorescence, we observed a decrease of membrane integrity at low concentration of BAK (0.0001%) and short time (30 minutes). A free radical production appeared with timolol BAK+ (0.1%-15 minutes). This phenomenon was concentration- and time-dependent and was more important with timolol BAK+ than with timolol BAK-. Production of free radicals lead to the decrease in mitochondrial activity. **Conclusions**. This study shows that benzalkonium chloride induces free radical production on conjunctival cells *in vitro*. These results can explain the ocular surface damage caused by preservatives.

199

CHANGES OF CONJUNCTIVAL MORPHOLOGY FOLLOWING THE TOPICAL ADMINISTRATION OF CHLORIDE FREE ISOOSMOTIC SOLUTION

ARAGONA P[1], MICALI A[2], PUZZOLO D[2], DI STEFANO G[1], STILO A[1] and FERRERI G[1]
1.Inst. Ophthalmology, University of Messina (Italy)
2.Dept. Biomorphology, University of Messina (Italy)

Purpose: The presence of chloride channels was demonstrated in several epithelia. They seem to play an important role for the epithelium homeostasis. No data are reported about the effect of chloride deprivation on the conjunctival epithelium. The effects of isoosmotic solutions with or without chlorides on mouse conjunctival epithelium were studied.
Methods: Fifteen Swiss CD1 mice were divided into 3 groups. Group 1 was untreated (control). The other animals were treated with the instillation of 5 drops/day for 10 days as follows: Group 2, Cl^- free isoosmotic solution (BSS); Group 3, BSS with Cl^-. On the eleventh day the entire conjunctiva was excised and processed for light and electron microscopy.
Results: Group 1 showed the normal variability of conjunctival epithelium. Group 2 showed an enhanced secretion (mucus and cellular debris), many mitoses and goblet cells of different cytoplasmic density. Group 3 showed no secretory activity of the epithelium, goblet cells with a dense cytoplasm and superficial cells with light cytoplasm.
Conclusions: Only Group2 (Cl^- free group) showed evident conjunctival alterations, indicating that Cl^- ions may play a role in maintining the ocular surface in good conditions.

200

INTERFERON GAMMA (IFNγ) INDUCES APOPTOSIS OF CONJUNCTIVAL CELLS *IN VITRO*.

DE SAINT JEAN M[1], DEBBASCH C[2], BRIGNOLE F[3], BAUDOUIN C[1] Depts of Ophthalmology[1] and Immunohematology[3], Ambroise Paré Hospital, University of Paris V, Dept of Pharmacology[2], CHNO des XV-XX, Paris, France

Purpose. Apoptosis and inflammation are present in the ocular surface in Sjögren's syndrome and the upregulation of IFNγ was recently reported. We investigated the pro-apoptotic and inflammatory actions of IFNγ *in vitro*. Methods. A continuous human conjunctival cell line was cultured during 24, 48 and 72h in presence of various concentrations of hrIFNγ with or w/o 3h pre-treatment with 100ng/ml TPA or 50µM staurosporine. Cell viability and number were analyzed with colorimetric assays. DNA content, expression of inflammation-related molecules HLA DR, ICAM-1, of apoptotic molecules Fas, p53, bax, and of IFNγ transcriptional factor STAT1 were evaluated by flow cytometry and/or Western Blot. Apoptosis was studied with DAPI, TEM, DNA electrophoresis and immunoblotting of PARP. Results. Cells treated with 300U/ml IFNγ presented a decrease in viability and number, cell cycle alterations, apoptotic chromatin condensation and fragmentation and cleavage of PARP. IFNγ upregulated HLA DR, ICAM1, Fas and bax. STAT1 was activated and translocated into nucleus. P53 was repressed. HLA DR and Fas were upregulated by staurosporine and repressed by TPA. Both enhanced ICAM1 expression. Conclusion IFNγ induces inflammatory changes and apoptosis of conjunctival cells *in vitro*. This fact could, in part, explain the coexistence of both processes in ocular surface inflammatory disorders.

201

ATRESIAS AND OBLITERATIONS OF LACRIMAL PUNCTS AND CANALICULI, TREATED BY MODIFIED METHODS OF DJ. ANGUELOV

ANGUELOV DJ. and ANGUELOV B.
Dept. of Ophthalmology, Medical University, Sofia (Bulgaria)

Purpose: The aim of the present work is the effective treatment of atresias and obliterations of lacrimal puncts and canaliculi.
Methods: The whole number of nosological units was 55 with duration of 6 to 30 years. The patients treated on were 19, aged 6 to 62 years. Of them four patients were with disorders of the lacrimal puncts, 3 with disorders of lacrimal canaliculi and 12 patients with disorders of both, lacrimal puncts and canaliculi. The following treating methods were used: 1) probing and dilatation by conical and cylindrical probes up to No 4; 2) partial intubation; 3) complete intubation of lacrimal passages with ascendant and descendant access for a period of 30 to 90 days.
Results: The latest results are: complete success due to the treatment with full passability of lacrimal passage was achieved in 51, partial success in 2 and failure in 2 of the whole 55 nosological units.
Conclusions: By using the modified methods of probing and intubation of Dj. Anguelov, effective treatment of atresias and obliterations of lacrimal puncts and canaliculi has been achieved.

202

ENDOLUMINAL ENDOSCOPY AND SILICONE TUBING OF THE LACRIMAL DRAINAGE SYSTEM

Maier M., Leipert K. P., Schmidt T., Schmidt M. (Augenklinik rechts der Isar, Technical University Munich, Germany)

Purpose: Operative procedures to manage lacrimal outflow obstruction were made traditionally without endoscopic assistance.

Methods: Since years we apply rigid endoscopes routinely to control endonasal manipulations and the location of the probe. In an attempt to perform microinvasive lacrimal surgery we used a 0,5 mm endoscope with a special wash cannula for endoluminal endoscopy of the lacrimal drainage system.

Results: Using the endoluminal endoscope we were able to visualize pathologic changes of the lacrimal outflow system prior to silicone tubing. Intraoperative situations are demonstrated from an endonasal view and with endoluminal endoscopy.

Conclusions: Endoluminal endoscopy and endoscopic controlled surgery of the lacrimal drainage system enables an atraumatic and minimal invasive surgery and helps to choose the adequate surgical method.

203

ANATOMIC AND ENDOSCOPIC STUDY OF LACRIMAL DRAINAGE SYSTEM WITH EVALUATION OF ERBIUM LASER : (BREMOND-GIGNAC D.[1,2], FEBBRARO J.L.[1,2], DEPLUS S.[1,2], ARON-ROSA [1], LASSAU J.P.[2], LAROCHE L. [3])

1. Dept. of Ophtalmology, Robert Debre Hospital, Paris, (France) ; 2. Institute of Anatomy of Sts Peres, Paris, ((France).; 3. Saint-Antoine Hospital, Paris, (France).

Purpose. To study the structure and the endoscopic aspect of the lacrimal drainage system and to evaluate the efficacy of the Erbium laser in lacrimal obstruction. **Methods**. Twenty lacrimal ducts from ten fresh cadaver heads were used to lead a special rigid probe of 1.1mm diameter (Schwind). This probe combined a flexible endoscopic probe of 500 μ, an Erbium laser fiber of 375 μ and an irrigation. The probe was introduced through the inferior canaliculus. Progressing in the lacrimal system, all the images were analysed. Then, we used the laser fiber to open the lacrimal sac mucosa and the bone. **Results**. The anatomo-endoscopic analysis was realised using endoscopic data. We appreciated essentially sinus of Maier and valve of Rosenmuller. Valves and sinuses appeared only functionnal when increasing the irrigation flow. The laser could easily open the mucosa and the lacrimal bone but not the maxilla. The laser parameters were evaluated. **Conclusions**. In this study we analysed the lacrimal system to adjust the surgery to the type of obstruction. This endocanalicular system permit, during the surgery, to control the opening. The endoscopic imaging with the irrigation will allow numerous applications in lacrimal diagnosis and surgical treatment.

204

TEMPORARY RETROBULBAR CATHETER FOR LONG-LASTING AND TITRABLE LOCAL ANAESTHESIA DURING AND AFTER OCULAR SURGERY

JONAS JB, BUDDE WM, HEMMERLING TM, DINKL M
Dept. Ophthalmology, University of Erlangen (Germany)

Purpose To evaluate a temporary indwelling retrobulbar catheter for repeatable injection of short-acting anesthetics for long-lasting and titratable intraoperative and postoperative local anesthesia.
Patients and Methods The study included 23 patients undergoing pars plana vitrectomy (n=10) or cyclocryo-coagulation (n=13). Using a commercially available 23-gauge retrobulbar needle 5 ml of mepivacaine 2 % were injected transcutaneously into the retrobulbar muscle cone. A commercially available 28-gauge flexible catheter was inserted through the needle, which was then removed. As soon as the patients complained about pain during or up to 24 hours after surgery, 2 ml of mepivacaine 2 % were injected.
Results Intraopreatively repetitive injections were necessary in 6 of the 10 patients undergoing vitrectomy and postoperatively in all patients who had undergone cyclocryo-coagulation. After all injections, the patients became pain-free within two minutes. No complication of the retrobulbar block nor the catheter itself such as optic nerve injury, globe perforation or retrobulbar hemorrhage were observed.
Conclusions A temporary insertion of a catheter into the retrobulbar space is a reliable technique to re-apply local anesthetics for prolongation of local anesthesia.

205

HISTOPATHOLOGICAL TOLERANCE OF ADAL-2® ADHESIVE FOR CONJUNCTIVAL SEALING.

MULET M.E.[1], JIMENEZ E[1], GOMEZ J.J.[2], MAHIQUES M.M.[3], MAS O[3], ALIO J.L.[2], MARTIN J.M.[3].

1. Research and Development Department of the Instituto Oftalmológico de Alicante.
2. Ophthalmology Department. Miguel Hernández University.
3. Adhesion Laboratories. Alicante University.

Purpose: To evaluate the effectiveness of Adal-2® as ocular Bioadhesive tissue and the histopathological tolerance of the conjunctive to its application.

Methods: Study was done on two groups of New Zealand Albino Rabbits. All rabbits had a superior periotomy performed. In group 1 the conjunctive was closed using Adal-2®. In group 2 it was closed by a vicryl 8/0 suture. Histopathologic studies were performed at 1, 4 and 6 weeks after the procedure.

Results: Efficacy of the conjunctival closure was observed in 100% of cases. Histopathological tolerance of the conjunctive to Adal-2® was comparable to the vicryl 8/0 suture. The adhesive was found to be totally eliminated after 6 weeks of its application.

Conclusion: Adal-2® bioadhesive tissue shows to be an efficient and safe alternative for conjunctival closure in ocular surgical procedures.

206

A NEW METHOD TO ASSESS THE STRENGTH AFTER SEALING OR SUTURING OF OCULAR TISSUES.

MULET M.E.[1], JIMENEZ E[1], MAHIQUES M.M.[3], ALVARADO C[2], ALIO J.L.[2], MARTIN J.M.[3].

1. Research and Development Department of the Instituto Oftalmológico de Alicante.
2. Ophthalmology Department. Miguel Hernández University.
3. Adhesion Laboratories. Alicante University.

Purpose: Determining an efficient and standard model for the measurement of the strength in joining different ocular tissues sealed both by sutures or adhesives.

Methods: Experimental model in Albino New Zealand Rabbits. Cyanocrilate (Histoacryl®), Fibrine (Tissucol®), Adal-1® tissue adhesive. Nylon 10/0 and Dexon 6/0 sutures. Dynamometer: Adamel L'Homargy. Two surgical models: 1.- Joint of muscle to sclera: Experimental Estrabismus surgery, and 2.- Scleral tunnel surgery. Measurement of the tensile strength: A section of 1 cm^2 of the implied tissues in the union. (Sclera in the scleral tunnel or muscle and sclera in strabismus surgery). Test of compression and decompression by the Dynamometer DY432-Adamel Universal testing Machine L'Homargy (France).

Results: The tensile strength in the immediate postoperative time in the strabismus surgery model was X=0.79 ± 0.02 N/mm with the Adal-1® adhesive group and X=1.23 ± 0.17 N/mm with Dexon 6/0 sutures at a week later with Adal-1® adhesive was X=0.89 ± 0.9 N/mm and with Dexon 6/0 group X=1.01 ± 0.1 N/mm there was no significant statistically difference (Student's test).

In the scleral tunnel model with Nylon 10/0 suture was X=0.08 ± 0.03 N/mm. In the group of cyanocrilate tissue was X=0.72 ± 0.02 N/mm with significant statistically difference, P=0.001 (U-Mann-Whitney) the fibrinogen tissue could not support the tension of the machine used and no measurement could be obtained.

Conclusion: This is an efficient method to measure the tensile strength able to support the unions in different ocular tissues. In the strabismus surgery the tensile strength was able to be supported by the union sealing with Adal-1® adhesive and it is comparable to the Dexon 6/0 sutures.

In the scleral tunnel the best support of the tensile strength was the cyanocrilate adhesive better than Nylon 10/0 sutures. The fibrine adhesive can only support minimum tension.

207

HEPARIN & HEPARIN-SURFACE-MODIFICATION REDUCE STAPHYLOCOCCUS EPIDERMIDIS ADHESION TO INTRAOCULAR LENSES

AL-KHARASHI SA[1], ABU EL-ASRAR AM[1], TABBARA KF[1] AND SHEBEL A[2]

1. Dept. of Ophthalmology, College of Medicine &
2. Dept. of Microbiology, College of Pharmacy, King Saud University, Riyadh (Saudi Arabia)

Purpose: Bacterial adherence to intraocular lenses (IOLs) could be the cause of endophthalmitis following cataract surgery and lens implantation. The majority of cases of postoperative endophthalmitis are caused by organisms in lid & conjunctival flora. Staphylococcus epidermidis commonly colonizes the eyelid margin and conjunctiva and is the most common organism causing postoperative endophthalmitis. We studied the in vitro adherence of S. epidermidis to regular poly-methyl methacrylate (PMMA) IOLs and to heparin-surface-modified (HSM) PMMA IOLs. The effects of heparin and antibiotics in solution on the adherence of bacteria to regular PMMA IOLs were evaluated.

Methods: Adhesion of bacterial cells to IOLs was determined by counting the viable cells attached to the lenses.

Results: Significantly fewer S. epidermidis attached to HSM-PMMA IOLs and to regular PMMA IOLs treated with heparin than to regular PMMA IOLs ($p < 0.001$). Bacteria attached in significantly lower numbers to regular PMMA IOLs treated with heparin than to HSM-PMMA IOLs ($p = 0.009$). Antibiotics in solution has no significant effect on bacterial adherence to PMMA IOLs.

Conclusion: This study indicates that the use of HSM-PMMA IOLs and treatment of regular PMMA IOLs with heparin could diminish the number of staphylococci adhering to IOLs during implantation.

208

AMMETROPY CORRECTION POST- OCULAR SURGERY

AUTHORS: GÓMEZ JOSÉ Mª, GENE A., MONTALT J.C.,PONS A.M.,SANCHEZ M.

Dpt. D' Òptica-UNIVERSITAT DE VALENCIA-Burjassot-SPAIN.

Purpose: in this work we present diverse clinical cases of contact lens adaptation post ocular surgery. CL are adaptec in order to solve different visual and aesthetic problems.

METHODS: In all cases a complete adaptation study was carried out. The methodology used was: external ocular inspection, evaluation of monocular and binocular capabilities, slit lamp, fluorescein test, ocular structures valorisation (pupil, anterior chamber depth, etc). Keratometry and topography help us to determine the idea CL to be adapted. We classify the patients in the following groups:1.-Keratotomies after traffic injury..2.- traumatic cataract with anterior chamber lesions. 3.- Congenital cataracts with retinal losses and leucoma 4.-Traumatic corneal alterations 5.- Monocular Afaquia with associated keratoplastia .6.- Herpes Keratoplastia

RESULTS: RGP CL adaptation improve visual performance in all cases, allowing the solution of ocular aesthetic alterations.

CONCLUSIONS: Patients after surgical techniques affecting refraction or ocular aesthetic due to previous ocular pathologies can improve their visual performance and aspect with the adaptation of special CL.

s

209

NEW MESHY LAVSAN FOR IRIDOPROSTHESIS

E.D.ISKO, E.W.MALTCEV, G.E.VENGER

1. Filatov Institute of Eye Diseases, Odessa,Ukraine
2. Filatov Institute of Eye Diseases, Odessa,Ukraine
3. Pirogov Medical University, Odessa, Ukraine

Purpose: In experiment biocompatibility of eye-tissues and synthetic material implanted into anterior chamber for long terms have been studied.
Methods: The experiment was performed in 80 rabbit eyes. Lavsan stained in blue, white, brown colours and lavsan with carbon-content covering was implanted into anterior chamber.
Results: Microscopic study of eyes show, that inflammatory process on implanted materials with carbon was expressed in degree compared with the non-carbon lavsan implantation. The eye reactions on blue lavsan was expressed less than the one on brown colours lavsan. The white and brown carbon lavsan incapsulation was less expressed in remote terms.
Conclusion: All types of lavsan are non-toxical. Lavsan with carboncontent covering caused the lower adhesion of cells in comparison with simple lavsan. This allows to recommend coloured lavsan with carbon-content covering into the clinical usage as iris implantation in traumatic aniridia.

210

LACRYMAL CRYSTAL OPTICS IN DIAGNOSIS OF INFECTED OPHTHALMIC WOUNDS.

SERGUSHEV S.G.(1), PROKOFIEVA G.L.(1), MOZHERENKOV V.P.
1.Dept. of Ophthalmology, Moscow Regional Scientific-Research Clinical Institute (Russia)

Purpose: Diagnosis of infection in penetrating ophthalmic wounds is very difficult, therefore working out new diagnostic methods is extremely actual.
Methods: We used our own modification of crystal-optical method to determine the relative amount of lacrymal protein. The group investigated consisted of 448 patients and 88 control persons.
Results: The relative coefficient (RC) giving evidence of normal level of lacrymal protein (determined in the control group) was 0.07±0.005. In patients with penetrating wounds but without signs of infection, RC was 0.18±0.04; in patients with wounds complicated with infection, it was 0.06±0.002.
Conclusions: Thus, in infected wounds, the level of lacrymal proteins was low, while that in penetrating wounds not complicated with infection exceeded normal level. The latter was indicative of the enhancement of organism defence reaction manifesting itself by increasing of protein components in tears.

211

PROGNOSIS VALUE OF CHOROID THIKNESS IN OCULAR TRAUMATOLOGY

P.PEGOURIE, D. SATGER, P. GENIN, M.MOUILLON, J.P.ROMANET
Dept. Ophthalmology C.H.U. GRENOBLE (France)

Purpose : The most severe complication of the eye traumas is the evolution towards atrophy. The echographic thickening of choroid is one of the signs of this complication as well as hypotony of the eye.
Methods: 23 patients were investigated in B mode echography with measurements of the scleral axial length, and of the choroidal thickness (C.T.) on at least three areas of the eye. Cilio-choroidal detachment was searched in each patient.
Results : At the first examination between D5 and D15 four patients had a C.T. of more than two millimetres. All of them evolved towards atrophy of the globe with diminution of the axial length. Four patients had a C.T. less than 2 millimetres : their evolution was favourable. Among the fifteen patients whose the C.T. was normal two patients evolved towards the atrophy (only one patient was hypotonic in the beginning).

Conclusions : Only echography can achieve the measurements of C.T. A great initial increase is a sign of a bad prognosis. The evolution towards atrophy can happen in spite of a normal C. T. and an initial normal IOP. Echographic examination with strict measurements must be rigorous and repetitive .

212

VITREOUS FLUOROMETRY VARIABLES IN CLINICAL PRACTICE

Oliveiros B, Ludovico J, Figueira J, Lobo C, Cunha-Vaz JG.
Center of Ophthalmology, Biomedical Institute for Research in Light and Image, Coimbra, Portugal

Purpose: To evaluate the methodological variables involved in performing vitreous fluorometry and to evaluate their relative importance for clinical practice.
Methods: A series of 40 diabetic patients with minimal to moderate retinopathy were examined by vitreous fluorometry. The parameters considered of interest were evaluated: total and free fluorescein (3 measurements), lens transmitance, Blood-Aqueous Barrier (BAB) and Blood-Retinal Barrier (BRB) permeabilities
Results: Statistical evaluation of the different parameters show that the measurement of free fluorescein does not reduce significantly the variability of the method in comparison with total fluorescein measurements. Lens transmitance measurements reduce variablity of the procedure by only 1,2%.BAB permeability correlates better with plasma rather than with BRB permeability.
Conclusion: Quantification of the permeability of the BRB may be performed in clinical practice using a BRB penetration ratio using only posterior vitreous fluorescence measurements and two measurements of total plasma fluorescence.

213

EPIMACULAR PROLIFERATION IN OPTIC NERVE AVULSION

Mª.S.Alforja ; J.García-Arumí ;L.Cavero ; M.Calatayud ; M.Garat ; E.Arrondo.
Vall d'Hebrón Hospitals.UAB. Barcelona (Spain).

Purpose. To describe the clinical and angiographic features of optic nerve avulsion. To determine the indications and surgical approach of epimacular proliferation due to optic nerve avulsion.

Methods. We studied a 20 years old man with a traumatic optic nerve avultion. Fluorescein angiography and CT scan were performed. There were no changes in the anterior segment of the eye nor associated sistemic lesions.

Results. A follow-up period of two years was made. We describe epimacular proliferation due to optic nerve avulsion. After pars plana vitrectomy was made, epimacular proliferation appeared again.

Conclusions.We describe epimacular proliferation due to optic nerve avulsion, an assocation not previously described, in our best knowledge.

214

TEST RELIABILITY WITH HUMPHREY SITA PERIMETRY IN THYROID-ASSOCIATED OPHTHALMOPATHY

FRENANDER C and ÅSMAN P
Dept. of Ophthalmology, Malmö University Hospital, Malmö, Sweden

Purpose To evaluate test reliability in modern automated perimetry in thyroid patients with and without infiltrative ophthalmopathy. **Methods** 58 Humphrey 30-2 SITA-standard field tests obtained from 58 patients with hyper-thyroidism were studied. All patients had experience with HFA threshold testing. The ratios of fixation losses, false positive and false negative responses were recorded in each field test. The patients were divided by one of us (PÅ) into two groups a) non-infiltrative and b) infiltrative ophthalmopathy based on the patient records. **Results** Reliability parameters are shown in the table (mean and range)

	n	FL %	FP %	FN %
Non-infiltrative	25	8,4 (0-47)	3,2 (0-19)	2,5 (0-11)
Infiltrative	33	9,5 (0-35)	3,5 (0-15)	3,5 (0-18)
Significance		p=0,3	p=0,5	p=0,7

There were no significant differences in any reliability parameter between the two groups (Mann Whitney U-test). **Conclusion** The Humphrey SITA-standard program is a short test associated with good patient performance in thyroid-associated ophthalmopathy and should be considered in the evaluation of these patients. Further studies are needed to give more detailed information regarding diagnostic precision.

215

OPTIC NEUROPATHY AS INITIAL PRESENTATION OF AN OCULO-CEREBRAL LYMPHOMA

SNYERS B., BOSCHI A.
Dept. Ophthalmology, St Luc Hospital, Catholic University of Louvain, Brussels (Belgium)

Purpose
Bilateral optic neuropathy associated with a mild pseudo-pigmentary retinopathy as initial presentation of an oculo-cerebral lymphoma.

Methods
Case report of a 63-year-old female with symptoms of a progressive bilateral optic neuropathy leading to the diagnosis of an oculo-cerebral lymphoma (B cell) which was confirmed histo-pathologically by a cerebral biopsy.

Results
High doses of corticosteroids followed by chemotherapy and external radiotherapy were sucessful in improving vision and visual fields in both eyes.

Conclusions
Optic neuropathy may be the initial manifestation of an oculo-cerebral lymphoma, even without ophthalmoscopic evidence of vitreous, retinal and optic nerve infiltration.

216

DURAL ARTERIOVENOUS FISTULA

DUBLANCHE S, VAREILLES M, VASDEV A, BESSOU P, MOUILLON M, ROMANET JP.

Service D'Ophtalmologie, CHU Grenoble (France)

Purpose: Dural carotid-cavernous fistula is an arteriovenous malformation supplied by duramatral branches of the internal and/or external carotid with cavernous sinus drainage. The diagnosis of a dural fistula is difficult because low-flow dural fistulas have a mild clinical course.

Methods: The case reported concerned a 71 year woman without antecedent, who presented a red eye, dilated episcleral veins, exophtalmos, elevated intraocular pressure and oculomotor nerve IV paralysis. A cerebral hyperselective angiography was performed.

Results: The cerebral angiography confirmed the diagnosis of a dural fistula. The treatment consisted in compressing the carotid artery. Recovery was achieved in three months.

Conclusions: The ophthalmological symptoms reveal the diagnosis. The cerebral angiography confirms the diagnosis and decides of the treatment. Vital pronostic is rarely touched but there can be some serious visual complications, if it is not diagnosed in time.

217

BILATERAL PAPILLEDEMA ASSOCIATED WITH CEREBRAL VENOUS SINUS THROMBOSIS

HERA R, DUBLANCHE S, BESSOU P, VASDEF A, MOUILLON M, ROMANET JP
Service d'Ophtalmologie CHU Grenoble (France)

Purpose: Case report of a patient with clinical features suggestive of intracranial hypertension caused by cerebral venous sinus thrombosis.

Methods: Computed tomography and magnetic resonance imaging disclosed indirect signs of cerebral venous sinus thrombosis. Angyo-magnetic resonance imaging confirmed this diagnosis.

Results: The patient was treated with oral anticoagulants (warfarine) and oral acetazolamide. Symptoms and ophtalmoscopic signs improved within two months.

Conclusions: Bilateral papilledema may be a sign of cerebral venous sinus thrombosis. This etiologic diagnosis worth be known, because this disease can be efficiently treated.

218

BENIGN ORBITAL TUMOR IN THE CHILD: A CASE REPORT

MASELLA JJ[1], ROGE A[1], PEOC'H M[2], BESSOU P[3], ROMANET JP[1] AND MOUILLON M[1]

1. Dept. Ophthalmology, Grenoble (France)
2. Dept. Pathology, Grenoble (France)
3. Dept. Radiology, Grenoble (France)

Purpose: Case report of a 11 year old child with evolutive and painless proptosis caused by an orbital tumor.

Methods: Computed tomography and magnetic resonance imaging turned the diagnosis on cavernous hemangioma. The arteriography proved that this mass was vascularised.

Results: A surgical biopsy was done and the histological analysis concluded to a very rare type of neurinoma, a cellular shwannoma. No complication was noted after the surgery.

Conclusions: Proptosis is usually the first sign of an orbital tumour. The neurinoma is a diagnosis to summon when the radiological exams do not conclue for a proptosis in the child.

219

WALKER WARBURG SYNDROME

BADA T*, FERRER C*, GONZALEZ I*, MELCON B*, OTEIZA C**, LOPEZ J**, HONRUBIA FM*.
(*)Department of Ophthalmology. (**)Department of Pediatrics. Miguel Servet Hospital. Zaragoza (Spain)

Purpose: The aim of this study is to analyze the major findings in a patient with Walker Warburg (WWS).

Patient and results: We report on the findings in a female patient with WWS who died at the age of one month.Ocular examination disclosed a complete afferent pupillary defect, cataract, severe retinal dysplasia and microphthalmia. Systemic abnormalities included cobblestone lissencephaly and congenital muscular distrophy.

Conclusions: The association of congenital muscular distrophy with brain and eye malformations has been reported in several clinical syndromes. Ocular symptoms are frequently observed in WWS. The majority of patients present malformations of the anterior segment and severe retinal dysplasia.

220

A COMBINED COGNITIVE AND ANATOMICAL ILLUSTRATION OF ESSENTIAL BLEPHAROSPASM

DIXON R S
Bon Secours Hospital, Grosse Pointe MI USA

Purpose: To map a symbolic neural machinery that addresses Essential Blepharospasm onto its anatomical terrain.

Method: A hypothetical network outlined from cognitive science is applied to its anatomical substrate derived from the clinical experience.

Result: Two levels of understanding exist simultaneously. A neural network and symbolic architecture compliments gross anatomy for the illustration of neural function and disease.

Conclusion: A deeper understanding of Essential Blepharospasm is available from cognitive science combined with neuroanatomy. Furthermore, this is a point of departure for the basis of neural function and disease.

221

EPIPHENOMENA AND DISEASE, SUCH AS ESSENTIAL BLEPHAROSPASM, FROM SYMBOLIC NEURAL MACHINERY

DIXON R S
Bon Secours Hospital, Grosse Pointe MI USA

Purpose: To Identify Essential Blepharospasm as a disease of implicit neural mechanisms...

Method: A symbolic neural machinery coupled with a biological information theory.

Result: The identified neural functions are unconscious routines within a symbolic mental architecture. Symbol-triggering patterns have suggestive value and metaphorical richness. The architecture facilitates spread of activity generation. Activity emerges as an epiphenomenon. In response to the environment, symbols play out probable or plausible scenarios from the past that may have no relevance other than as metaphors. Statistics determine response. There is simulation by abstraction and shrewd guessing, based on analogy and experience. Simulations effect approximations for interpretations that range from crude but effective to inappropriate and excessive.

Conclusion: Essential Blepharospasm and its associated syndromes result from a symbolic neural machinery triggered by symbols for internal or external events. This observation is also a point of departure for the appreciation of the concept of epiphenomena that relate to cognitive functions.

225

VISUAL PERFORMANCE OF PRE-MOUNTED LENSES

PONS A.M., ILLUECA C., HERNANDEZ C., VIQUEIRA V., BALAGUER A.
Dept. D'Optica. Universitat d'Alacant. (SPAIN)

Purpose: Pre-mounted lenses are widely used for the presbita as a low-cost aid for near vision. These lenses are mounted following standard parameters and manufacturing in plastic materials. In our study we have compared the visual performance of pre-mounted lenses with the one obtained from specifically designed lenses.

Methods: The comparison between the two types of optical compensation was carried out by evaluating the Contrast Sensitivity Function (CSF), Visual acuity (VA), Modulation Transfer Function (MTF) and Binocular vision.

Results: Our results shows a decrease of visual quality in a significative percentage of cases, which is more important in the cases of binocular function. We have obtained important deviations on longitudinal horopter, indicating induced aniseikonia.

Conclusions: From the results of our work we must advise against the use of pre-mounted lenses, due to the important induced effects over binocular vision, specially in phorias and anisometropy.

226

THE DISSOCIATION OF GRATING- AND OPTOTYPE ACUITY DEPENDS ON ACUITY AND LUMINANCE.

FOSSE P[1] AND VALBERG A.[2]
1. Tambartun National Resource Centre for the Visually Impaired (Norway)
2. Dept. of Physics, Section of Biophysics, Norwegian University of Science and Technology (Norway)

Purpose: To establish the relationship between optotype and grating acuity as a function of luminance for persons with age-related macular degeneration (AMD). Methods: 14 subjects with AMD and three with normal vision were tested with optotype acuity charts and Teller grating cards. Luminance ranged from mesopic (0.4 cd/m²) to high photopic levels (1 200 cd/m²). Results: Generally, acuity improved with increasing luminance, although individual variations were large. Regardless of luminance level, for optotype acuity (OA) below about 0.2, significant differences were found between the two acuities. The mean ratio between optotype and grating acuity was close to 0.4. For higher acuity values the differences were much smaller. Conclusions: For AMD subjects with optotype acuity below about 0.2, optotype acuity cannot at any luminance level be derived from grating acuity. With regard to the WHO's criterion for low vision ($OA<0.33$), we caution against inferring optotype acuity from grating data.

Supported by grants from Thonning Owesen Foundation and The Norwegian Association of the Blind and Partially Sighted.

227

VARIATION OF DETECTABILITY OF ORIENTED LINE TARGETS WITH VISUAL-FIELD QUADRANT

DOHERTY, L. M. and FOSTER, D. H.
Vision Sciences, Aston University, Birmingham B4 7ET (United Kingdom)

Purpose. Observers can often detect a uniquely oriented line element ('target') among uniformly line oriented elements even if viewing duration is brief. Does performance in this task depend on the visual-field location (left, right, upper, or lower) of the target?

Methods. Observers detected randomly placed targets in displays comprising 20 oriented line elements. Displays were presented briefly and then masked. The probability of target presence on each trial was 0.5. All observers were English-speaking and aged 18-35 yr.

Results. Percent-correct scores were found for targets in each visual-field quadrant. For 8 of the 14 observers, the effect of quadrant was significant ($p < 0.01$ for 7 observers; $0.01 < p < 0.05$ for 1 observer). For 7 observers showing a significant effect, the quadrant giving poorest performance was in the right visual field.

Conclusions. Some observers performing a rapid-detection task show an uneven distribution of processing resources across the visual field. Detection performance is often poorest for targets in the right visual field, possibly because the observers usually read from left to right.

228

EFFECTS OF DIVING ON CONTRAST SENSITIVITY, COLOUR VISION AND VISUAL FIELD. A RETROSPECTIVE STUDY IN 21 DIVERS.

MACAREZ R[1], DORDAIN Y[1], KOVALSKI JL[1], COLIN J[2].
1.Dept. Ophthalmology, HIAClermont-Tonnerre,Brest(France)
2.Dept. Ophthalmology, CHU de Brest (France)

Purpose
To evaluate the long term effects of professional diving on Spatial contrast sensitivity, colour vision and visual field.
Methods
Complete ophthalmological examination, spatial contrast sensitivity, colour vision (desaturated 15 hue test) and visual field (Humphrey® Fastpac central 30-2 threshold test) was performed in 21 professional divers and in a comparison group of 21 non-divers. The mean number of dives was 3472 and the mean diving history was 14 years. All the subjects were non-smokers.
Results
None of the divers had any loss of spatial contrast sensitivity. Divers make a significantly more important number of errors in the desaturated 15 hue test ($p < 0,01$), with an important frequency of yellow-blue axis colour vision defects (45%). Corrected Pattern Standard Deviation of the central 30-2 threshold test was significantly higher in divers ($p < 0,01$), but no difference was found in the foveal threshold ($p = 0,47$).
Conclusions
These findings suggest that iterative diving may cause infra-clinical functional effects on vision. Further studies will be needed to determine the exact setting of this repercussion upon macula and/or the optic nerve.

229

LIGHTNESS MEMORY MATCHING ANALIZED USING DIFFERENT REPRESENTATION SPACES

DE FEZ, MD, DIEZ A, GÓMEZ J, CAPILLA P, PONS AM
Dept. Optica, Universitat de València, València, Spain.

Purpose: The choice of the representation space is relevant when analysing the results of a colour memory experiment. The aim of the present work is to study how the perceptual attribute lightness of the remembered colours differ from these of the reference colours. We analized four differents representation spaces: CIELAB, SVF, RLAB and LLAB.

Method: We used 10 gray cardboard circle panels on which we arranged 20 comparative chips, chosen round 10 reference tests from Munsell Atlas. 100 observers took part in the experiment. The observer looked at the reference test for 10 sec in order to memorise it. After that time, the observer was asked to recognize the comparison test, which matched the memorised one, 15 sec, 15 min and 24 h later.

Results and discussion: For most colours and in all spaces, reference colours above a particular lightness value are remembered as even lighter, whereas below certain value they are remembered as darker or equally light.

230

BIOFEEDBACK THERAPY IN AMBLIOPIC ADULTS.

M RAPINESE, L LOBEFALO, A BAIOCCHI, C CRUDELI, PL DI CARLO, F DI CRESCENZO, T MARSILIO, L MASTROPASQUA, PE GALLENGA
Institute of Ophthalmology and Legal Medicine
"G.d'Annunzio" University, Chieti - Italy

Purpose: to evaluate the usefulness of a treatment based on biofeedback in the improvement of visual function in ambliopic patients

Methods: Eighty adults (mean age: 27.12 yr± 4.57 range 20-38 yr) affected with unilateral anisometropic ambliopia were enrolled in a prospectic randomized controlled study. In all patients visual acuity (ETDRS) was evaluated at the beginning of the treatment and weekly for 6 months. Forty patients underwent weekly treatments with the Improved Biofeedback Integrated System for 6 months, while the other 40 patients were not treated.

Results: In the treated group 70% of patients showed an improvement of visual acuity of at least 2 lines and in 47.5% of cases this improvement was greater than 3 lines. In no control cases an improvement of at least 2 lines was found.

Conclusions: Biofeedback therapy is useful in improving visual acuity in patients affected with anisometropic ambliopia. More informations on the duration of this therapy are needed.

231

REFRACTIVE STATE OF A MEDITERRANEAN POPULATION

Authors: López-Alemany A.(1), Montés-Micó R.(1), Serra-Plá S.(2)
(1) Departament d'Òptica. Universitat de València. SPAIN.
(2) Ophthalmology Clinic "Daniel Miguel". Alzira. SPAIN.

Purpose: In this work a complete study of the refractive state of a Mediterranean population was made.

Methods: At this stage 5527 subjects were examined. 227 subjects with ocular abnormalities were excluded from the study. The subjects were classified by age in three groups.

Results: We obtained an spherical and cylindrical mean value of ammetropia of -0.24 D and -1.20 D respectively. The results obtained showed a prevalence of emmetropia (41.4%) whereas hyperopia and myopia appeared only in 31.0% and 27.6% of the subjects, respectively. We found a change in the direction of astigmatism from with-the-rule to against-the-rule and astigmatism value increment with increasing age. We obtained a mean near addition similar for men and women and greater than Donders values.

232

REFRACTIVE STATUS OF TWO POPULATIONS WITH DIFFERENT CULTURAL AND GENETIC BACKGROUNDS

RODRIGUES, M.L.V.[1], CRUZ, A.A.V.[1], SILVA, F.L.M.[1], MABTUM, E.A.[1], CARVALHO, R.A.C.[2], THORN, F.[3] and ROMÃO, E.[1]
[1] – Medical School of Ribeirão Preto, University of São Paulo, Brazil; [2] – Instituto de Olhos de Manaus, Amazonas and Medical School of Ribeirão Preto; [3] – New England College of Optometry, Boston, MA, USA.

Purpose: to compare the refractive status of two populations from different geographic Brazilian regions and different cultural and genetic backgrounds.

Methods: Refractive measurements were performed, in a population of indigenous descendent (Group 1) near the Equator Line; and in medical students (Group 2), in the University Hospital – Medical School of Ribeirão Preto, located near the Capricorn Tropic.

Results: In Group 1 the vast majority is emmetropic, and the prevalence of myopia is 1.6%. In Group 2 the most frequent condition is myopic astigmatism (48.8%).

Conclusion: If myopia is genetically determined, the indigenous population should have shown a large percentage of myopia. Our results, on the contrary, support the hypotheses that cultural environment appears to affect the development of myopia and that the prevalence of myopia is associated with the level of education or amount of reading.

233

VISUAL ENVIRONMENT INFLUENCE ON EYES MOVEMENTS IN VISUAL APRAXIA.

DEFOORT -DHELLEMMES S, DE SEZE J, ARNDT CF, VERMERSH P, BUQUET C, PASQUIER F, HACHE JC.
Depts. of neuro-ophtalmology and neurology,
LILLE, FRANCE

Purpose: to study the visual scanning strategy and the influence of the visual surrounding on the eyes movements in the oculomotor apraxia.
Methods: Eye movements were recorded with a bright pupil -corneal refflex technique (photo-oculography) in 2 patients with a right parietal atrophy and a progressive visual apraxia without hemianopia or hemineglect. Reflexives saccades and visual pursuit were tested.The stimulus is a red laser target elicited in front of the patients on a screen with and without pictures. Scanning visual strategy including free scanning and reading tasks were also performed.
Results : During the visual scanning, the patients were unable to explore the left hemifield but could report the text or the scene. They had a left predominant visual apraxia and left pursuit impairment when pictures or peoples were in front of them. Saccades and pursuit were normal when there is no picture on the screen.
Conclusions: This troubles occurring only with a visual stimulus in front of the patient could be related to the parietal atrophy and probably due to a parieto-collicular disconnection.

234

REFRACTION ERRORS AND EYE SUBJECTIVE SYMPTOMS OF VDT OPERATORS

URBAN E, SALOMON E, BORODULIN-NADZIEJA L, JANOCHA A.
Dep. Physiology, Medical University, Wroclaw (Poland)

Purpose The aim of the study was to estimate relationships between refraction errors and eye subjective symptoms concerned with work of video display terminals operators.
Methods Examinations were carried on 150 VDT operators of similar age (39,5 ± 2,3 years) and seniority (15,6 ± 1,5 years). They were chosen after refraction measurements by autorefractometer (50 – myopic, 50- hypermetropic and 50 – emmetropic, as control operators).They performed 5,2 ± 1,5 hours task of dialogue type. Persons with refraction errors used corrective eyewear during the work with computer.The questionare they filled in afterwards provided the data to study the effects of work with VDT on manifestation of subjective eye symptoms.
Results Statistical analysis of the data didn't reveal any relationships between refraction of the eye and frequences or kinds of eye subjective symptoms of VDT operators.
Conclusions The obtained results suggest that work with VDT evoke eye subjective symptoms independly on refraction state of the eye.

235

PREVALENCE AND VISUAL DISORDERS IN CHILDREN IN SOFIA DISTRICT, BULGARIA

VASSILEVA P., PETROV D. and CHAUSHEV V.

University Hospital "St. Anna"-Eye Department (Bulgaria)

Purpose Early diagnosis of children with sight threatening diseases is of main importance for prevention of childhood blindness. Screening is necessary for identification of visually impaired children, that could benefit from surgery.
Methods A screening project for eye disorders in children was undertaken in orphanages and among general population in underserved area of Sofia district. The team consisted of two ophthalmologists and seven residents. A workshop on pediatric ophthalmology was conducted prior to the screening with participation of local neonatologists and pediatricians.
Results We screened total of 1996 children, 1015 up to 6 years and 981 between 7 and 15 years (315 of them were institutionalized in orphanages). Congenital eye pathology was more common in orphanages: strabismus had a prevalence of 8.74 %, and systemic disorders-4.94%. Significant number of children with strabismus, amblyopia, glaucoma and cataract were identified among general rural population, that have unfavorable prognosis due to late diagnosis.
Conclusions Eye screening programs in collaboration with neonatologists and pediatricians is of decisive importance for early diagnosis and timely treatment of visually impaired children.

236

CAUSES OF BLINDNESS AND SEVERE VISUAL IMPAIRMENT IN BULGARIEN CHILDREN

POPOVA-TASHKOVA, A.
Chair of ophthalmology, Medical University, Sofia, Bulgaria

Purpose: The autor studies the ocular pathology in 4I4, 6-I8 years old children, from the school for students with visual disorders in Sofia. The study covers the period from I984-I989.

Methods: Clinical, genetical, genetical-matematic and statistical.

Results: The leading significance of the hereditary ocular pathology among the causes for blindness and severe visual impairment in discassed group of children is marked/77,3% of all children and 93,8% of the children with inborn diseases/. The total number of clinical-genetic forms described in this work is 59/AD-I7;AR-40;X-linked-2/. The relative part of the patients with AD disease is I9,I%, with AR-80,3% and X-linked-0,6.

Conclusion: Clinical-genetic polymorphism is established within the studied nosological units. Interfamilial and intrafamilial analyses with respect to the phenotype is carried on and the existence of interfamilial correlations and intrafamilial dyscorrelations as well as the existence of interfamilial discorrelations and intrafamilial correlations is established.

237

VISUAL ABILITIES OF YOUNG FOOTBALL PLAYERS

Authors:
Montés-Micó R, Bueno-Gimeno I, Gené-Sampedro A.
Dept. Òptica. Universitat de València. SPAIN

Purpose: We developed an optometric study and determined visual abilities related to football practice over young football players of the VALENCIA Football Club. Also we realized the same test over non-football players.

Methods: The abilities studied were static and dynamic visual acuity, ocular motility, stereopsis, visual field, visualization, visual location, contrast sensitivity and colour vision. Subsequently the football players went through a two-month period of visual training, with the purpose of improving their visual abilities.

Results: The results showed that the football players had better visual abilities than the non-football players except for visual contrast sensitivity, and that these visual abilities improved with the visual training, except for visual contrast sensitivity and visual estereoacuity.

238

STUDY OF BINOCULAR FUNCTIONS AND OPHTHALMO-ERGONOMICAL EVALUATION OF THE EFFICIENCY OF INTRAOCULAR APHAKIA CORRECTION

ALIYEV AHD, ISMAILOV MI
Daghestan State Medical Academy

It is known that decentration. of the IOL is accompanied by additional optical aberrations in the "eye-intraocular lens" system. These induced aberrations result in a series of optical phenomena that negatively affect functional indices and thus considerably diminish efficiency of the operation.
The problem being insufficiently investigated, we have undertaken a study of how optical aberrations in the "eye-intraocular lens" system caused by decentration of the posterior IOL affected mono- and binocular optic functions in 44 patients (47 eyes).
We have developed and followed a certain procedure of measuring the posterior IOL decentration. According to the place taken by the IOL in the posterior chamber the patients were divided into 4 groups: 15 patients (15%) with the centred IOL, 12 (25.5%.) - with up to 0.5 mm decentration, 11 (23.4 %) - with decentration from 0.5 to 1.0 mm and 9 patients (19.1%) with decentration of more than 1.0 mm.
There has been revealed statistically authentic decrease of visual acuity depending on the IOL deviation from the visual axis.
Investigation of sight characteristics showed that 36 patients (81.8%) had binocular vision, in the rest 8 patients (18.2%) simultaneous perception was observed.
Investigation of anyseikonia was carried out with the traditional anyseikonimeter. When there were detects in binocular sight we used our original device which made it possible to conduct eikonometric study in these cases as well.
Anisophoria and depth vision have also been investigated. Study of optical efficiency in the aforementioned group of patients shows that decrease of binocular indices is followed by worsening of optical efficiency.
Analysis of the data obtained testifies to the fact that IOL decentration does not only result in decrease of monocular visual acuity in the operated eye, but obviously produces a negative effect on binocular functions and ophthalmoergonomical indices.

239

HOW TO PREPARE OR ADAPTE QUESTIONNAIRES OF QUALITY OF LIFE

LEITE E, PEDRUCO A, OLIVEIROS B, TAVARES C.
Centre of Ophthalmology, Biomedical Institute for Light and Image Research, Coimbra, Portugal

To describe the impact of cataract surgery in terms of visual function and health related quality of life. Several questionnaires have been elaborated and validated accordingly to certain "local" parameters. The purpose of this study was to compare several quality of life questionnaires (4) and establish the main advantages and drawbacks. A group of 22 patients submitted to cataract surgery with IOL implantation were evaluated with different questionnaires (NEI-VFQ, VF-14, CATQUEST, RAND VISION) before surgery and six week after surgery. All the four questionnaires showed an improvement on the global score of quality of life. However several differences were detected between them. NEI-VFQ is the most complete and dettailed one, since it covers most of the items, namely, general health, physical health, pain cognition function, anxiety/depression, self control, social health, vision perception, difficulties in activities, driving and limitations. VF-14 is the simplest one since it covers only daily activities and driving. CATQUEST and Rand-Vision are in between the other two. The time consuming in its aplication goes from 15 min. (VF-14 and 50 min. NEI-VFQ). As conclusion all the questionnaires should be validate to the target population. NEI-VFQ seems to be the most complete questionnaire and CATQUEST appears to be in a clinical basis the most equilibrate (n° of items covered, time-consuming). However, as final conclusion in this type of quality of life evaluation, all patients psychological profile should be defined.

240

EFFCTS OF WORK WITH VDT ON VISUAL ORGAN STATE

SALOMON E, BORODULIN-NADZJEJA L, URBAN E, JANOCHA A.
Dep.Physiology ,Medical University, Wroclaw (Poland)

Purpose Performing their work VDT operators stay in contact with source of physical factors that can affect their health.The aim of the study undertaken was to evaluate the condition of the eye in the chosen VDT operators group.
Methods Examinations were carried on 100 VDT operators and 100 office workers - non-VDT (control) of similiar age with emmetropia.The seniority of VDT operators was 15,5 ± 3,2 years.They performed 5,4 ± 1,2 hours task of dialogue type. The anterior segment of the eye was examined before and after the work and then after dilating of the pupil we tested lens and vitreous in a slit lamp and the fundus of the eye after work.
Results The study of operators group revealed : chronic conjunctivitis – 24% , blepharitis – 8 % and irritation of conjunctiva after work – 12%.In the control group except 5% of chronic conjunctivitis, no changes in the organ of vision were observed.
Conclusions The study proved that the VDT operators suffered more often from the chronic inflammation of the protective apparatus of the eye than the control group did.

241

MODIFIED DEM: A TOOL FOR SACCADIC EVALUATION IN ADULTS

GENÉ A, PONS A.M., MONTALT J.C.
Dept. D'Òptica.Universitat de València. Dr. Moliner, 50. Burjassot (SPAIN)

PURPOSE: To determine effects of aging on visual motion processing we measured saccade dynamics in young, middle-aged and elderly normal patients using a reading type tests to objectively record time eye movements to evaluate the developmental aspects of the saccadic velocity with the age.

METHODS: Saccades movements of a large number (n= 500) of normal subjetcs of different ages (9-68 years-old) were investigated applying the Developmental Eye Movement Modificaded (DEMM)

RESULTS: For children under In children tested to date saccadic velocities were lowest for the youngst children and increased progressively with increased age.

CONCLUSIONS: with increase in age, the velocity showed a tendency to decrease. The results indicate that the diagnosis of saccadic dysfunction should be qualified by the age of the patient.This quantitative study provides anew test with norms for the detection of oculomotor dysfuntions in young, middle-aged and elderly subjetcs.

243

FRESNEL DIFFRACTION ON A THEORETICAL EYE: A FRACTIONAL FOURIER TRANSFORM APPROACH

ILLUECA C(1), LORENTE A (1), PONS AM(1), ARTIGAS JM(2), FELIPE A(2)
1. Dcpt. d'Òptica. Universitat d'Alcant. PO.Box 99. Sant Vicent del Raspeig. (SPAIN). 2. Dept. d'Òptica. Universitat de València. Dr. Moliner 50. 46100 Burjassot (SPAIN)

Purpose: The use of Fresnel diffraction theory to characterise the optical behaviour of a theoretical eye, although it can be the most powerful method, has several methodological problems when it is applied to an arbitrary axial distance. In this work we implement a new model of theoretical eye based on the properties of the Fractional Fourier Transform (FRT).

Methods: The FRT has been recently introduced in optics by Mendlovic and Ozaktas (1993) as a new tool for image analysis. The FRT provides a correct expression for Fresnel diffraction at any axial distance. We have introduced the FRT algorithms in a modification of the schematic Gullstrand-Emsley eye model in order to obtain the PSF and the MTF of the eye.

Results: With our model a complete scheme of Fresnel diffraction on the theoretical eye can be obtained. We show different cases of theoretical results in ammetropia.

Conclusions: This methodology can be used in order to design optics elements for ophthalmic compensation or for the assessment of optical quality in refractive surgery.

244

REACTION TIME (RT) MEASUREMENTS ALONG DIFFERENT DIRECTIONS IN AN OPPONENT MODULATION SPACE.

M. J. Luque, P. Capilla, M. A. Díez, A. Felipe

Purpose: We aim to study the dependence of RT on the signal amplitude along different directions in a opponent modulation space (DKL-space), including the achromatic (A), the red-green (T) and the blue-yellow (D) channels and two additional directions on the isoluminant plane.

Methods: A white background of 20 cd/m2 subtending 4 degrees was presented to the observer on a computer-controlled display. After a random lapse, a test, subtending 1 degree, and producing a given modulation on the white background along one of seven directions in DKL-space was displayed. The observer signaled when the test was perceived by pressing a key, and the time elapsed from the test apparition to the observer response was recorded. For each direction, eigth different test signals were used, with 400 presentations per test, in 100-presentation runs.

Results and discussion: Our data may be fitted assuming that RT verifies a law of the Pieron type in the isolated channels and that for an arbitrary signal, RT is determined by the channel yielding the smallest RT. The asymptotic RT proved to be minimum for the A channel and maximum for the D channel, in agreement with physiological data.

245

SPACE PERCEPTION DEVIATIONS FROM THEORETICAL HOROPTER INDUCED BY ANISOMETROPY.

GENÉ A.1, PONS A.M.1, ILLUECA C.2, VIQUERA V.2, ALBARRAN C.1, HERNANDEZ C.-2

1Dept. D'Òptica.Universitat de València. Dr. Moliner, 50. Burjassot (SPAIN)

2Dept. D'Optica. Universitat d'Alacant. PO.Box.99. Sant Vicent del Raspeig(SPAIN)

Purpose: In this work we have derived theoretically the curves of equal Convergence and Accommodation, comparing these results with the ones obtained empirically of longitudinal horopter with induced anisometropy.

Methods: From the classical expressions of Physiological Optics, we have derived general expressions for binocular convergence, obtaining theoretical curves of C=A. We have measured empirically the longitudinal horopter by the method of the longitudinal horopter as it was described by Ogle.

Results: The rotation of horopter around fixation point is reproduced in a simple way with this approach, and new curves of C=A are showed. These curves allows us to redefine a more general ACA relationship and to compare convergence and accommodation in the peripheria.

Conclusions: The use of C=A curves in non-symmetrical convergence allows the definition of a general expression of ACA relationship.

246

STARGARDT: REHABILITATION TREATMENT

S.Z. Scalinci., P. Simoni., F. Bartolomei., L. Scorolli., R. Meduri.
Department of Physiopathologic Ottica
University ol Bologna (Italy)

PURPOSE: The use of optical and electronic aids, helped by rehabilitation cycles, after accurate ophthalmologist visits, permitted us to stimulate an area of eccentric fixation in patients affected by Macular Degeneration.
METHODS: The Authors selected five patients affected by Stargardt's Desease with mean age of 35+/-5. The ophthalmogist visit consisred of Visual Acuity Test, Perimetry, F.A.G., E.R.G., V.E.R., Chromatic Sense Test, and Contrast Sensitivity Test. The aids used were: half-eye-system spectacle magnifiers, telescopic systems, CCTV, V-MAX sistem. The rehabilitative cycle consisted of ten weekly sessions during which the patients made reading and fixation exercices and Biofeedback.
RESULTS: Four patients otained binocular eccentric fixation; on the other hand only one patient achived monocular eccentric fixation.
CONCLUSIONS: The use of eccentric retina by additional fovea let the patients with macular degeneration increase their visual capability.

247

COMPARISON OF MAGNIFICATION AND VISUAL ACUITY IN HIGHLY MYOPIC EYES FROM DIFFERENT CORRECTING PLANES

García-Valldecabres M, López-Alemany A, Montés-Micó R

Optometry, Cornea and Contact Lens Research Group. Department of Optics. University of Valencia. SPAIN.

Purpose: To calculate and compare the change in retinal magnification and visual acuity (VA) in highly myopic eyes resulting from moving the correction from the spectacle plane to the contact lens plane.

Methods: The relative retinal magnification (RRM) was used to calculate the change in retinal image size due to different systems of correction using the matrix method. RRM is the ratio of retinal image size in the eye under study (eye corrected with contact lens) to that in reference eye (eye corrected with spectacle lens). The VA was calculated in proportion to change in magnification. The RRM and VA expresions were applied to theoretical cases of high myopia corrected with contact lenses or spectacle lenses. These myopic eyes correspond to the combinations of different corneal powers and axial lengths.

Results: We found an increase in RRM and VA with increasing corneal power and axial length. Moving myopic correction from the spectacle plane to corneal plane increases retinal magnification, therefore it increases the AV. Conclusions: Visual Acuity in myopic eyes corrected with a contact lens is better than that in myopic eyes corrected with a spectacle lens.

248

EIDOLON HAND HELD SLIT LAMP IN CONTACT LENS FITTING

CANO-PARRA J[1,2], BUENO I[2], MONTÉS R[2], ILLUECA I[2], ESPAÑA E[2]

1. Dept Ophthalmology, Municipal Hospital of Badalona
2. Dept. Optics, University of Valencia.

__Purpose:__ To evaluate the efficacy of a new hand held slit lamp in contact lens practice.
__Methods:__ Eidolon hand held slit lamp was used in 50 soft contact lens users and in 50 hard contact lens users to evaluate contact lens fitting.
__Results:__ Eidolon hand held slit lamp provides a good illumination without magnification to observe lids, conjunctiva and cornea, and it is useful to evaluate contact lens centration and movement. However the illumination with the blue filter is not appropiate to evaluate the fluorescein pattern of hard contact lenses
__Conclusions:__ Eidolon hand held slit lamp is a useful instrument in contact lens fitting.

249

THE EMPIRICAL LONGITUDINAL HOROPTER IN PHORIAS.

MONTALT JC, GENÉ A, GÓMEZ JM, PONS AM, SÁNCHEZ M.

Departamento de Optica. Facultad de Fisica. Universitat de Valencia. Spain.

PURPOSE: Our objective is to atempt the horopter as a way to detect and to analyze heterophorias by deviations related to the normal horopter,explaining reasons for its not use in daily practice.

METHOD: The studied population is made up with 85 non presbyopic subjects. The method used was the Apparent Frontoparallel Plane.

RESULTS: Depending on the horopter´s shape for each subject we classify them in the five groups with the following results: Group I (aniseikonia in the left eye): 7% of subjects ; Group II (aniseikonia in the right eye) 15%; Group III (exophoria): 13%; Group IV (esophoria): 15%; Group V (normal binocular vision): 50%.

CONCLUSIONS: Average horopters coincide with the pre-established in every group. The subjects classification depending on its convexity in the esophoric and normal binocular vision´s group requires a comparative method and a sufficient data basis. An main advantage is the possibility of analyse some binocular properties that cannot be detected by another methods

250

TESTING SIGHT IN REAL ENVIROMENTS

VILLANI S., RONCHI R.L. and VILLANI G.
Associazione Ottica Italiana, Pescia (PT) (Italy)

PURPOSE- Visual functions are usually assessed, at photopic levels, by the use of standard techniques. The individual is expected to be "adapted" to their relative balance. Our research program aims at investigating whether the exposure to unconventional sceneries, like those met in a city at night, and classified as "gloomy" by lighting engineering may interact with the individual by producing the breakdown of the above said balance. through uncorrelated deviations of the responses to various tests.

METHODS- A number of individuals are tested at photopic levels by the use of conventional techniques, and, at high mesopic levels by the use of a properly designed setup, free of constraints (that is, by including the "contextual" influences, of a real enviroment), for refraction, binocularity. functional visual field, as well as gloom (with differential semantic scales)

RESULT AND CONCLUSIONS - The multiple handicap, artificially induced by the enviroment at high mesopic levels, in the city-by-night, is found to be correlated with the sensation of weariness and discomfort (gloom), the relative balance of various visual functions being upset. The "luminance signals", popping out from the assumed average level, seem to play a vital role. Accordingly, also the test stimuli of the testing devices should be properly chosen.

251

ON/OFF CONES PATHWAY AND FUCTIONAL STATE OF THE RETINA

SHAMSHINOVA A.

Moscow Helmholtz Research Institute of Eye Diseases

Purpose. To determine the role of functional topography of on/off channels of the cone system in initial diagnostics of the retinal and optic nerve pathology.

Methods.The computer monitor was used to show on the gray background the achromatic stimulus darker and brighter than the background in different points of the visual field. Reaction time (RT) was registered in the process of the equasion in brightness of the stimulus and background.

Results. In the normal patients the RT symmetrically decreased in accordance with the increase of difference between the target and the background symmetrically for brighter and darker stimuli. The early stages of glaucoma and CSB are characterized by an increase of the RT for the stimuli darker then background in 10° from the center. In patients with cones dystrophy RT has an asymmetrical increase for brighter targets in the central zone, suggesting severe reduction of on- channels of cone system sensitivity.

Conclusions. The reaction time of human subject for the detection of the target against the illuminated background rather depends not of the absolute intensity of target stimulus, but on the brightness differences between the background and the target. RT reflects the functional state of the brightness (on-) and darkness (off-) neuronal channels of the cone system and can be used in differential diagnosis of the retina and optic nerve diseases.

252

0NE STEP JUST BEYOND THE SIMPLE VISUO MOTOR REACTION TIME (RT)

RONCHI L.R.(*) and VOGELIN M.R. (**)

(*) Dept. Visual Sci, INO, Florence, (Italy)
(**) Dept. Clin Physiopathol. Univ. Florence (Italy)

Purpose- The present experiment concerns the foveal RT and its dependencies on a number of attention-related factors. It represents a first step beyond the classical simple RT. We aim at linking, gradually, the simple RT to the choice or disjunctive RT, where higher cognitive factors are hard difficult to be quantitatively correlated with task difficulty, stimulus complexity, influences of distractors etc.

Methods- Suprathreshold stimuli are computer generated.Fixation is maintained at a small green cross.In some session the target is presented only at the fovea and RT is recorded in a cued situation. In other sessions the target is also presented (in succession) at other (uncued) locations, at 5 0r 10 deg.

Results and conclusions- Foveal RT is shorter when the target (a square) is presented only at the fovea, and increases when attention is to be divided and splitted to other locations. This holds for both simple and choice RT (where the square is faced with a cross,in succession and a decision is to be taken). Moreover data treatment is found to be difficult because data are not unimodally distributed and the meaning of the Mean and Standard Deviation is questionable. In addition learning takes a long time.

253

CONTRAST SENSITIVITY IN DIABETICS WITH AND WITHOUT RETINOPATHY

G DELLA LOGGIA[1], A VERROTTI[2], L LOBEFALO[1], F CHIARELLI[2], A AVERSANO[1], G MORGESE[2], PE GALLENGA[1]
[1]Institute of Ophthalmology and Legal Medicine
[2]Department of Pediatrics
University "G.d'Annunzio" Chieti - Italy

Purpose: to evaluate the relationship between contrast sensitivity (CS) and metabolic control in diabetic patients

Methods: twenty diabetics without retinopathy and 40 with diabetic retinopathy at different stages were enrolled in the study; 20 healthy subjects similar for age and sex served as controls. CS was assessed with the CSV-1000 contrast testing instrument, testing 4 spatial frequencies.

Results: a weak, but significant difference at 18 cpd was found in diabetics with no retinopathy than in controls ($p=0.04$) while diabetics with background retinopathy showed a significant reduction of CS at 12 and 18 cpd when compared with controls ($p<0.001$). Patients with preproliferative/proliferative retinopathy showed a significant reduction of CS at all frequencies in comparison with controls and a significantly lower mean CS than patients without retinopathy. After a significant amelioration of metabolic control an improvement of CS was found in diabetics without retinopathy and with background retinopathy, while diabetics with severe retinopathy showed no modification.

Discussion: diabetic patients have a loss of CS, which is more severe in those patients with preproliferative/prolife-rative retinopathy. A significant amelioration of metabolic control is associated with an improvement of CS in all patients except in those with fluorescein angiographic signs of preproliferative/proliferative retinopathy.

254

PSEUDO REGRESSIONS AND PSEUDO LINE LOSSES WHEN READING A FULL TEXT WITH A CENTRAL SCOTOMA

DURET F, SAFRAN AB, ISSENHUTH M, MERMOUD C.
Neuro-ophthalmology unit, Geneva University Hospital.

Purpose. Investigating the combined use of several PRLs, in patients with central scotoma of about 15 deg. in diameter during reading tasks.

Methods. Full texts were successively projected onto the retina of patients with macular disorders, using a SLO. Recordings of the fundus image, on which the projected targets were superimposed, were analyzed frame by frame.

Results. Patients used two to three preferred retinal loci (PRL) in association during reading tasks. To read full texts, a PRL offering a large visual span onto the left of the scotoma was employed to search for the beginning of a line, and a PRL with a large visual span onto the right was employed to read a line from left to right. When deciphering a particularly difficult word, up to three PRLs were used in association. Interestingly, in our recordings, most of backward or vertical saccades corresponded to switches of PRL.

Conclusion. Apparent regressions (backward saccades) and apparent line losses (vertical saccades) should not necessarily be considered as uneconomical eye movements, as they may represent adaptive changes of PRL. The functions of PRL may vary according to the visual requirements of the task. This fact is important when considering laser treatment and rehabilitation procedures.

255

EARLY DETECTION OF THE OCULAR PROGRESSION DISEASE IN CICATRICIAL PEMPHIGOID

RIVAS L, SANZ AI, SHALABY O and OROZA MA
Dept Ophthalmology. Hospital Ram6n y Cajal. Madrid. Spain

Purpose: Therapy of cicatricial pemphigoid (CP) depends on the extent and severity, so, it is important obtains a quick diagnosis of the disease during the first stages in order to start the treatment as soon as possible. Drugs against CP are more useful in acute grade than in chronic grade, so an early therapy and management need a minimal dose, and, ederly patients could improve their health even with this relative intolerant systemic treatment.
Methods: We analysed bistering and scarring dispositions, dry eye features (clinic tests, laboratory tests, impression cytology and biposy), presence of immunoglobulins and complement at the epithelial basement membrane zone, circulating antibodies and inflamatory cellular infiltrates, Then, we included the patients in 3 groups according their severity, and study only acute patients.
Results: We obtained 11 patients with acute CP. Immunoglobulins and complement were found in 4 patients (36.4%); IgA was the most frequent deposit. Circulating IgG antibodies were found in none of the patients. Dry eye tests showed a great decrease in goblet cells. None acuous tear components were modified in acute patients. Lacunar folds were decreased in size in 6 patients (53.6%). We also found many neutrophils and macrophages.
Conclusion: Immunogloblulin and complement depositions at basement membrane, impression cytology and lacunar folds confirm the diagnosis of CP. Inflammatory cells may be useful in the assessment of disease activity. Early diagnostic of disease progression should allow a better therapy and preservation of vision.

256

COMPLEX INVESTIGATION OF INTRAOCULAR TUMOR

PAUNKSNIS A[1], BARZDZIUKAS V[1], DAUKSA K, CERNIAUSKIENE L[2], VAICAITIENE R[2], LUKOSEVICIUS A[3], KRIAUCIUNIENE L[1].

1.Lab.of Ophthalmology, Institute for Biomedical Research
2.Lab. of clin.biochemistry, Kaunas Medical Academy
3.Kaunas University of Technology (Lithuania)

Purpose. To develop the complex of differential diagnostic parameters for intraocular tumors.
Methods. Ultrasonic A, B scan, CDI, reflected radiofrequency (RF) signal analysis, histopathological, biochemical (fluorimetrical for vitamin E and A in serum).
Results . Using standardized ultrasonic echography and analysis of reflected RF signal, some differential parameters were determined for diagnosis of intraocular tumors. They were identified with histopathological data. The data obtained allowed to identify microstructure of tumor in vivo.
Conclusions. After complex investigation, performed for 173 patients with intraocular tumors, it was occured that investigated parameters are informative for diagnosis (ultrasonic A, B scan, CDI, reflected RF analysis) or for evaluation of development of pathology (biochemical).

257

STUDIES ON VASCULATURE OF HAMSTER MELANOMA GROWING IN THE EYE

ROMANOWSKA B.[1], CIĘSZKA K.[2], ELAS M.[2], PAJĄK S.[2], CICHOCKI T.[3], MIODOŃSKI A.[4]
1. Dept. Ophthalmology, CM UJ, Kraków, Poland
2. Inst. Molecular Biology, UJ, Krak6w, Poland
3. Dept. Histopathology, CM UJ, Kraków, Poland
4. Dept. Otolaryngology, CM UJ, Kraków, Poland

Purpose The vascular pattern of the Bomirski Hamster Melanoma (BHM) implanted into the anterior chamber of the hamster's eye was evaluated using scanning electron microscopy (SEM) of vascular casts and histopathological examination.
Methods The casts of the eye vasculature were inspected in SEM JSM 35 CF (Jeol) at 20 kV. Eyeballs were also examined histopathologically.
Results The tumor vasculature develop from iridical and limbal vessels. The newly formed vessels originated from capillaries, postcapillary venules and small veins. The induced vascular networks consisted of dilated venous and capillary vessels of different caliber. The vascular bed of untreated tumor revealed chaotic pattern of strongly tortuos capillaries and small veins of surfaces decorated by nodular outgrowth. Histhopathology confirmed the presense of numerous and large vessels, thin walled with visible extravasations.
Conclusions Both histhopathology and eye vasculature casts showed features characteristic of rapidly growing tumors.

259

BILATERAL CHOROIDAL OSTEOMA.REPORT OF A CASE

Arrondo Murillo E, Navarro Alemany R, Alforja Castiella S, Cavero Roig LL, Martínez Castillo V, Calatayud Pinuaga M.
Department of Ophthalmology. Val d'Hebron Hospital. Barcelona. Spain

Purpose: To present a case of a bilateral choroidal osteoma.

Methods: We report the case of a 39 year-old female who suddenly refered a loss of vision of the right eye. The visual acuty was: RE hand movement, LE 1.0. In the right eye fundus we found a yellow-orange lesion affecting the RPE of the posterior pole, involving the macula, and a similar lesion, but in a lower grade in the inferior temporal arcade of the right eye. We asked for a CT which showed in both eyes the existence of a bone density tissue located inthe posterior pole. Within the next months a decrease in the visual acuty of the right eye was acused by the patient, and it became no light perception. The fluorescein angiography demonstrated a neovascular subretinal membrane. Besides, a decalcification of the primary lession was observed. The left eye's lesion remained estable and and there was no decreased visual acuty.

Conclusions: Choroidal osteoma is a benign, rare and usually unilateral tumor that affects the posterior pole of otherwise healthy young females. It can be asymptomatic but over 1/3 of the patients will develop a subretinal neovascular membrane sooner or later, which results in a great visual loss. Eventhough its low fecuency, it should be considered in the differential diagnosis of all subretinal masses, to avoid unnecessary agressive behaviours. There is nowadays no effective therapy to stop the evolution of this disease, and the only chance we have is the fotocoagulation of the subretinal neovascular membrane.

260

CHOROIDAL FOLDS ASSOCIATED WITH OPTIC NERVE MENINGIOMA

Calatayud Pinuaga M, García-Arumí J, Puig Galy J, Escalada Gutiérrez F, Arrondo Murillo E, Garat Chifflet M.
Department of Ophthalmology. Vall d'Hebron Hospital. Barcelona. Spain.

Purpose: to present a case in which retinochoroidal folds appear in association with an optic nerve meningioma previously diagnosed.

Methods:A 58 year-old woman is sent to our department because of a progressive loss of visual acuty in her right eye from 2 months ago. In clinical examination we observed a corrected visual acuty of 0.3 in OD, accompanied by severe colour vision disturbance. Anterior pole examination and IOP were normal.The fundus examination revealed optic disc edema. Visual field showed an importan concentric reduction, and MRI confirmed what was diagnosed in CT as an optic nerve meningioma, because of a diffuse intraorbitary thickening of the nerve.

Results: The patient denied treatment, either surgery or radiotherapy, so we decided just periodical observation. It became a slowly progressive decrease of vision until hands movement, but there is not intracraneal extension.

Conclusions: Choroidal folds may appear as idiopatic pathology or associated to multiple ethiologies such as ocular hipotony, choroidal tumors, posterior escleritis or thyroid ophthalmopathy. It's the first description of a case with the association of optic nerve meningioma to choroidal folds, which we have considered produced by the tumor.

261

COMBINED HAMARTOMA OF THE RETINA AND RETINAL PIGMENT EPITHELIUM : A CASE REPORT

Freixes Puig S, García-Arumí J, Puig Galy J, Martínez Castillo V, Escalada Gutierrez F, Cavero Roig LL.
Department of Ophthalmology. Vall d'Hebron Hospital. Barcelona. Spain

Purpose: Combined hamartomas of the retina and retinal pigment epithelium are rare, benign tumors.They are located in the posterior pole or at the disc and pigmented. These tumors are elevated lesions with retinal vascular tortuosity and epiretinal membrane formation. They usually occur in patients without evidence of systemic disease and their main clinic features are basically progressive visual loss, and strabismus. The fluorescein angiography shows vascular anomalies in the midphase.

Methods: We report the case of a five years old female who showed an strabismus and a painless visual loss. The ophthalmoscopic appearance was an elevated pigmented lesion with vascular tortuosity that affected the posterior pole and with an epiretinal membrane.

Results: No treatement was performed in this case.

Conclusions: Combined hamartomas show a visual loss due to involvement of the disc or macula by the tumor and to the complications , like vitreous hemorrhage or progressive surface contraction by epiretinal membrane. It can be treated by vitrectomy and epiretinal membrane surgery but visual acuity rarely improves.

262

IRIDOCYCLECTOMY OF THE IRIS AND THE CILIARY BODY MELANOMA MALIGN

TANEV V.[1], KAMENOV I.[1], KOEV K.[1], TANEV I.[1]
[1] Medical University - Sofia

Purpose: Iridocyclectomy is organ-preserving operation in cases of iris and ciliary body tumor (melanoma malign).
Material and Method: Fourteenth patients (14 eyes) with a clinic diagnosis iris and ciliary body melanoma malign are treated by the iridocyclectomy. The operation includes: a scleral T-incision under the ciliary body directed to the limbus. The scleral thickness is separated on two parts by the sclerectomy—anterior one (2/3 of the scleral thickness) and the posterior one (1/3 of the scleral thickness). The tumor and the sclera's posterior 1/3 part are extracted simultaneously.
Results: The following events are observed during the postoperative period: cornea edema (3 eyes); hyphema (2 eyes); one eye with cataract progression, followed by a cataract extraction and than by a keratoplastic after a keratopathy appeared; one enucleated eye caused by an endophthalmitis. However all eyes have no visus modification. The histology fixes: an iris melanoma malign (6 eyes), a ciliary body melanoma malign (4 eyes), an iris and a ciliary body melanoma (2 eyes) and 1 eye with a nevus. The tumor size between 3 to 8 mm in the different cases. The extracted tumor scleral part does not contain a melanoma malign cells.
Conclusion: The described method of iridocyclectomy ensures a good anatomic and functional eye preservation.

263

INDOCYANINE GREEN ANGIOGRAPHY OF CHOROIDAL NEVI & MALIGNANT MELANOMAS

LAFAUT BA & DE LAEY JJ
Ophthalmology, University Hospital Gent (Belgium)

Purpose To analyse the indocyanine green angiograms of choroidal nevi and malignant melanomas.
Methods 105 choroidal tumors (nevi and malignant melanomas) are examined including ultrasonography, fluorescein and indocyanine green angiography and classified according their dimensions (height ; largest basal diameter).
Results The series includes 13 nevi (1 <= height <= 1.5 mm) and 92 malignant melanomas : 32 small (1.5 < height <= 3 mm), 30 medium (3 < height <= 6 mm) and 30 large tumors (height > 6 mm). Nevi mask the choroidal vascular pattern or an attenuated pattern with normal course of vessels is seen in less pigmented nevi. The lesions are invariably hypofluorescent in the late phase. In malignant melanomas tumor vascularization can often be recognized in less pigmented parts : parallel or irregular coursing vessels. In the late phase foci or zones of (hyper)fluorescence on a hypofluorescent bed may be seen even when vessels are not seen in the arterial or venous phase. Tumor that has broken through the Bruch's membrane is vascularized by engorged tortuous vessels with leakage.
Conclusion Indocyanine green angiography shows a spectrum of features according to the tumor's dimensions.

264

BILATERAL BEAR TRACKS HYPERTROPHY OF THE RETINAL PIGMENT AND FAMILIAL ADENOMATOUS POLYPOSIS.

BERTHEMY S,[1] ROMANET J.P,[1] MOUILLON M,[1]
1. Dept. Ophthalmology, C.H.U. Grenoble (France)

PURPOSE : FAP is an autosomal dominant disease affecting the colon. It may be associated with solitary or multifocal CHRPE.

METHODS : We examined three patients with bilateral « bear tracks » fundus lesions and four of their children. Biomicroscopic fundus examination, color retinograph and angiography were performed in each people. Two of them had a colonoscopy for a polyp's ablation. None had the other disorders described in the Gardner syndrome.

RESULTS : The three patients had blood relatives with an history of colon cancer. N°1, 34 y., his grandfather died by a colon cancer, his father had a total colectomy, his children have a normal fundus. N° 2 y., his grandfather and his father had a colon cancer, his son have pigmented lesions, his daughter was healthy. He underwent a polyp's ablation. N° 3, 36 y., his uncle died by a colon cancer and his aunt have an CHRPE.

CONCLUSIONS : Bilateral multifocal CHRPE seems to be highly correlated with a risk to develop a colorectal cancer especialy if there is a family history of that disease. It may be a variant phenotype of the FAP.

265

OCT IMAGING IN CONGENITAL GROUPED PIGMENTATION OF THE RETINA

A LIBERATOSCIOLI, L LOBEFALO, M RAPINESE, AP D'AURELIO, G DE NICOLA, L MASTROPASQUA, PE GALLENGA
Institute of Ophthalmology and Legal Medicine
University "G.d'Annunzio" Chieti - Italy

Purpose: To describe the features of congenital grouped pigmentation of the retina by optical coherence tomography.
Methods: A 10-year-old boy with congenital grouped pigmentation of the retina was discovered to have congenital grouped pigmentation in the right eye during a routine ocular examination. Automated visual field, ERG, EOG, color vision testing were performed. We also performed OCT scans passing through and away from the lesions.
Results: Functional test were all within normal limits The neuroretinal structure and thickness were comparable in affected and normal regions. An increased reflectivity of the red band corresponding to the retinal pigment epithelium was noted with a moderate degree of choroidal shadowing.
Conclusions: Our findings are consistent with previous ultrastructural data according to which neither hypertrophy nor hyperplasia of the RPE cells are present within the lesions, but only an increased number and size of melanosomes.

266

FLUORESCEIN AND INDOCYANINE GREEN ANGIOGRAPHY FEATURES OF OCULAR LYMPHOMA

LUMBROSO L. FARDEAU C. CASSOUX N. LEHOANG P.
Dept. Ophthalmology, Hôpital Pitié-Salpêtrière, Paris, France.

Purpose : To describe the fluorescein and ICG angiographic feautures in ocular lymphoma.
Methods : The charts of patients with proven ocular lymphoma (vitreous biopsy) were reviewed. Fluorescein angiograms and ICG were analysed . All patients were presenting an active disease.
Results : All eyes presented with vitreous infiltration, 3 eyes had serous retinal detachment, 5 eyes Retinal pigment épithelium detachments, 14 eyes Vasculitis, 2 eyes cystoid macular edema, 1 eye a subretinal tumor.
3 ICG angiographies were realised. None showed major anomalies.
A dilated choroidal vasculature seemed to be the most important feature.
Conclusion : Fluorescein and ICG angiography are a useful tool to asses the involvement of retina in ocular lymphoma. They are not of a diagnostic help as their features are often very similar to posterior uveitis. Their results must always be compared to clinical examination.

267

TREATMENT OF CORNEO-CONJUNCTIVAL INTRA-EPITHELIAL NEOPLASIA WITH TOPICAL MITOMYCIN C

BURTIN T, MOREL X, D'HERMIES F, LEGEAIS J.-M, and RENARD G.
Dept. Ophthalmology, Paris VI University, Hôtel-Dieu, Paris (FRANCE)

Purpose To evaluate the clinical efficacy of topical mitomycin C on corneo-conjunctival intraepithelial neoplasia.

Methods Five eyes of five patients with recurrent intraepithelial neoplasia were treated with one drop of topical mitomycin C 0.02% four times a day for 21 consecutive days. In all eyes, the diagnosis of intraepithelial neoplasia was confirmed by histopathology before the onset of therapy.

Results The mean follow up was 4 months (range 2 to 6 months). All patients recovered the same visual acuity as they had before the occurrence of the neoplasia. They all had a complete clinical regression of the conjunctival intraepithelial neoplasia. One patient needed a retreatment for a small clinical tumor recurrence. This topical therapy was associated in three eyes with a mild degree of conjunctival hyperemia and ocular discomfort.

Conclusion Topical mitomycin seemed to be an effective treatment for recurrent corneo-conjunctival intraepithelial neoplasia.

301

A FAST AND OBJECTIVE TEST TO MEASURE THE DENSITY OF THE MACULAR PIGMENT.

BERENDSCHOT TTJM, VAN DE KRAATS J and VAN NORREN D.
Dept. Ophthalmol., Utrecht University (Netherlands)

Purpose: Macular pigment (MP) may protect against age-related macular degeneration. It is therefore of great importance to have a fast and easy to use setup to determine the MP density. The purpose of this study is to evaluate spectral fundus reflection as a means to determine the MP density

Methods: Spectral fundus reflectance was measured with a home build reflectometer and a Scanning Laser Ophthalmoscope on 12 healthy subjects. Model analysis of the spectral fundus reflectance provided estimates for the MP density. Psychophysical estimates were obtained using heterochromatic flicker photometry.

Results: MP densities obtained by fundus reflectance correlate significantly with the psychophysically obtained values.

No differences were found between fellow eyes.

Conclusions: Spectral fundus reflectance may be used as a fast and objective test to measure the density of the macular pigment.

302

MACULAR PIGMENT MEASUREMENT WITH A NOVEL PORTABLE INSTRUMENT

MELLERIO J, PALMER D, RAYNER M
Biosciences, University of Westminster, London, UK

Purpose To develop an inexpensive & portable instrument for measuring macular pigment optical density (MPOD).
Methods The method of Werner *et al* (1987) was modified, whereby a minimum flicker match was made in the fovea and in the parafovea for an alternating blue and green 0.5 deg field. The field was a circular aperture in a small integrating chamber illuminated by 2 light emitting diodes (LED's) flashing in square wave counter phase at 17 Hz. For one LED λ_{max}=530nm (FWHM 19nm) & for the other λ_{max}=470nm (FWHM 11nm). A concentric field (5 deg) from an array of LED's (λ_{max}=425nm, FWHM=21nm) adapted the S cones. Subjects adjusted the brightness of the blue LED for minimum flicker for each retinal location. The log of the ratio of the blue intensities gave the MPOD.
Results Over thirty subjects of both sexes and different ages yielded MPOD values from zero upto 0.50. A number of subjects' MPOD were measured by reflectometry & the correlation between the two methods was good (r^2 = 0.84).
Conclusions A small portable device for measuring MPOD has been constructed and its results verified. It is suitable for screening macular pigment in the clinic as it takes subjects only 10-12 minutes to complete their measurements.

Ref Werner JS, Donnelly SK, Kliegl R. *Vis. Res.*, **27**:257-268, 1987

303

OSMOTIC SHOCK AS A NEW MODEL FOR VASCULAR CELL ENRICHMENT OF RETINAL EXTRACTS

STITT A.W., JAMISON P.L., MURPHY G.M. & ARCHER D.B.
Dept of Ophthalmology, The Queen's University of Belfast, Northern Ireland, UK

Purpose The retinal vasculature is of special interest to vision scientists since they are at the centre of a number of important retinal diseases. Despite their role in maintaining the retina, vascular cells represent a minute fraction amidst glia and neurones present in the mammalian retina. In the current study we sought to enrich for the retinal vasculature by using an osmotic shock model which exploits the sensitivity of the retinal neuropile to osmotic imbalance and the protective basement membrane enshrouding the retinal vascular cells.
Methods Fresh retinas were dissected off rat posterior eye cups and immediately immersed in RNase free distilled water at 4°C. After 30min the retinas were gently agitated, treated with DNase and processed for RNA extraction. These retinas were designated "shocked" (S^h) retinas. Other retinas were processed immediately for RNA extraction and designated "whole" (W^h) retinas. After quantification of the RNA, RT-PCR was performed on all RNA's using primer pairs designed according to the rat gene sequences for von Willebrand Factor (vWF), rhodopsin, and cyclophillin. In addition, a number of retinas were immediately fixed in 2.5% glutaraldehyde and processed for TEM.
Results Results suggest that the S^h retinas had much greater proportion of vWF mRNA's present than the W^h retinas. Cyclophillin and rhodopsin mRNA's did not appear to alter between treatments. TEM indicated that the retinal neuropile was osmotically disrupted with little recognisable cytoplasm or nuclei present. By contrast, the retinal vascular endothelial cells and pericytes appeared relatively normal, protected within the vascular basement membranes.
Conclusions This study outlines the use of osmotic shock in the mammalian retina. By allowing significant enrichment of the vascular fraction from whole retinas, it may represent a valuable tool for analysing the gene expression of the retinal vasculature *in vivo*.

304

EXPERIMENTAL MODEL FOR PRODUCTION OF SUBRETINAL HEMORRHAGE IN RABBIT

GOMEZ-ULLA F[1], TABARA J[2], CUEVAS J[1], LOPEZ E.[3], CENTENO A.[3]
1. Comp. Hosp. Universitario de Santiago. Facultad Medicina.(Spain)
2. Serv. Ophthalmology. Hospital "Juan Canalejo". La Coruña.(Spain)
3. Experimental Surgery Unit. Hospital "Juan Canalejo".La Coruña.(Spain)

Purpose
Standarised production of subretinal hemorrhage in rabbits. Description of difficulties arrised and solutions found in the development of the technique.
Methods
Albino rabbits weighing 1 to 4 kg. Transscleral injection of autologous blood into the subretinal space inferior and adjacent to the optic disc and medullary rays. Direct visual control by surgical microscope and a planocóncave vitrectomy contact lens. Operating controls of the tipe and sice of hemorrhage by indirect ophthalmoscopy inmediately after the surgical procudure. Evolution controls by retinografy and histology
Results
Despite of previous training and standarization of this technique a great variety of results were obtained. Most common difficulties have been: 1.-early disparition of hemorrhage induced by reflux of blood through scleral perforation after removal of the needle. 2.-partial injection due to blockage of the needle by clots. 3.- partial injection of blood by movement of the needle during hemorrhage induction. 4.- Retinal perforating-breaking with the needle during passage into the subretinal space.
Two sorts of hemorrhage were obtained: ampullar hemorrhage and superficial hemorrhage.
Conclusions
Induction of subretinal hemorrhage is an experimental technique hard to standarise. Nevertheless, this method allows a comparative study of evolution of subretinal hemorrhage withaut and with differen treatments.

305

THE ROLE OF THE EXTRACELLULAR MATRIX IN OXIDANT-INDUCED CELL DEATH IN RETINAL MICROVASCULAR PERICYTES

Gardiner, TA, Clint S, Archer DB.
Division of Ophthalmology and Vision Science,
The Queen's university of Belfast, BT12 6BA, N Ireland, UK.

Purpose: To examine cell death responses of retinal pericytes exposed to an oxidative insult when propagated on different substrata.
Methods: Bovine retinal pericytes were grown on laminin, Martigel or glycated Matrigel. Cells were exposed to 1.0,1.5 and 2mM hydrogen peroxide for 2 hrs. After initiation of cell death but prior to detachment (~18 hrs) cultures were fixed with formalin and cell death assessed by a morphological assay.
Results: Cells grown on laminin proved most resistant to oxidant-induced death in spite of the fact that cell density was lower than on Matrigel coated dishes. Cell numbers were lowest in glycated Matrigel cultures although susceptibility to oxidant-induced death was not markedly increased compared to cells grown on non-glycated matrix. Apoptosis in control cultures of the glycated Matrigel group was much higher than in the other controls.
Conclusions: As Matrigel is a complete cell matrix substitute containing all the major extracellular matrix (ECM) components and facilitated greater cell growth than either plastic or laminin, it was of interest that a simple laminin substratum proved more supportive of retinal pericytes during a severe oxidative injury. As non-enzymatic glycation of long-lived ECM proteins has been implicated in microvascular cell dysfunction in diabetes, it was also notable that cells grown on glycated Matrigel should demonstrate a greater vulnerability to apoptosis, even in the absence of overt oxidative stress.

306

IMMUNOHISTOCHEMICAL LOCALIZATION OF EXTRAVASCULAR ALBUMIN IN AN EXPERIMENTAL ISCHAEMIA/REPERFUSION MODEL OF THE RAT RETINA

CARVALHO M. PROENÇA R. CUNHA-VAZ J.G.
Dept. Ophthalmology, Biomedical Institute for the Research on Light and Image, Coimbra (Portugal)

Purpose
To study the breakdown of the Blood-Retinal Barrier (BRB) occurring in an experimental ischaemia / reperfusion model of the rat retina using albumin (69KDa) as an endogenous marker.
Methods
Retinal ischaemia has been induced by increasing the intraocular pressure to 160 mmHg, in the Wistar rat. The selected duration of the ischaemia and reperfusion periods was 30,60 minutes and 7, 30 days respectively. For immunohistochemistry we used the ABC method and the policlonal anti-albumin (69 KDa) antibody.
Results
Periods of ischaemia of 30 and 60 minutes followed by 7 days of reperfusion induced only a breakdown of the inner BRB. However, after 60 minutes and 30 days of reperfusion there was breakdown of both inner and outer BRB.
Conclusions
The inner and outer BRB showed different thresholds for breakdown in the ischaemia/reperfusion model. Histochemical staining of endogenous albumin is a sensitive method for the evaluation of BRB breakdown.

307

ACUTE TOXIC EFFECT OF MONOSODIUM-L-GLUTAMATE IN RABBIT RETINA .

BADA T[1], FERNANDEZ FJ[1], ALVAREZ R[2], SANCHEZ A[1], GUERRA E[1], MARCUELLO B[1], CARCELEN J[3], HONRUBIA FM[1].
Dept. Ophthalmology[1], Dept.Pathology[2], Dept. Pharmacology[3], Hosp Miguel Servet. Zaragoza (Spain).

Purpose : To evaluate acute toxic effects of monosodium-L-glutamate in the rabbit eye.

Methods : 15 New Zeland albino rabbits underwent an intravitreal injection of monosodium-L-glutamate (MLG) prepared in 0.1 mol/l phosphate buffer (pH 7.4). Only one eye was treated in each case. Three groups of 5 animals each were formed: group 1: 5 mol/ml, group 2: 10 mol / ml and group 3: 25 mol / ml. A volume of 0.1 ml of saline solution was injected into the fellow eye. Animals were sacrified 1 and 24 hours after the procedure and a light and electron microscopy study was performed.

Results : A mean reduction in the ganglionar cells number was found in the eyes treated with MLG when compared with control eyes (938 ± 57 cgr). Group 3 showed a greater cell loss (125 ± 68 cgr / cm) ($p < 0.05$). Apoptotic changes were observed at light and electronic microscopy in ganglionar cells of eyes treated with MLG. Bipolar cell population was also reduced

Conclusions : These data suggest that glutamate has a toxic effect on retinal ganglionar cells. This effect is mediated by apoptosis.

308

TRANSPLANTATION OF NEURAL STEM CELLS INTO THE EYES OF THE RETINA INJURED BY TRANSIENT ISCHEMIA.

KURIMOTO Y[1], SHIBUKI H[1], KANEKO Y[1], KUROKAWA H[1], YOSHIMURA N[1], and TAKAHASHI M[2]
1. Dept. Ophthalmology, Shinshu University School of Medicine (Japan)
2. Dept. Ophthalmology and Visual Science, Kyoto University Graduate School of Medicine (Japan)

Purpose. To examine whether the stem cells of the central nervous system, which are capable of differentiating along multiple central nervous system cell-type lineages, can be integrated into the retina injured by transient ischemia.
Methods. Transient retinal ischemia was induced in adult rats by raising the intra-ocular pressure to 110 mmHg for 60 minutes. Immediately after the reperfusion, the ß-galactosidase labeled stem cells derived from hippocampus of adult rat were injected into the vitreous cavity of the treated eyes. The rats were sacrificed 1, 2, or 3 weeks later, and the eyes were processed for immunohistochemical studies.
Results. The transplanted cells were found to invade into the retinal ganglion cell layer 1 week after the transplantation, and they were found to be integrated into the retinal inner nuclear layer and show the appropriate morphology of retinal neuronal cells 3 weeks after the transplantation.
Conclusions. It was suggested that neural stem cells may possibly be used as the donor of neural transplantation to reconstruct the neural network of ischemic-injured retina.

309

GROWTH OF PORCINE RPE CELLS ON PORCINE ANTERIOR LENS CAPSULE

PRAUSE JU[1,2], KIILGAARD JF[1], NICOLINI J[1], WIENCKE AK[1], RÖPKE C[3], NISSEN MH[3], SCHERFIG E[1] AND LA COUR M[1].

1. Dept. Ophthalmology, Rigshospitalet, University of Copenhagen
2. Eye Pathology Institute, University of Copenhagen
3. Dept. Anatomy; University of Copenhagen (Denmark)

Purpose Transplanting large sheets of RPE cells requires a suitable support. The anterior lens capsule is a readily available basement membrane that could serve as support. We examined the growth and morphology of porcine RPE cells cultured on porcine anterior lens capsule.

Methods Porcine anterior lens capsules were prepared from freshly enucleated eyes of domestic pigs weighing approximately 20 kg. Primary cultures were grown on bovine ECM. On this substrate RPE cells were subcultured up till the 8th passage. P_1 - RPE cells were plated on the humoral side of lens capsules.

Results RPE cells obtain epithelial morphology with regular hexagonal cells from P_0 through P_5. After P_6 the morphology started to deteroirate. Cell density at confluency decreased from 2000 cells/mm^2 in P_1 to 560 cells/mm^2 in P_5. RPE cells grown on porcine lens capsule showed excellent morphology in P_1.

Conclusions Porcine RPE cells can be grown with excellent morphology on porcine anterior lens capsules. This material may be useful as a support for cells used in transplantation.

310

AN INVESTIGATION OF THE EFFECT OF ADVANCED GLYCATION ENDPRODUCTS ON ENDOCYTOSIS IN THE RETINAL CAPILLARY ENDOTHELIUM.

J.Connolly, T.A. Gardiner, A.W. Stitt, & D.B. Archer
Dept. of Ophthalmology, Queen's University of Belfast

Purpose: Diabetes has been shown to increase endocytosis in the retinal vascular endothelium and in vitro studies suggest a role for advanced glycation endproducts (AGE's). This study investigated the influence of AGEs on endocytic activity in the retinal endothelium and dysfunction of the blood-retinal barrier (BRB).
Methods: Non-diabetic rats were given AGE-albumin for 10 days and the retinas either perfused with FITC-dextran (40kDa) and flat-mounted or assayed for endocytic activity in the retinal vascular endothelium using i.v. horseradish peroxidase (HRP) and ultrastructural stereology. In addition, STZ-diabetes was induced in rats and half of the diabetic animals treated with oral aminoguanidine (AGE-inhibitor). After 8 weeks the retinal vasculature was assayed for endothelial endocytic activity.
Results: There was a marked increase in FITC-dextran leakage from the retinal vasculature of AGE-infused rats compared to controls indicating overt breakdown of the BRB. Ultrastructurally, HRP was confined to the endosomal system of the retinal vascular endothelial cells with no obvious egress of HRP beyond the endothelium in any of the groups of animals used in this study. There was no significant difference in the volume fraction of HRP-containing endosomes in the endothelium of AGE- treated rats and control rats. Aminoguanidine had no effect on endothelial endocytosis in the diabetic animals although a difference was confirmed between diabetic and control rats.
Conclusions: AGE's cause BRB dysfunction but the phenomenon is not mediated by increased endothelial endocytosis.

311

BREAKDOWN REDUCTION OF THE BLOOD-AQUEOUS BARRIER IN A EXPERIMENTAL UVEITIS. COMPARATIV STUDY OF FOUR NSAIs

RUIZ O, CUEVAS R, TORRON C, FERRER E, POLO V, HONRUBIA FM.

Purpose: To study the effect of four NSAI (pranoprofen, ketorolac, diclofenac and flurbiprofen) in the breakdown of blood-aqueous barrier in endotoxin-induced-uveitis.

Methods: Endotoxin-induced uveitis (EIU) was produced in albino rabbits by intravitreal injection of 10 ng of Salmonella typhymurium lipopolisacharide A in 5 ul saline solution. We have used 6 groups of 12 animals each. Control group (G-I) was injected with 5 l of saline solution and 5 l of ET solution were injected in rest of groups. These groups were treated with two topical drops 2 hours before intravitreal injection, immediately after and every 2 hours during 24 hours (G-III: pranoprofen, G-IV: ketorolac, G-V: diclofenac and G-VI: flrubiprofen). Proteins and E2 prostaglandine concentration in the aqueous humour were determined.

Results: In all treated groups we observed a significant reduction ($p<0,01$) in the parameters studied comparing with the endotoxin group. Four drugs didn't show differences in the proteins concentration. We observed differences in the E2 prostaglandine concentration.

Conclusions: The NSAI reduce the prostaglandin E2 concentration, without increase the B4 leukotriene level.

312

ULTRASTRUCTURAL CELLULAR BASIS OF INCREASDED MICROVASCULAR PERMEABILITY IN VEGF-INDUCED RETINOPATHY IN MONKEYS

HOFMAN P[1], BLAAUWGEERS HGT[1], TOLENTINO MJ[2], ADAMIS AP[2], VRENSEN GFJM[3], SCHLINGEMANN RO[1]
[1]Departments of Ophthalmology, Academic Medical Center, Amsterdam (NL) and [2]Massachusetts Eye and Ear Infirmary, Boston (USA) and [3]Department of Morphology, The Netherlands Ophthalmic Research Institute, Amsterdam (NL)

Purpose: To investigate the ultrastructural vascular changes in vascular endothelial growth factor (VEGF) induced retinopathy in cynomolgus monkeys in relation to increased vascular permeability in this model. **Methods:** Two monkeys received 4 injections with 0.8 µg VEGF in one eye and PBS in the other eye before sacrifice at 9 days. One monkey received 12 injections with 1.25 µg VEGF before sacrifice at 24 days. After enucleation retina samples were either snap frozen for immunohistochemistry or fixed for electron-microscopic evaluation. **Results:** Immunohistochemistry demonstrated massive leakage into the neuro-retina of IgG in VEGF treated eyes. Electronmicroscopically these eyes showed signs of endothelial cell activation and a marked shift of endothelial pinocytotic vesicles from an abluminal localization in control eyes to a more luminal localization in VEGF injected eyes. The ratio luminal / abluminal located vesicles was increased by 2 to 10-fold in these eyes compared to control eyes. No endothelial fenestrations were found. **Conclusion:** Increased permeability for plasma proteins in VEGF-induced retinopathy is not associated with formation of fenestrations, but may be based on a change in direction and/or specificity of pinocytotic endothelial transport.

313

NITRIC OXIDE IS AN IMPORTANT REGULATOR OF HUMAN RETINAL TONE

DORNER GT,[1] POLAK K,[1] BOBR B,[1] FINDL O,[3] and SCHMETTERER L.[1,2]

1. Dept. of Clinical Pharmacology, University of Vienna (Austria)
2. Inst. of Medical Physics, University of Vienna (Austria)
3. Dept. of Ophthalmology, University of Vienna (Austria)

Purpose: There is evidence from a variety of studies that nitric oxide is an important regulator of choroidal blood flow. The role of nitric oxide (NO) in the retinal vasculature has, however, not yet been studied in humans.

Methods: We performed a placebo controlled, three way cross-over study in 9 healthy male volunteers with two different doses of N-monomethyl-L-arginine (3 mg/kg and 6 mg/kg), an inhibitor of NO-synthesis. The effect on retinal arterial and venous diameter was investigated with the new Zeiss retinal vessel analyzer. In addition, we investigated the effect of diffuse luminance flicker periods between 1s and 16s of duration on retinal vessel diameters as well as the NO-dependence of this effect.

Results: L-NMMA significantly reduced arterial (-7%, $p<0.005$) and venous (-5%, $p<0.001$) retinal diameter, although it significantly increased mean arterial pressure (+13%, $p<0.001$). 16s flicker induced an increase in arterial (+16%, $p<0.001$) and venous (+12%, $p<0.001$) diameter. This flicker-induced vasodilation was blunted by L-NMMA in the artery (+11%, $p=0.07$) and in the vein (+6%, $p<0.001$), although only the effect in the vein was significant.

Conclusions: Our data indicate that NO plays an important role in the maintenance of vascular tone in human retinal vessels in vivo. In addition, endogenous NO seems to be involved in the retinal vasodilator response induced by diffuse luminance flicker.

315

DOES "OPPURTUNISTIC SCREENING" FOR DIABETIC RETINOPATHY RESULT IN TIMELY AND APPROPRIATE REFERRAL?

PRASAD S[1], JONES K[2], KAMATH GG[1], PHILLIPS RP[1].
1.Dept. Ophthalmology, Arrowe Park Hospital,Wirral, (UK)
2.Diabetes Register Manager, Wirral, (UK)

Purpose: To assess if referrals to the ophthalmology unit for diabetic retinopathy were appropriate and timely before the introduction of a formal screening programme.
Methods: Case records of 121 referrals for diabetic retinopathy in the period before the implementation of a formal screening system were analysed retrospectively. As formal grading was not available, surrogate measures were used to assess the severity of retinopathy at referral. We looked specifically at visual acuity (VA), retinal status and recommended action at their first ophthalmic consultation.
Results: 80/121 patients had a VA of ≥ 6/12 in the better eye at first consultation. 27 of these had sight threatening retinopathy (STR). 29/121 had a VA of ≤ 6/12 in the worse eye at first consultation. 16 of these had had STR.
Conclusion: We have used "findings at first ophthalmic consultation" as proxy measures for STR. Although the methodology is limited the very high proportion of patients with STR at presentation in patients with poor vision in either eye (16/29) and the fair proportion of patients (27/80) with STR in patients with good binocular vision suggest that "opportunistic screening" identifies patients with STR only at a late stage. It is hoped that the introduction of a formal screening programme will lead to more timely referral.

316

EDUCATION TO INCREASE OPHTHALMOLOGIC CARE IN DIABETIC PATIENTS

DIEZ A, LOPEZ MI, BERCIANO A, VELILLA S AND PASTOR JC
IOBA, Unixersidad de Valladolid. Valladolid, Espana

Purpose: To investigate if education of both physicians and diabetic persons about the need for regular examinations to prevent blindness would increase the compliance with guidelines on ocular examinations for diabetic persons.
Methods: The population consisted on 3223 diabetic persons (1040 younger onset and 2183 older onset) participating in the program to prevent blindness caused by DR that nowadays is being hold in our country. Study subjets and primary care physicians received educational material on diabetic eye disease. A medical history in wich subjects were asked about previous eye examinations was taken and the presence of DR was determined by an ophthalmologist by using dilated ophthalmoscopic examinations. Examination findings were conveyed to each participant and their primary care physicians.
Results: Only 20,7% had had an eye exam in the previous year. Younger-onset persons were more likely to have had the exam than older-onset persons. However, after intensive intervention the ophthalmologic patterns of the diabetic population improved and 75,2% participated in the program and had an eve examination. DR was diagnosed in 21,9% of all patients and 88,6% of them had the non proliferative form, 70% without clinical significant macular edema and 18,6% with clinical significant macular edema. Proliferative DR was present in 11,4% of the patients. None of the macular edema and 50,0% of the proliferative forms had been properly treated.
Conclusions: These data indicate a need for further education of diabetic population and an educational program about diabetic retinopathy screening for family practioneers.

317

VISUAL PROGNOSIS AFTER RETINAL LASER PHOTOCOAGULATION FOR DIABETIC MACULOPATHY A 3 MONTHS FOLLOW-UP STUDY.

Bodil Klausen, Flemming Møller, and Toke Bek
Department of Ophthalmology, Århus University Hospital

Purpose: Diabetic retinopathy complicated by clinically significant macular oedema is a frequent cause of visual loss. The visual prognosis can be improved by treating the retinal oedema with photocoagulation outside 400 microns from the fovea. However, only little attention has been given to quantitatively evaluating the visual outcome after treatment.
Methods: 121 eyes of 103 consecutive patients who had undergone macular laser photocoagulation because of diabetic retinopathy complicated with clinically significant macular oedema were included. Visual acuity and fundus photography were performed before and 3 months after treatment. The relation between the change in visual acuity and pre-treatment age, diabetes type, diabetes duration, number of laser applications, visual acuity, and quantitative measures of individual retinopathy lesions were studied.
Results: 95 patients had complete data at follow-up. On average there was no significant change in visual acuity after treatment (mean= -0.04, SD=0.15), however with wide variation (range: -0.44 to 0.33). There was no correlation between the change in visual acuity and any of the studied background parameters.
Conclusions: The study gives information that can be used to inform patients about the visual prognosis after laser photocoagulation for diabetic maculopathy.

318

COLOR DOPPLER IMAGING IS A TOOL FOR PREDICTION OF RETINAL ISCHEMIA IN CENTRAL RETINAL VEIN OCCLUSION

CELLINI M, PELLE D, ROSSI A, MORETTI M
Institute of Ophthalmology - University of Bologna (Italy)

Purpose: To determine the blood velocities and the resistive index in the orbital vessels in patients with central retinal vein occlusion (CRVO)
Methods: The ophthalmic artery (OA), the central retinal artery (CRA), the posterior ciliary arteries (PCA) and the central retinal vein (CRV) of 26 patients with CRVO and 30 control subjects were investigated by color Doppler imaging (CDI). The patients were examined by ophthalmoscopy and fundus fluorescein angiography to estimate the degree of retinal ischemia.
Results: After three monthes we found an haemodynamic alterations in the orbital circulation of patients with CRVO. The peak systolic velocity (PSV) was lower and the resistence index (RI) was higher both in the OA , in the PCA and in the CRA but only the PSV reduction in CRA was statistical significant: 13.426±4.213 cm/sec vs 15.526±3.516 cm/sec ($p<0.018$) and after six monthes the PSV in CRA was 12.100±3.112 cm/sec vs 16.455±4.799 cm/sec ($p<0.047$) and RI 0.699±0.107 vs 0.598±0.056 ($p<0.025$).
For the CRV we found at three monthes a mean velocity (MV) of 5.995±4.614 cm/sec vs 9.432±4.151 cm/sec ($p<0.050$) and after six monthes 6.282±1.461 cm/sec vs 7.682±2.212 cm/sec ($p<0.049$). In the eye with CRVO that developed an ischemia at three monthes the MV was 4.960±0.666 cm/sec vs 6.200±0.644 cm/sec ($p<0.002$) and after six monthes 4.120±0.217 cm/sec vs 6.260±0.456 cm/sec ($p<0.001$).
Conclusions: Blood velocity was reduced in the retinal circulation of patients with CRVO and reduced further in the ischemic form. We think that CDI may play a role in the routine assessment of patients with CRVO.

319

HYPERBARIC OXYGEN THERAPY (HOT) IN THE TREATMENT OF CENTRAL RETINAL VEIN OCCLUSION (CRVO): EFFECT ON VISUAL FIELD.

L LOBEFALO[1], G DELLA LOGGIA[1], L COLANGELO[1], MA D'INCICCO[1], L MASTROPASQUA[1], PE GALLENGA[1]
[1]Institute of Ophthalmology and Legal Medicine
University "G.d'Annunzio" Chieti - Italy

Purpose: we evaluated the efficacy of HOT of CRVO in patients with steroid and anticoagulation treatment.
Methods: Sixty patients affected with CRVO were enrolled in the study: 20 underwent HOT and 40 (age and sex-matched) were used as controls. All patients underwent visual acuity, central visual field and fluorescein angiography. HOT was performed at 2.0 ATA by air for 60 minutes a day 5 days a week for 2-3 weeks (mean 12.6±2.7 days).
Results: 34 patients presented an ischemic type CRVO (12 treated) and 26 (8 treated) an oedematous type. At the end of follow-up, visual acuity showed a significant increase in the treated group ($p<0.05$). Treated patients affected with edematous CRVO type showed a reduction of MD (-8.67db±2.08 vs -4.67 db ±1.15: $p<0.001$), while those with ischemic type showed no modification(-7.50 db±1.51 vs -7.86db±1.95: $p>0.05$). No modifications were found in untreated subgroups.
Conclusions: HBO treatment is useful in patients with edematous CRVO to improve central visual field sensitivity.

320

SELECTIVE OPHTHALMIC ARTERY FIBRINOLYSIS IN ACUTE CENTRAL RETINAL ARTERY OCCLUSION (CRAO).

FERNANDEZ FJ[1], GUELBENZU S[2], BARRENA C[2], SANCHEZ A[1], BADA T[1], MELCON B[1], PUEYO M[1], HONRUBIA FM[1].
1 Dept. of Ophthalmolgy, Zaragoza (Spain).
2 Dept. of Neuroradiology, Zaragoza (Spain).

Purpose: To evaluate the efficacy and reliability of local intra-arterial fibrinolysis (LIF) in CRAO.
Methods: We have studied 12 patients with CRAO. Seven patients (group I) were treated with traditional forms of therapy, and 5 patients (group II) were treated with urokinase via transcutaneous femoral catheter into ophthalmic artery. Thereafter, the patients received heparin sulfate for 3 days.
Results: The mean follow-up was 14 months and the mean time from the onset of the symptoms to the beginning of the therapy was 11 hours. In one patients of group I an improvement of visual acuity was observed (count fingers to 0.1). In all patients of the group II angiographic evidence of improved perfusion of the retinal arteries was seen and 4 patients (80 %) showed improvement of visual acuity. The best results were obtained where LIF was performed before 10 h. No complications were observed after fibrinolysis.
Conclusion: The LIF in ophthalmic arteries for treatment of CRAO reduces the doses of fibrinolytic agents and is a safe and useful treatment during the first hours post CRAO.

321

DIET IN RETINOPATHY PREVENTION

Fco. Olmos Carrillo.(Departament d´Óptica. Universitat de València. SPAIN), Magda Minguez Blas. (Licenciada Farmacia. Licenciada Ciencia y Tecnología de los Alimentos por la Universidad de Valencia. Facultad de Farmacia.)

The eye of the diabetic patient can be affected by various pathological processes, the most important being diabetic retinopathy due to hyperglycemia.

This study pretends to find foods will avoid this complication improving glucose metabolism. We used the glycemic index of some foods and the relation between hypertriglyceridemia-hypeglyceridemia- retinopathy and the effects in animals with type II diabetes of dietary fructose, fiber, high-fat diet, effects in person with type II diabetes of a commercially prepared risk reduction program, effect of postpandrial exercise of moderate intensity.

Fructose further increases hepatic triglyceride production with a resultant deterioration in fatty rats. High-fat diet in mice, develop defective glycemic control, hiperglycemia and obesity. But tuna fish oil and palm oil are less diabetic that lard oil.

Conclusion: An appropriate diet can reduce risk factors for retinopathy enclose with a commercially prepared and wit moderate exercise after breakfast.

322

IN VITRO ANGIOGENESIS MODEL USING AN OCULAR CELL LINE (RF/6A)

BIZEC JC, GRÜNINGER M.
Ciba-Vision Preclinical Ophtha Unit, Basel (Switzerland).

Purpose: Tube-like formation with lumen was evidenced from capillary endothelial cells (in absence of pericytes or smooth muscle cells) in gel containing extracellular matrix (ECM) components such as fibronectin, collagen I, laminin. Cell culture on ECM extracted from Engelbreth-Holm-Swarm mouse sarcoma (Matrigel®) can induce a fast tube-like organization of vascular endothelial cells (VEC). As far as we know, no established ocular VEC line has been investigated in this way. The well-established choroido-retinal endothelial cell line RF/6A from Maccaca mulata (ATCC CRL-1780) was studied and compared to the umbilical one ECV 304 (ATCC CRL-1998) in order to develop an in vitro model of ocular angiogenesis. Angiogenesis inhibitors from main classes were tested. **Methods**: The tube formation assay was performed as modified from Kleinman's method. Matrigel® was used to coat 24-well cluster plates. The drug and the endothelial cells ($5x10^4$ cells/well) were successively added in 1 ml final medium (low glucose DME medium containing FBS). Cell organization was photographed and evaluated under light microscopy for 24 hours. **Results:** While anastomosis maintained 24 hours after ECV304 seeding, it moved into a less reticulate network as soon as 12 hours after RF/6A seeding. In both cell lines, cytochalasin D fully inhibited the network formation. Inhibitor response was observed with inhibitors of protein synthesis (cycloheximide, mitomycin C), of metalloprotease (1,10-phenanthroline), of PKC (staurosporine, hypericin) and of PTK (herbimycin A), then with fumagillin (antimalarial) and thalidomide. Inhibition of cell proliferation was also determined (BrdU test). **Conclusion**: Such a model with cell line RF/6A appeared to be suitable for investigating angiogenesis modulators in posterior segment of the eye.

323

INHIBITORY EFFECT OF ALPHA-TOCOPHEROL SUCCINATE AND 13-CIS RETINOL ON FIBROBLAST PROLIFERATION.

PINILLA I[1], PIAZUELO E[2], JIMENEZ P[2], LARROSA JM[1], POLO V[1], ABECIA E[1], HONRUBIA FM[1].
1. Dept. Ophthalmology. Miguel Servet Hospital. Zaragoza (Spain)
2. Mixed Investigation Unit. Zaragoza University (Spain).

Purpose: To determine the inhibitory effect of alpha-tocopherol succinate (ATS) and cis-retinol on the proliferation and migration of cultured fibroblasts.
Methods: In vitro wound repair was determined in confluent fibroblast monolayers. Conjunctival fibroblasts were incubated with serum-deprived medium for 24 hours. After this time an mechanical wound was made and the cells were incubated with fresh medium and the drugs to be tested. The cell-free area was monitored at 0, 18, 24 and 48 hours.
Groups of treatment: Group 1/ ethanol 0.1%. Group 2/ ATS 50 μM dissolved in ethanol (final concentration 0.1%). Group 3/ 13-cis retinol 10 μM in 0.1% ethanol. Each experiment was carried out in triplicate and repeated 4 times.
Results: There were no differences among groups within the first 24 hours. ATS showed larger cell-free area after 48 hours (statistically significant).
Conclusions: ATS 50 μM presents an inhibitory effect on wound repair.

324

VITAMIN K3 EFFECT ON FIBROBLASTIC PROLIFERATION AND MIGRATION.

PINILLA I[1], PIAZUELO E[2], JIMENEZ P[2], POLO V[1], LARROSA JM[1], ABECIA E[1], HONRUBIA FM[1].
1. Dept. Ophthalmology. Miguel Servet Hospital. Zaragoza (Spain)
2. Mixed Investigation Unit. Zaragoza University (Spain).

Purpose: To evaluate the dose-effect relationship of vit k3 on the wound healing mechanisms.
Methods: Conjunctival fibroblasts were incubated with serum-deprived medium for 24 hours. After this time a mechanical wound was made and the cells were incubated with fresh medium plus doses of vit k3 to be tested. The wound repair was monitored (cell free area) at 0, 18, 24 and 48 hours.
There were 5 different groups depending on the supplemented drug: Group 1/ ethanol 0.1%. Group 2/ vit k3, 1 mg/l dissolved in ethanol (final concentration 0.1%). Group 3/ vit k3, 2 mg/l. Group 4/ vit k3, 4 mg/l. Group 5/ vit k3, 6 mg/l. Each experiment was carried out in triplicate and repeated 4 times.
Results: There were no differences among groups at the initial time. Wound repair was slower in groups 3, 4 and 5. There were no differences between controls and vit k3 1 mg/l group. Groups 4 and 5 showed cellular toxicity with ulcers that increased in size throughout the study.
Conclusions: Vit k3 is able to inhibit fibroblast proliferation at 2 mg/l or higher doses, showing cellular toxicity at 4 and 6 mg/l.

325

EXPERIMENTAL USE OF DEXAMETASONE LIPOSOMES IN THE INHIBITION OF PROLIFERATIVE VITREORETINOPATHIES.

SARAROLS L(1), GARCIA ARUMI J(1), CAVERO L(1), REIG F(2), CUNILLERA D (2), SALVADOR F(1).
1. Department of Ophthalmology. Hospital Vall d'Hebron, Barcelona.
2. Department of Peptide and Protein Chemistry. CSIC. Barcelona.

Purpose: To study the effect of dexametasone (DXM) loaded liposomes in the inhibition of proliferative vitreoretinopathy (PVR) in an animal experimental model.
Methods: Belgian white pigs are used as experimental animals. An experimental model of PVR based on vitrectomy, retinotomies, injection of platelet-concentrate and cryoaplications is used. We studied the pharmacokinetics of liberation of DXM liposomes in the vitreal cavity comparing it to the clearance of free DXM in the vitreal cavity. The efficacy of supressing PVR is studied after injection of DXM liposomes observing the retina 1, 2 and 4 weeks after the surgery.
Results: Preliminary results show adequate inhibition of PVR in this animal experimental model. Clearance of these liposomes is specially slow observing residual liposomes in the vitreal cavity 3 weeks after injection.
Conclusions: Our preliminary results show good supression of PVR injecting DXM loaded liposomes in our PVR experimental model.

326

APOPTOSIS IN PROLIFERATIVE VITREORETINAL DISORDERS AND IMMUNOHISTOCHEMICAL EXPRESSION OF P53 AND P21/WAF1 GENES

OSNAGHI S[1], BERTI E[2], GALIMBERTI D[1], ROSSI A[1], MARCHI L[1], RATIGLIA R[1]
1) Dept. Ophthalmology 2) I[st] Institute of Dermatology; Hospital Maggiore - IRCCS, University of Milan (Italy)

Purpose The growth of the epiretinal membranes (ERMs) is the result of the rates of cellular proliferation and spontaneous cell death. In this study we report the occurrence of apoptosis and the expression of apoptosis-related genes in the ERMs.
Methods With a perspective and randomized study we examined 25 ERMs obtained from patients with primary PVR (pPVR n=14), post operative PVR (post op PVR n=7), proliferative diabetic retinopathy (PDR n=4).The "In Situ Cell Death Detection Kit" is the test for evidence of apoptotic cells based on labeling of DNA strand breaks. With specific monoclonal antibodies we evaluated the expression of genes related to apoptosis: P53 (able to induce cell cycle arrest to allow DNA repair or apoptosis) and P21/WAF1 (activated from P53, it's a reversible inhibitor of cell cycle progression).
Results The incidence rate of positive samples for this stains was low for P53 (pPVR=28,5%, post op PVR=28,5%, PDR=25%), high for P21/WAF1 (pPVR=78,5%, post op PVR=71,4%, PDR=100%) and high for apoptosis (pPVR=78.5%, post op PVR=71.4%, PDR =100%). No correlation between the expression of these genes and respectively the duration of the disease and the kind of PVR was observed.
Conclusions The low expression of P53, the high expression of P21/WAF1 and the high apoptotic index lead us to think that the programmed cell death in epiretinal membranes is due in a small measure to the activation of P53 in consequence of the cellular damage, and in a larger one to growth factors like βTGF and αTNF (released during PVR), which induce P21/WAF1 gene activation with arrest of the cellular cycle in G1 or G2 phse.The apoptosis could play a prospective role in the PVR process and could represent a good way to remove damaged cells.

327

DIFFERENTIAL EXPRESSION OF THE VEGF GENE FAMILY IN A MURINE MODEL OF PROLIFERATIVE RETINOPATHY

Simpson DAC, Stitt AW, Murphy GM, Gardiner TA, & Archer DB. Dept. of Ophthalmology, The Queen's University of Belfast, Northern Ireland, UK

Purpose Many proliferative retinopathies are driven by potent vasoactive growth factors. One of these, the angiogenic peptide vascular endothelial growth factor (VEGF), plays a crucial role, but is only one of a growing family of peptides which share sequence and functional homology and include platelet derived growth factors (PDGF) A and B, placental growth factor (PlGF) and VEGF-B, -C, and -D. This investigation aims to determine which factors are expressed in the retina and how their level of expression varies during proliferative retinopathy in a murine model.
Methods Ischaemic retinopathy was induced in neonatal mice by exposure to hyperoxia for 5 days. Gene expression of all the VEGF family members was examined using RT-PCR and Southern blotting.
Results All the members of the VEGF family were expressed in the retina - this is the first time that VEGF-B, -C and -D have been demonstrated in this tissue. VEGF expression was reduced during hyperoxia and then increased above normal levels within 12 hrs of ischaemia. The reduction in VEGF-D expression during hyperoxia was less marked but increased above normal levels under ischaemic conditions. Expression of PDGF A and B was unaltered and VEGF-C decreased. VEGF-B was expressed at very low levels throughout. Expression of PlGF doubled during hyperoxia and remained ~50% above normal levels under hypoxic conditions.
Conclusion The expression of the VEGF family in normal retina suggests that all these growth factors play a role in maintaining the retinal vasculature. The fact that expression of most of these factors changes during proliferative retinopathy according to different patterns suggests that they are involved in this process with different, if likely related functions. They therefore provide novel targets for future therapeutic interventions aimed at preventing proliferative retinopathy.

328

VITREOUS LEVELS OF IGF!1 and IGFBP1/ IGFBP3 IN PRLIFERATIVE DIABETIC RETINOPATHY; A CASE CONTROL STUDY:

F.Escalada,C.Mateo, R. Simó, R.Burgos,A.Lecube. Diabetes Unit and Ophthalmology Dept. Hospital general Vall D´Hebrón. Barçelona.

Insuline-like growth factor-1(IGF-1) has been implicated en the pathogenesis of diabetic retinopathy(DR). and elevated intravitreous IGF-1 levels as well as IGFBP1/IGFBP3 have been reported in diabetic patients with retinal neovascularization. The source of vitreal IGF-1,IGFBP1 and IGFBP3 is presumably ischaemic retina. The aim of tht study was to determine levels of IGF-1,IGFBP1 and IGFBP3 in diabetic patients with RD and to investigate whether serum levels could contribute to its intravitreal concentrations. For this porpose we compared 21 diabetic patients with proliferative retinopathy (group A) and no diabetic patients (group B) in whom a vitrectomy was performed. Both groups sre equipared by age.IGF-1 and IGFBP3 were measured by RIA and IGFBP3 byimmunoenzymometric assay. Vitreal levels of IGF-1 were elevated in group A in c comparison with group B.After adjusting by vitreal proteins, the difference remainded sgnificant (p 0.005). Vitreal levels of IGFBP1 and IGFBP3 werw also elevated in diabetic patients. Howewer, when the ratio IGFBP/protein wae considered thr differences werw not significant. We concluded that elevated vitreous levels of IGF-1 found in diabetic patients are origined by intraocular synthesis rather than serum diffusion. By contrast, unspecific increase of intravitreal proteins could contribute to elevated vitreous levels og IGFBP1 and IGFBP3 found in diabetic patients.

329

Epidemiological date from the Ufa perinatal center on the incidence of retinopathy of prematurity over a five year period

SAIDASHEVA E., AZNABAYEV M.

Dept.Ophthalmology, Ufa Eye Research Institute (Russia)

Purpose. To evaluate the incidence of ROP morbidity under the conditions of a perinatal center.
Methods. There were 227 premature infants randomized to examination at the specialized perinatal center. Their birth weight (BW) varied from 850 g to 2700 g, gestational age (GA) was26-37 weeks. The fundus was first examined at 2-6 weeks of life.
Results. ROP was diagnosed in 85(37,4%) children. Severity of ROP was classified according to the International Classification of ROP. The majority of the infants 52(61,2%) had stage 1 disease involving 2-3 zones. The disease regressed spontaneously during different follow-up periods. In 25(29,4%) children the process progressed to stage II and then regression occurred. Only 8(9,4%) babies developed severe disease and reached stage III. In these infants the process progressed more guickly and developed threshold disease after 3-4 weeks when the first signs of the disease appeared.
Conclusions. The incidence of ROP under established standard of care in Ufa was 37,4%.

330

ROLE OF OXYGEN-DERIVED FREE RADICALS IN THE COURSE OF THE VITREORETINOPATHIES

Verdejo C, Marco P, Renau-Piqueras J and Pinazo-Durán MD.
Ophthalmology Unit of the Hospital Peset and Research Center of the University Hospital La Fé, Valencia (Spain)

Purpose: Fibro-vascular-proliferative vitreoretinopathies represent an important medical and social problem, because the pathogenical mechanisms of the vitreoretinal diseases remain unknown. The present work investigates the oxygen-derived free radical formation and antioxidant activity in advanced diabetic retinopathy (DR) and proliferative vitreoretinopathy (PVR).
Methods: 41 vitreous samples from patients undergoing vitrectomy because of rhegmatogenous retinal detachment, macular hole and/or epiretinal membranes (control group CG, n= 14), DR (n=15) and PVR (n=12) were analysed for protein content, basal lipid peroxidation as determined by the thiobarbituric acid test, and the antioxidant activity for superoxide dismutase (SOD) and catalase (CAT). An approach to the molecular basis of free-radical damage in the vitreoretinal tissues was carried out by determining the genomic DNA content in the samples, using the Hoechst 332258 commercial kit.
Results: MDA-like metabolites were measured to assess basal lipid peroxidation and the results were significantly higher in DR and PVR cases ($p \leq 0.0001$) than in the CG. SOD activity was significantly elevanted in DR and PVR vitreous ($p \leq 0.001$), as compared to those from the CG. CAT levels displayed significantly greater values in DR and PVR eyes ($p \leq 0.0001$) than in the CG. Finally, when compared with the controls, DNA values showed statistically significant higher values ($p \leq 0.001$) in those patients with vitreoretinopathies.
Conclusions: DR and PVR are correlated with an increased FR formation and DNA content and a decreased antioxidant activity in the human vitreous.

331

IS PRIMARY BUCKLING SURGERY FOR TREATMENT OF PSEUDOPHAKIC RETINAL DETACHMENT STILL UP-TO-DATE?

RONZANI M, KODOMSKOI L, JANKNECHT P
Dept. Ophthalmology, University of Freiburg (GERMANY)

Purpose: Therapy of pseudophakic retinal detachment (PRD) is not standardized. Our approach is to treat PRD by a buckling procedure and -if not succesful- by vitrectomy. We compare our results to the literature.
Methods: The charts of 79 eyes from 77 consecutive (1/95-12/96) patients were retrospectively analyzed. Patients with additional eye diseases were excluded. Mean follow up was 7.5 months.
Results: Primarily, 69 (87%) of the eyes received a buckling procedure and 10 a vitrectomy (VE) depending on the severity of the PRD. After buckling the retina was reattached in 74%. Non attached retina were treated by VE. Several VE´s were necessary in 7 eyes. Preoperative visual acuity (VA) was 0.02 and the final visual acuity was 0.07 (N=79).
Conclusions: We think that pseudophakic retinal detachment can be treated by a buckling procedure. If this fails VE is necessary.

332

THE LASER INTERFEROMETRY IN RETINAL DETACHMENT AND FELLOW EYES

ROLDAN-PALLARES M[1], OSSAMA IA[1] and BRAVO C[2].
1. Dept.Ophthal.,Hosp.S.Carlos.Madrid (Spain)
2. Dept.Statistics,C.Cálculo UC.Madrid (Spain)

Purpose. To study value of Laser Interferometry (LI) to predict VA improvement in retinal detachment (RD) and changes in its fellow eyes.
Methods. 38 eyes with unilateral rhegmatogenous RD, macular involvement and VA $\geq 1/10$ were selected. VA (Snellen) and LI (IRAS) with test field diameters of 3º and 8º, both with (CL) and without light (SL) were tested in RD and its fellow eyes, in both before and after surgery (1week; 1, 3 and 7 months). X^2 test and Spearman correlation test were used.
Results. Average preoperative Snellen VA was 0.27 ± 0.19. Statistically significant postoperative improvement ($p = 0.02$) was found after 7 months follow-up (0.39 ± 0.14). Statistically significant postoperative LI improvement was found after 3 months follow-up ($p = 0.05$, LI 3º). Statistically significant ($p < 0.05$) difference was found with each LI test between RD eyes (worse values) and fellow eyes preoperatively and during follow-up. 88 % of patients in whom LI (3º SL) predicted improvement experienced it ($R = 0.71$, $p = 0.002$).
Conclusions. LI shows improvement shortly after SB surgery but values always remain below fellow eyes. Prediction of VA improvement may be done correctly with LI (3º SL).

Supported by FISS 98/0718.

333

ROLE OF OCT IN THE POSTOPERATIVE FOLLOW-UP OF RETINAL DETACHMENT.

GALLENGA PE, MASTROPASQUA L, CARPINETO P, CIANCAGLINI M, RAPINESE M, FALCONIO G, DI STEFANO N
Inst. Ophthalmology, University of Chieti (Italy)

Purpose We investigated the utility of OCT in detecting macular reattachment after episcleral surgery for retinal detachment without drainage of subretinal fluid.
Methods The authors studied by OCT 12 eyes of 12 patients subjected to retinal detachment surgery. Preoperatively all the eyes showed macular detachment. Episcleral technique without subretinal fluid drainage was performed to all patients. Macular study by OCT was performed postoperatively on days 1,3,7,15,30,60,90.
Results No eyes showed flat macula in the first postoperative day. In 9 eyes out of 12 (75%) OCT macular study revealed the reattachment of the foveal area at the 7-day control. After 1 month only 1 eye showed a dark signal beneath the fovea, probably linked to long-standing subretinal fluid. A correlation between the preoperative duration of RD and the time of macular reattachment was evident.
Conclusions OCT may be useful in detecting delayed macular reattachment during the postoperative follow-up. Long-standing detachments may lead to slower macular reattachment.

334

SILICON OIL TAMPONADE AND OCT NERVE FIBER ANALYSIS.

CARPINETO P, MASTROPASQUA L, DELLA LOGGIA G, DI STEFANO N, GALLENGA PE
Inst. Ophthalmology, University of Chieti (Italy)

Purpose We investigated the reproducibility of nerve fiber measurement by optical coherence tomography (OCT) in silicone oil filled eyes.
Methods The authors studied by OCT 5 eyes of 5 patients operated on for rhegmathogenous retinal detachment. The retina was reattached by vitrectomy with fluid-silicone oil exchange in all cases. Each patient underwent five repetitions of a series of scans on five separate occcasions within a 15-day period. Each series consisted of five circular scans around the optic nerve head (1.5 R). Each series was performed separately using external fixation technique. Contralateral healthy eyes were used as a control.
Results Reproducibility was better in a given eye on a given visit than from visit to visit. The intersubject and intrasubject standard deviation was approximately constant among the control eyes. Analysis for the intrasubject standard deviation confirmed that silicon oil leads to higher variation ($P < 0.05$).
Conclusions Reproducibility results for OCT measurement of NFL thickness in silicon oil filled eyes were not as encouraging as in control eyes. Contralateral eyes provided a higher degree of reproducibility than silicon oil filled eyes.

335

THE ROLE OF PROTEOLYTIC ACTIVITY OF CATHEPSIN A IN THE PATHOGENESIS OF RHEGMATOGENOUS RETINAL DETACHMENT

STANKIEWICZ A. and OBUCHOWSKA I.
Dept. Ophthalmology, Med. Academy, Białystok (Poland)

Purpose
To evaluate cathepsin A activity in the subretinal fluid in the rhegmatogenous retinal detachment.
Methods
The studies were performed on subretinal fluids taken from 42 patients. Duration of the detachment was contained between 1 week and 6 months. Cathepsin A activity was determined by the ninhydrin colorimetric method with synthetic substrate (N-Cbz-Phe-Ala) at its optimum pH 5.0.
Results
Proteolytic activity of cathepsin A was demonstrated in all investigated fluids. The highest activity was found at about the 4th week of the detachment.
Conclusions
The increasing proteolytic activity in the subretinal fluid in the rhegmatogenous retinal detachment could be an important factor in gradual degrading of the detached retina structure. Probably cathepsins, including cathepsin A, are involved in digestion of outer segment proteins of cones and rods and in degradation of mucopolysaccharide interphotoreceptor matrix.

336

A CALCULATION OF THE RISK OF FAILURE AND PRESENCE OF COMPLICATIONS AFTER PNEUMATIC RETINOPEXY

ABECIA E, PINILLA I, OLIVÁN JM, LARROSA JM, POLO V, HONRUBIA FM
Dep. of Ophthalmology. Hospital Miguel Servet. Zaragoza (Spain)

Purpose: Pneumatic retinopexy may increase the risk of proliferative vitreoretinopathy. Profile of risk is calculated by means of contingency tables and logaritmic linear regression.
Methods: 219 consecutive cases of SF6 pneumatic retinopexy are presented.
Results: Initially, 179 (81.73%) of 219 eyes were successfully treated. High risk of failure was associated with criopexy, aphakia or pseudophakia and breaks localized on horizontal meridians. Early complications appeared in 31.05% of the eyes. Patients with detachment of the macula and breaks on the horizontal meridians had higher risk of early complications. Late complications were observed in 6.84% of the eyes; refractive errors, extension of the detachment and cryopexy were related to the presence of these complications.
Conclusions: Aphakic and pseudophakic patients and breaks localized on horizontal meridians may present a high rate of failures and complications when pneumatic retinopexy is performed to reattach the retina. Criopexy has a potential high risk to cause complications than laser photocoagulation.

337

LIPID PEROXIDATION PRODUCTS IN SUBRETINAL FLUID OF MYOPIC AND NON-MIOPIC PATIENTS WITH RETINAL DETACHMENT

BELDA-SANCHIS JI[1]; VILELA C[2]; BOSCH-MORELL F[1]; MARIN-BENITA N [1]; QUIJADA A[1] ; DIAZ-LLOPIS M[3]; ROMERO FJ[1].
1. Experimental Toxicology and Neurotoxicology Unit. Dept. Physiology. University of Valencia. Valencia. (Spain).
2. Dept. Neurophysiology. Univ. Hospital La Fe. Valencia. (Spain).
3. Dept. of Ophthalmology. University of the Basque Country. Leioa. Vizcaya. (Spain)

Purpose: To determine the role of lipid peroxidation in the pathogenic process or retinal detachment (RD) in myopic and no-myopic patients.
Methods: We have studied 55 patients with non complicated RD, divided into 3 groups: group 1= non myopic; group 2=0-6 D; group 3> 6 D. We determined malondialdehide level (MDA) in subretinal fluid (SRF) with high pressure liquid cromatography (HPLC).
Results: There were significant levels of MDA in the SRFs studied. We found a significant correlation between diopters of myopia and the level of MDA ($R=0{,}91$; $p<0{,}001$). There were also a correlation between age and MDA, but considering only non-myopic patients ($R=0{,}72$; $p<0{,}001$).
Conclusions: These results suggest a possible role of lipid peroxidation in the pathogenesis of the RD. There is a clear relation between the degree of myopia of the patients with the amount of lipid peroxidation.

341

EFFECTS OF SILDENAFIL ON RETINAL HISTOPATHOLOGY AND ELECTRORETINOGRAM (ERG) IN DOGS

WALLIS RM, LEISHMAN D, PULLMAN L, GRAEPEL P, HEYWOOD R
Pfizer Central Research, Sandwich, UK.

Purpose. Sildenafil, an inhibitor of phosphodiesterase type 5 (PDE5; IC_{50} 3.5 nM), is an effective oral treatment for erectile dysfunction. Since sildenafil has been shown to inhibit retinal PDE6 enzymes (IC_{50} 27-58 nM), we evaluated the effects of high doses on retinal histopathology and ERGs in the dog.
Methods. The effects of iv sildenafil on ERG recordings from 5 dogs were investigated. To assess toxicological effects, oral sildenafil (80 mg/kg/day; approx. 65 times the max. human recommended dose) was administered to dogs for 12 months.
Results. Free plasma sildenafil levels of 51-532 ng/ml (human therapeutic range: 3.5-13 ng/ml) induced dose-related increases in the implicit time of the a- and b-wave and reduced the amplitude of the a-wave of ERGs; 16 ng/ml had no effect. Effects on ERGs were reversible and declined in a manner consistent with the plasma half-life of sildenafil. There was no histopathological evidence of toxicity to visual pathways after long-term exposure to these sildenafil levels.
Conclusion. At therapeutic plasma concentrations, the effects of sildenafil on ERGs were modest. Higher concentrations produced more marked effects on ERGs but had no effect on retinal structure in long-term toxicology studies.

342

CELL DEATH IN THE RETINA AFTER BLUE LIGHT EXPOSURE

Wu J, Chen E and Seregard S
St. Erik's Eye Hospital, Karolinska Institute (Sweden)

Purpose: To investigate cell death in blue light induced retinal damage
Methods: Cyclic light reared albino rats, 170-180 g, were exposed continuously to diffuse blue light (400-480 nm) at 0.64 W/m² for 3 or 6 hours after 22 hour dark adaptation. The rats were kept in darkness and sacrificed immediately, 8, 16, 24 and 48 hours following light exposure. The enucleated eyes were processed for pathological and biochemical analysis.
Results: Immediately after 3 hour exposure, the blue light did not cause a discernible loss of visual cells. However, a few TUNEL positive cells were identified at the upper temporal area. There was a slight reduction in the thickness of the outer nuclear layer (ONL) just after light exposure for 6 hours. Comparably, a certain amount of visual cells, mostly distributed in the inner aspect of ONL, were TUNEL positive. With prolonged staying in darkness, the TUNEL staining reached a climax between 8-16 hours post exposure. The presence of DNA ladder and morphologic changes following light exposure indicated an apoptotic pathway through which the visual cells died.
Conclusion: Apoptosis is a considerable mechanism involved in blue light induced retinal degeneration.

343

A NOVEL DEVICE FOR LONG TERM LIGHT EXPOSURE TO INDUCE RETINAL DAMAGE IN RATS

Chen E, Wu J and Söderberg P
St. Erik's Eye Hospital, Karolinska Institute (Sweden)

Purpose: To establish an experimental device which provides an even irradiance to the retina among a group of rats.
Methods: This device consisted of two rat cages which rotated about a horizontal axis in a speed of 0.25 spin/min. The rotatinig was motorized by an electric motor with an adjustable speed. The cage was made of stainless steel wires, with a wire diameter of 2 mm and a space of 8 mm between wires. Two rats were kept in each cage therefore four rats were exposed simultaneously. This device was surrounded by a ring of blue light fluorescent tubes. The irradiance at 24 points in the cage was measured. The rate of rat's falling into sleep (constant closure of the eyelids) was counted at 10 one-min-observation points during 6 hour light exposure. Similar observation was done during the same period when the cage stood still.
Results: The uniformity of light intesity was SD/mean=14%. The sleeping rate was 0 and 45% in rotated and static cage, respectively, during 6 hour light exposure
Conclusion: The device efficiently keeps rat's eye open during light exposure and provides an even illumination. Therefore it ensures a meaningful dose-response estimation with the current exposure model.

344

CYTOTOXICITY IN LARGE TIME INTERVALS OF DIFFERENTS CONCENTRATIONS OF ACQUEOUS FERROFLUID AS A PRELIMINARY STAGE TO ITS INTRAOCULAR USE.

SARMIENTO B[1], TEJADA P[1], ALONSO MJ[2], VILLAFRUELA IM[1], CORCUERA MT[2], PICAZO A[2], MÉNDEZ MJ[1], GOMEZ F[2], CASADO I[2]
1.- Dept. Ophthalmology, 12 de Octubre Hospital, Madrid (Spain)
2.- Dept. Pathology, Carlos III Institute, Madrid (Spain)

Purpose: To study an aqueous ferrofluid biological tolerance previous to test it as ophthalmic biomaterial.
Methods: Ferrofluids constitute a new generation of synthetic materials characterized by their ability to change their position and viscosity when subjected under a magnetic field. To perform the study we inoculated 0,1 ml of ferrofluid diluted with destiled water to different concentrations under the skin of 8 groups of rats. They were sacrifized after 15 and 30 days. Lesions observed were studied microscopically.
Results: A chronic inflammatory reaction without free ferrofluid was observed histologically.
Conclusions: A mild tisular response was observed comparable with those achieved with other biomaterials.

345

LONG TERM BIOCOMPATIBILITY STUDY OF A SILICONE FERROFLUID IN RATS PREVIOUSLY TO ITS USE AS VITREOUS SUBSTITUTE

VILLAFRUELA IM[1], TEJADA P[1], ALONSO MJ[2], SARMIENTO B[1], CORCUERA MT[2], PICAZO A[2], MÉNDEZ MJ[1], GOMEZ F[2], CASADO I[2]
1.- Dept. Ophthalmology, 12 de Octubre Hospital, Madrid (Spain)
2.- Dept. Pathology, Carlos III Institute, Madrid (Spain)

PURPOSE: To study the tisular reaction after intradermal injection of a silicone ferrofluid at concentrations of 1/4,1/8 and 1/1 6 in rats
METHODS: 30 rats were employed. A intradermal injection of 0.1 ml of ferrofluid at concentrations of 1/4,1/8 and 1/16 was carried out in the back foots of Wistar rats. Control animals were inoculated with silicone oil and controls without inoculum were studied
RESULTS: A chronic inflammatory reaction with polymorphonuclears, lymphocytes and macrophages (siderophages) cells were present. The inflammation were similar with the different concentrations of ferrofluid employed. Free ferrofluid was present in the tissues of animals that received the less diluted ferrofluid.
CONCLUSIONS: The inflammatory response and the presence of iron particles points to the occurrence of degradation of the ferrofluid. This fact would preclude its clinical employment. We will continue on studying if ferrofluids with different coverings of the magnetic particles are biocompatible.

346

ANTIBODIES ANTISILICONE (ANTI-S Ab) IN OPHTHALMIC SURGERY PATIENTS CARRYING SILICONE MATERIALS.

RODRIGUEZ DE LA RUA E[1] ,PASTOR JC,[1] SANCHEZ H[1].CARRASCO B[1].PUENTE B[1].CORTES A[2].TELLERIA J.[3]

1.Instituto de Oftalmobiologia Aplicada (IOBA). Universidad de Valladolid (Spain).

2.University of Puerto Rico. Puerto Rico.

3.Instituto de Biologia y Genetica Molecular. Universidad de Valladolid (Spain)

Purpose : Protheses and implants of silicone are used at present with high frequency in surgery.Different reactions . both local and general . apparently immunomediated . have been seen .connective-tissue diseases being the most often observed. In this study we have tried to detect the presence of anti-S Ab in patients who had undergone ocular surgery for retinal detachment with the use of some of the following elements: encircling bands. soft scleral sponges and intraocular silicone oil. We also tried to investigate the incidence of immunological diseases in these patients. Methods: Three groups of patients were established with similar distribution rates of sex and age . Group 1(control) 36 patients underwent cataract surgery ; Group 2: 28 patients underwent retinal detachment surgery with encircling bands and /or silicone sponges; Group 3 : 40 patients had intraocular silicone oil injected. In groups 2 and 3 the permanence of silicone material was longer than 12 months in all the cases. After informed consent was obtained, an epidemiologic questionnaire to identify immunological diseases was performed on all patients and samples of blood were taken to detect serum levels of reumathoid factor (RF) . antinuclear antibodies (ANA) . Scl 70 and anti S- Ab. Results: Relative levels of anti S -Ab (absorbance units) were : 0.012 (0.023) in group 1 ; 0.060 (0.077) in group 2 and 0.218 (0.178) in group 3.Differences were statistically significant between the three groups. RF.ANA,and S cl 70 values were negative in all the patients, and no one had clinical evidence of immunological diseases.Conclusions: These results suggest that silicone used in ocular surgery produces an immunological reaction in most patients . being higher in those with intraocular silicone oil.Although none of the patients has developed clinical manifestations of immunological disease. further studies are required to establish the clinical relevance of the high serum levels of anti S -Ab.

Supported by FIS 96/0929.Spain; AC2 supported by FIC Program, NIH.USA.None.

347

EXPERIMENTAL RETINAL TOLERANCE OF A NEW INTRAOCULAR TAMPONADE FOR VITREORETINAL SURGERY

TISSIÉ G[1], DRIOT J.Y.[1], GROSMAIRE V.[1], MATHIS A.[2], RICO-LATTES I.[3], PYNSON J.[1],

1.CHAUVIN Montpellier et Toulouse, France

2.Service d'Ophtalmologie,Hôpital Rangueil,Toulouse, France

3.U.M.R. 5623 Université Paul Sabatier, Toulouse, France

Purpose : To assess retinal tolerance of a new vitreous substitute with a specific gravity superior to 1 which could offer advantage to tamponade the inferior retina in retinal detachment surgery.

Methods : Right eye of twenty-five New-zealand white rabbits have been vitrectomized from the pars plana and the vitreous cavity was filled with 4 different fluorinated olefine-silicone mixtures with densities of 1.01 and 1.03 and viscosities of 600 or 3000 centistokes or with a silicone oil (density 0.97) as a control. At 8, 30, 60, 90 days after surgery, IOP determination with a Tonopen® and clinical assessment of the eye and of the retina with an ophthalmic microscope (ZEISS) and a Volk lens (90 D) were performed. Animals were sacrificed at 90 days and the eyeballs collected for light and transmission electron microscopy of the retina.

Results : No clinical signs of toxicity of the mixtures could be observed during the 3 months following surgery. There was no difference in IOP between eyes filled with the different mixtures and the control oil. Light and electron microscopic examinations of the retinas did not reveal any toxic changes.

Conclusion : These results demonstrate the good tolerance of this new compound suggesting it could be useful as an intraocular tamponade in vitreoretinal surgery for management of giant retinal tears and inferior retinal breaks.

348

EXPERIMENTAL TOXICITY OF INTRAOCULAR SILICONE OIL BY DETERMINATION OF LIPID OXIDATION IN LENS AND RETINA

MARCOS PRIETO M and CORDERO PEREZ Y.
BIOCHEMISTRY UNIT. INSTITUTO DE OFTALMOBIOLOGIA APLICADA (IOBA). UNIVERSITY OF VALLADOLID, SPAIN

Purpose: Injection of silicone oil for internal tamponade after vitrectomy is an useful technique in the treatment of vitreo-retinal disorders, although its different composition respect to the vitreous can produce some problems. This experimental study try to evaluate the toxicity of two different types of silicone oil. (A-high purity and B-commercial) by determination of lipid oxidation products (MDA-Malondialdehide and 4-Hydroxynonenal-4HNE), in lens and retina at different times after vitrectomy.

Methods: The experiment were done using 9 groups of albino rabbits: 1.- Control; 2.- 15 days silicone A; 3.- 15 days silicone B; 4.- 1 month silicone A; 5.- 1month silicone B; 6.- 3 months silicone A; 7.- 3 months silicone B; 8.- 6 months silicone A; 9.- 6months silicone B. Determination of lipid oxidation products were made using a commercial assay kit and spectophotometry at 586 nm.

Results: Results in lens (MDA + 4 HNE, in nmol/gr) were: 1=3.80; 2=4.57; 3=2.78; 4=1.33; 5=2.21; 6=1.35; 7=1.30; 8=3.27; 9=3.18. In retina, results were: 1=38.78; 2=53.37; 3=36.87; 4=23.12; 5=39.10; 6=28.22; 7=37.17; 8=39.20; 9=41.58. Comparison among control group and the other groups showed no statistical difference ($p<0.05$).

Conclusions: Based on these results, the toxicity of intraoculat silicone oil by measuring of lipid oxidation products seems to be not very important although it is necessary a long time study.

349

RETINAL SENSITIVITY OVER DRUSEN DETERMINED WITH THE SLO: COMPARISON BETWEEN BLUE-ON-YELLOW AND RED-ON-RED PERIMETRY

Remky A.[1,2], Elsner, A.E.[1]

[1] Schepens Eye Res. Inst, Harvard Medical School, Boston (USA)

[2] Augenklinik der Med. Fak. der RWTH Aachen (Germany)

Purpose To determine retinal sensitivity in areas with and without drusen in patients with age-related macular disease (ARM), comparing red-on-red with blue-on-yellow perimetry.

Methods: Five patients with ARM were tested in a 10° central test field with static perimetry and simultaneous infrared fundus illumination (850 nm). Blue stimuli (200 ms) and a dim, blue background were produced by an Argon laser (458 nm). A bright yellow background (594 nm) was superimposed. Red-on red perimetry (633 nm) was performed with equiluminant conditions.

Results: With red-on-red perimetry, sensitivity over areas with drusen, compared to those without, was not significantly less: 16.5 dB ±1.3 vs. 18.5 dB ± 0.3, respectively. In contrast, with blue-on yellow perimetry, sensitivity over areas with drusen was significantly less than those without: 14.8 dB ± 1.8, 18.5 dB ± 0.1, respectively (p <0..01).

Conclusions: These results confirm the reports of a selective sensitivity loss of short-wavelength sensitivity mediated mechanisms in ARM. Drusen are likely to mark loci of functional changes, representing damage to photoreceptors considerably prior to atrophy.

350

FULL THICKNESS MACULAR HOLES TREATED WITH AUTOLOGOUS PLATELET CONCENTRATE. A FIFTY CASES PROSPECTIVE STUDY.

VAREILLES M, ALBINET P, ROMANET JP, MOUILLON M.
Dept. of Ophtalmologie, CHU of Grenoble.

Purpose :The authors present the surgical result of a full-thickness idiopathic macular holes series of patients operated with autologous platelet concentrate as adjuvant therapy.
Methods: Fifty non-selected consecutive patients has been operated between may 1996 and march 1998.The surgery consisted of a central and periferic pars plana vitrectomy, removal of the posterior hyaloid and the epiretinal gliosis, instillation of autologous platelet concentrate on to the posterior pole and gas tamponated.The patient was left supine for 24 hours after surgery and then remained face down for 12 days. Age, sex, duration of symptoms, best visual acuities, stage of macular hole, postoperative results and complications were recorded. Angiography and photography were made before and six month after surgery.
Results: Anatomic and fonctional success were analysed at 6 months and compared with stage and age of the hole, and epiretinal gliosis associated.
Conclusion: Peeling of epiretinal gliosis and using autologous platelet concentrate seems to improve the surgical results of full-thickness macular hole treatment. Despite of a wellknown surgical technic, this surgery is not without complications.

351

FOLLOW UP OF RETINAL PIGMENT EPITHELIAL DETACHMENT WITH CHOROIDAL NEOVASCULARIZATION AFTER TREATMENT WITH DIODE LASER.

GÓMEZ-ULLA F[1], RODRÍGUEZ MJ[1], SEPÚLVEDA G[1], ABELENDA D[1], GÓMEZ M[1].

1.- Dept. Ophthalmology, Galician General Hospital, Santiago de Compostela (Spain).

Purpose:
To evaluate the benefit of the diode laser in the treatment of retinal pigment epithelial detachment (RPED) asociated with choroidal neovascularization (CNV), using indocyanine green angiography (IGA) for diagnose.

Methods:
Visual acuity, fluorescein angiography and IGA was taken in people with age-related macular degeneration and vascularized RPED. We include CNV persistent and/or recurrent and treatment with diode laser in the past too.

Results:
The outcome of the treatment was 54 % . The position of the RPED with regard to the fovea is an important risk factor.

Conclusions:
We use IGA in all cases of occult CNV. The photocoagulation with laser must be made to ensure the closure of the membrane.

352

SUBRETINAL NEOVASCULARIZATION AND HEMORRHAGES IN ANGIOID STREAKS.

PUIG J, GARCÍA-ARUMÍ J, ESCALADA F, MARTÍNEZ V, CALATAYUD M, FREIXES S.
Dept. Ophthalmology, "Valle de Hebrón" Hospital, Barcelona (Spain).

Purpose: To evaluate the occurrence of subretinal neovascularization and/or subretinal hemorrhages in patients with angioid streaks.
Methods: 38 eyes of 19 patients with angioid streaks were included in our study. Angioid streaks were diagnosed basing on the ophthalmoscopical and angiographic picture of the fundus. A complete ocular examination, including fluorescein angiography and fundus examination, was performed every six months.
Results: In this group of patients a subretinal neovascularization was observed in 39% of them. Subretinal hemorrhages, with or without neovascularization, were present in 67%.
Conclusions: Angioid streaks represent discontinuities or breaks in thickened and calcified Bruch's membrane. The most visually significant complication of them is the development of subretinal neovascularization and hemorrhages from breaks in Bruch's membrane. No treatment is known to prevent these conditions. Patients should be informed of the risk of subretinal hemorrhages after relatively minor ocular trauma.

353

RADIOTHERAPY TREATMENT FOR MACULAR DEGENERATION - 3 YEAR FOLLOW UP

CHURCHILL AJ.
Dept. Ophthalmology, St James's University Hospital (UK)

Purpose: To determine the long-term effects of radiotherapy as a treatment in age related macular degeneration (ARMD).
Methods: Eighteen individuals (age range 67-87 yrs) with sub foveal neovascular membranes confirmed by fluorescein angiography underwent radiotherapy to the macular region. Each received a total of 13.3 Gy ionising radiation in 6 fractionated doses, using a less costly method to that initially described. Visual acuities and fundus photographs were compared before and after treatment.
Results: Thirty six months after radiotherapy 10/18 (56%) showed stable visual acuities (less than 2 line change in Snellen acuity). Only 8/18 (44%) demonstrated a deterioration in acuity. No individual suffered any unpleasant side effects from the treatment.
Conclusions: Several studies have illustrated the steady decline in visual acuity when ARMD is treated conservatively. Less than 25% of untreated individuals would be expected to maintain a stable acuity 3 years after diagnosis. These results demonstrate that radiotherapy is not only a safe and effective form of treatment for subfoveal neovascular membranes but the benefits appears to last at least 3 years.

354

ELECTRONTHERAPY FOR MACULAR LESIONS IN PATIENTS WITH AGE-RELATED MACULAR DEGENERATION

MEZMATE K, KOENIG F., BENCHABOUNE M., SCHMITT T. , MAUGERY J.P.
Hôpital de BELLEVUE, Saint-Etienne, France.

Purpose To describe the long-term results of irradiation on subfoveal neovascular membranes (SNVM) in age-related macular degeneration (AMD).
Methods 54 consecutive AMD patients with SNVM were treated between february 1995 and december 1996 with external irradiation. 20 Gy were delivered in one week and 4 or 5 sessions using a calibrated electronbeam. All patients had clinical and angiographic follow-up at 3 month-intervals, the first year and then every six months.
Results After one year, visual acuity remained stable or increased in 31 out of 54 patients. These results maintained after longer follow-up. In these patients, after a transient exsudative reaction, F.A. showed disparition of subretinal diffusion and mottled RPE reaction. In the 23 other patients, this treatment failed to stop the course of the disease. Some complications were observed : 2 cataracts, 2 subretinal massive hemorragies, 5 optic neuropathies with radiation retinopathy.
Conclusion First results of radiotherapy in the treatment of AMD are still controversed. These preliminary results need to be confirmed by controlled trials.

355

EVALUATION OF CHOROIDAL NEOVASCULAR MEMBRANE REGRESSION AFTER Sr-PLAQUE RADIOTHERAPY FOR AMD

Immonen I, Jaakkola A, Tommila P & Laatikainen L
Dept. Ophthalmology, Helsinki University Hospital

Purpose.To evaluate the choroidal neovascular membrane (CNVM) regression occurring after Sr-plaque radiotherapy for age-related macular degeneration (AMD).
Methods. Planimetry and masked subjective analysis of the baseline, 3, 6 and 12 month angiograms of 20 patients treated using Sr plaque radiotherapy for exudative AMD was performed . Baseline and 12 month angiograms of 8 untreated AMD patients were similarly analyzed.
Results. The angiograms of 8 patients could only be evaluated subjectively. Of these the CNVM rgressed in 6. In the remaining 12 patients, the CNVM regressed in 8 and progressed in 4. In eyes with regression the size of the CNVM at 12 months decreased into 21.4% and leakage into 1% of baseline value. In eyes with progression the corresponding percentages were 900% and 520% of baseline value. All eyes showing a decrease in CNVM area or leakage by planimetry were considered to have a regression of the CNVM by subjective evaluation.
Conclusion. A clear regression of the CNVMs occurs in 70% of patients treated with Sr-plaque radiotherapy. Subjective evaluation and planimetry give similar results.

356

SURGICAL REMOVAL OF SUBFOVEAL NEOVASCULAR MEMBRANES IN YOUNG PATIENTS

MOUILLON M. (1), GONZALVEZ B. (1), VAREILLES M. (1), PINEL N. (2), PEOC'H M. (2)

(1) Department of Ophthalmology, C.H.U GRENOBLE
(2) Department of Pathology, C.H.U GRENOBLE

Surgical removal of subfoveal choroïdal neovascular membranes give its best results in the young patients presenting this affection (angioïd streaks, myopia, traumatic choroïdal rupture).

About 12 cases, the authors define the indications and present their visual, clinical and angiographic results.

The histological study allows to precise the histologic finding and specific characters of these membranes and their topography.

This restoration surgery of the threatened macular function ins certainly about to know a big expansion.

357

THE USE OF OPTICAL COHERENCE TOMOGRAPHY (OCT) IN THE DIAGNOSIS AND FOLLOW-UP OF PATIENTS ELEGIBLE FOR MACULAR SURGERY.

STALMANS P., SPILEERS W., DRALANDS L.
Dept. of Ophthalmology, KULeuven, Belgium

Purpose: To demonstrate that OCT can deliver additional information in the diagnosis and follow-up of several macular diseases and degenerations that cannot be obtained using other fundus imaging techniques.
Methods: Patients that underwent macular surgery for macular holes, epiretinal membranes, vitreo-macular traction syndrome or long-standing macular edema were examined using OCT before and after macular surgery.
Results: Preoperative differential diagnosis and staging of macular holes was facilitated in approximately one third of patients with a macular hole. Postoperatively, the size of the macular hole could be quantitized to evaluate the success-rate of hole closure. In patients with epiretinal membranes, the secondary effects of the membrane that induce a decreased visual acuity such as retinal folds and macular edema could be objectively evaluated pre- and postoperatively. The anatomical properties of the vitreo-macular interface in patients with a vitreo-macular traction syndrome could be determined and visualized using OCT, helping to determine when vitrectomy was indicated. Finally, grading of the extent of macular edema could be done using OCT without the need to inject fluorescent dyes.
Conclusion: OCT is a powerful instrument in the objective evaluation and the quantitative analysis of various macular pathologies, and is of particular use in the pre- and postoperative evaluation in macular surgery.

358

OCT AND ECHOBIOMETRY IN THE DIAGNOSIS OF MACULAR EDEMA.

L LOBEFALO[1], A LIBERATOSCIOLI[1], L COLANGELO[1], A MANCINI[1], G DELLA LOGGIA[1], M RAPINESE[1], PE GALLENGA[1].
[1]Institute of Ophthalmology and Legal Medicine University "G.d'Annunzio" Chieti - Italy

Purpose: to determine if the relative sensitivity of OCT and echobiometry in detecting the presence of macular edema in patients with diabetic retinopathy.
Methods: One hundred diabetic patients (44 male and 56 female) were enrolled in a prospective, double masked study. Fifty patients had fluorescein angiographic signs of retinopathy with macular edema, while the other 50 patients had no signs of retinopathy. In all patients A-scan echobiometry and OCT scan of the macular area were performed.
Results: Both echobiometry and OCT scans found retinal thickness values significantly greater in edematous than in non-edematous eyes ($p<0.001$). Echobiometry showed a sensitivity of 64%, a specificity of 82% and an accuracy of 73%. Sensitivity, specificity and accuracy of OCT scans were respectively 90%, 96% and 93%.
Conclusions: OCT is more sensitive than a-scan echobiometry in detecting macular edema. However, this last technique can have a role in consideration of his high specificity, greater diffusion in eye departments and particularly for the possibility to be performed with opaque media where the OCT cannot be performed.

360

TREATMENT OF EXUDATIVE NEOVASCULAR MACULAR DEGENERATION WITH OCTREOTIDE

KUIJPERS RWAM[1], VINGERLING JR[1], MOOIJ CM[1,2], VAN HAGEN PM[3]
1. Dept Ophthalmology, Universtity Hospital Roterdam-Dijkzigt. 2. Dept Pathology, Erasmus University Rotterdam. 3 Dept of immunology and internal medicine III, University Hospital Rotterdam (Netherlands)

Purpose: Exudative macular degeneration is a major complication of age-related macular degeneration (AMD). For subfoveal subretinal neovascularisation, currently no treatment is available, that protects the central vision. Octreotide, a Growth Hormone inhibitor, previously shown to have effect on macular edema, was tested for its usefulness in stabilising exudative AMD.
Methods: In a pilot study of 13 cases of AMD with recent exudative lesion, we evaluated the effect of octreotide, given subcutaneously for 3 - 6 months.
Results: Macular edema diminished in all cases. After 6 months, visual acuity improved in 2 cases, remained within one Snellen line in 9 cases and deteriorated in one case.
Conclusions: Octreotide may prove an effective treatment for exudative AMD by diminishing retinal edema and arresting neovascular growth. The results of this pilot study warrants the start of a prospective randomised trial

359

Functional and anatomical changes after surgery for retrofoveal neovascularization in age related macular degeneration

LE ROUIC JF[1], BEHAR-COHEN F[1], CHAUVAUD D[1].
1 Department of ophthalmology, hôtel-Dieu de Paris, Paris (France)

Purpose : To evaluate the anatomic and functional changes of the macula after surgery for retrofoveal neovascularization in age related macular degeneration (ARMD).
Methods : Thirteen eyes of 13 patients suffering from well defined retrofoveal neovascularization due to ARMD were included in a prospective study. Pre and post operative examination included visual acuity and central field testing with the Octopus perimeter. Mean follow-up was 6.9 months (3-14). Pre operative neovascular membrane, retinal pigment epithelium (RPE) alteration and serous retinal detachment and post operative choriocapillaris (CC) atrophy and RPE alteration were determined on fluorescein angiograms.
Results : At 3 months, 54 % of the patients could read 20/200[e]. At the end of follow-up, 31 % could still read 20/200[e]. Post operative visual field study showed a loss of retinal sensitivity in central 3° field at 3 months. At 3 months, post operative CC atrophy was larger than the neovascular membrane. RPE alteration was larger in post operative, and was correlated to the pre operative serous retinal detachment. One recurrence of neovascularization occurred 5 months after surgery
Conclusions : Post operative central scotoma is deeper after surgery. Post operative CC atrophy is greater than the neovascular membrane on fluorescein angiograms.

365

NEAR CONVERGENCE POINT AND AMETROPIA

Felipe A, Sánchez M, Montalt JC, Gené A, Gómez JM
Dpto de óptica. Facultad de Física. Universitat de València

PURPOSE: Our objective is to analyse the NCP change compensating the refractive error and to remark when compensation is clinically harmful, proposing in this case some alternatives to improve binocular vision and at the same time to compensate the refractive error. METHOD: The study has been preceded by an analisys of the NCP behaviour on a emetropic population with a binocular addition of positive and negative lenses.Before, we have analysed the NCP behaviour when compensating the refractive error on a ametropic population. Both approximation and separation methods are used. RESULTS: We classify the subjects in the following groups: Group I-Myopes for whom NCP comes closer when compensating. Group II-Myopes for whom NCP comes further when compensating. Group III- Hyperopes for whom NCP comes closer when compensating. Group IV- Hyperopes for whom NCP comes further when compensating.CONCLUSIONS: The NCP position when lenses are added depends on the accomodative and fussional reserves, and the behaviour with positive and negative lenses is not symmetrical. All our hyperopic subjects belong to group IV. Myopic subjects belong to group I if they have been compensated for a long time and to group II if they have been compensated for a short time. The NCP without compensation does not show clinically significant differences between the myopic and hyperopic population

366

BIOMETRIC FINDINGS IN MYOPIC CHILDREN WITH RETINOPATHY OF PREMATURITY

TANASIJEVIC -FILIPOV I, LATINOVIC S, OROS A

Clinical Center, University Eye Clinic, Novi Sad (Yugoslavia)

Purpose To analyze the factors contributing to myopia in premature children with regressed retinopathy of prematurity after cryotherapy and to compare them with a) prematurely born children without ROP b) myopic fullterm children of the same age, with same range of myopia.

Methods We performed A scan ultrasonography to measure the axial length, anterior chamber depth, lens thickness and the equatorial diameter, as well as keratometry in myopic preterm and fullterm children at the age of 12 months and repeated them annually during the mean follow-up time of 6 years.

Results In premature children treated with cryo higher keratometric values, lower values of axial length and equatorial diameter were found.

Conclusions. The obtained results suggest that the high refractive power seems to play the major role in children with ROP and that different mechanisms were involved in the development of myopia.

367

THE STATE OF BRAIN HEMODYNAMIC IN AMBLYOPIA PATIENTS

SLOBODYANIK S., PONOMARCHUK V.
Filatov Institute of Eye Diseases, Odessa (Ukraine)

Purpose .To determine the particularity of the brain hemodynamic and its relationships to the visual acuity and eye refraction in patients with amblyopia.

Methods. We examined 92 patients with amblyopia including 41 - refractive binocular, 30 - monocular anisometropic, 21 - monocular strabismic and 15 normal persons - control. There were used the reoophthalmography methods for the brain blood hemodynamic study.

Results. There were determined the significant decrease of the brain blood vessel filling level in the region aa. vertebrobasilaris in patients with anisometropic and strabismic amblyopia by 7-15 % compared with control group and the increase of the small vessel elastic properties in this area by 14.3-15.3% compared with control group ($p<0.01$). There was determined the direct correlation between the brain blood vessel filling level and degree of the visual acuity decrease of amblyopic eye.

Conclusions. The amblyopia is accompanied by brain and eye hemodynamic disturbances which depend on degree of visual function decrease and refraction type of amblyopic eyes.

368

MONOCULAR ACCOMMODATION FACILITY : IS IT A PREDICTOR OF DECREASED VISUAL ACUITY?

NAVARRO MJ[1], GONZALEZ E[2] ,BARRA F[2]
1Instituto Iberoamericano de Investigación
2 Departament of Optics Universidad Complutense de Madrid (Spain)

Purpose
to establish the existing association between accommodation facility an visual acuity.

Method
a correlational study was performed after a vision screening. 1041 students from 4 to 8 degree were evaluated.

Results
9% of the studied subjects (n=89) who passed the binocular accomodation facility test and failed the monocular accommodation test showed heterophoria conditions and a high correlation with visual acuity in a multiple regression analysis ($R2 = .81$ $p<.01$).

Conclusions
monocular accomodation facility is a good predictor of visual acuity in heterophoric population and this test must be performed in all school vision screening.

369

VERGENCE FACILITY TEST AND NEARPOINT OCULAR SYMPTOMS

BARRA F[1] GONZÁLEZ E[1] NAVARRO M[2]
1. Dept. Optica, UCM, Madrid (Spain)
2. Instituto Iberoamericano de Investigación

Purpose
To compare two powers of prism flipper test for assessment of nearpoint vergence facility in relation to predicting ocular symptoms.

Methods
In two groups of subjects (symptomatic and asymptomatic in nearpoint activities) two prism flipper tests (8BI/8BO and 5BI/15BO) was performed.

Results
The symptomatic group (n = 26) showed significant worse performance than asymptomatic group (n = 26) but only in the 5BI/15BO prism flipper test. The null hypothesis that there is no significant difference between the two powers of prism flipper tests in discriminating between symptomatic and asymptomatic subjects is reject ($p < 0.05$).

Conclusions
The vergence facility test with flipper of 5BI/15BO prism power, is a good predictor of nearpoint ocular symptoms.

370

FUNCTIONAL STATE OF FIXATING AND AMBLYOPIC EYE IN CHILDREN WITH STRABISMIC AND NON STRABISMIC AMBLYOPIA

BOYCHUK I.
Lab. of Binocular Vision Disturbances and Functional Methods of Investigations, The Filatov Institute of Eye Diseases (Ukraine)

Purpose The goal of complex investigation was to reveal disturbances in function of fixating (F) and amblyopic (A) eye and their interaction
Methods Children of 5-7 years old (40): unilateral strabismic amblyopia (15) - I gr., alternative squint (13) - II gr., unilateral non strabismic amblyopia (12) - III gr. were examined. Visual functions, state of retina, optic nerve were investigated by routine methods, EEG and flash VECP on Medicor EEY8S.
Results Increasing of values of the main indices of retina were established on F and A eyes in the I gr. in dependence on monocular fixating excentricity (r=0,85), lower on the A eyes and the lowest in the III gr. Indices were equal and normal on both eyes in II gr., exept cone light sensitivity - it was low. Function of axial fasciculus was better on F eyes in I gr. and in A eyes in III gr., equal in II gr. Threshold of electric sensitivity by phosphen were normal on the F eyes and higher on the A eyes in I and equal in II, III gr.
Conclusion Functional state of fixating and amblyopic eye depend on character of strabismus: unilateral, alternative, microtropic. Better indices in amblyopic eye in comparison with fixating eye indicate on binocular interaction between them.

371

CORNEAL EXCENTRICITY IMPORTANCE IN ORTO-K: ABOUT A CASE

Authors: García-Lázaro S. (1), Albarrán-Diego C. (2) Montés-Micó R. (2)
(2) Dept. Òptica. Universitat de València. SPAIN.
(1) Optometric Centre "+ Visión". Oliva. SPAIN.

Purpose: To demostrate the importance of corneal excentricity in an Orthokeratology treatment as a predictive toll both for the myopia reduction degree which can be reached, and for programming a contact lens use timetable

Methods: "OK" reverse geometry lenses were used in night therapy over a subject with astigmatism and myopia. Corneal changes were studied with an EyeSys video-keratoscope.

Results: It is shown that if there is a good correlation between corneal excentricity and refractive defect, the sucsess probability with these lenses is higher. A higher correlation produces higher possibility of reducing the contact lenses use (wearing them in alternating nights, for example)

Conclusions: It has been demostrated that corneal excentricity is an important factor in orto-K treatment also for prediction and procedure contact lenses use.

372

BIOLOGICAL OXYGEN APPARENT TRANSMISSIBILITY OF CONTACT LENSES FOR EXTENDED WEAR

LOPEZ -ALEMANY A.
Optometry, Cornea and Contact Lens Research Group.
Department of Optics School of Optometry.
University of Valencia. Spain.

Purpose: We want to know of B.O.A.T. (Biological Oxygen Apparent Transmissibility) described by Fatt (1996) of contact lenses for extended wear and to evaluate if these contact lenses for extended wear transmit a minimum level of oxygen through them.

Method: The value of transmissibility (Dk/l) has been obtained by the standard electrochemical method described by Aiba (1968). From this value, we have calculated the B.O.A.T.

Material: We have analysed twelve commercial contact lenses for extended wear: Seequence, Acuvue, Newvues, Precision UV, Terapeutic 04, Plano B, CW 79, Optima FW, Plano T, BL 70, Permalens, Terapeutica.

Results: The B.O.A.T. of twelve commercial contact lenses for extended wear ranged from 8.42 to 10.51 x 10-9 cm3 of oxygen (STP)/cm2 . s . mm Hg.

Conclusion:

None of these lenses have a minimum level of B.O.A.T. for safe extended wear.

373

COMPARATIVE STUDY OF THE ACCURACY OF THE MEASURE OF HYDRATION OF HYDROPHILIC CONTACT LENSES WITH TWO METHODS

LOPEZ ALEMANY A(1) and REFOJO M F.(2)
1. Optometry, Cornea and Contact Lens Research Group. Department of Optics. University of Valencia. Spain.
2. Schepens Eye Research Institute. School of Medicine. University of Harvard. USA.

Purpose: We want to value which of two methods is the more accurate to determine the hydration of hydrophilic contact lenses.

Method: We measured the refraction index of each hydrophilic contact lenses 100% hydrated in water. We then determined concentration of a saccharose solution in water that has the same refraction index. In this way, we know the percentage of saccharose/polymer corresponding to this refractive index. We measured the weight of the lens hydrated to the 100% and dehydrated. The difference indicated us the percentage of hydration.

Results: The hydration calculated with the refraction index method differed more from the values indicated by the manufacturer of the contact lens than the results we obtained by the gravimetric method.

Conclusion:

We consider that the gravimetric method is more accurate than the refraction index method for the determination of the hydration of hydrophilic contact lens.

374

CORNEAL MOULDING BY DISPOSABLE CONTACT LENSES

Authors: Montés-Micó R, Albarrán-Diego C,
Pons-Moreno AM, Artigas-Verde JM, Gené-Sampedro A.
Dept. d'Òptica. Universitat de València. Spain

Purpose: In this work, we try to characterize the corneal moulding due to the adaptation of daily disposable contact lenses and look for a relation between corneal radius variation and the contact lens material hydrogel and its hydration.

Methods: 46 subjects were fitted with etalfycon contact lenses (58% of hydration) and 50 subjects with polymacon contact lenses (38.6% of hydration). The corneal radii were measured at 0° and 90° during a 10 month period.

Results: The results showed a decrease in horizontal and vertical curvature radii after one day of fitting the contact lenses, these values remaining constant during the testing period without statistically significant differences ($p > 0.01$). The reductions obtained provoke an increment in the refractive power lie within the range of eye depth focus. Therefore no vision decreasing is due to contact lens wear.

Conclusions: Our results also confirm that it does not exist a relation between the material hydrogel and the

variation (0 t-test values of significance).

375

ACCELERATED ORTHOKERATOLOGY: A CLINICAL STUDY

MONTALT JC, GENE A, PONS AM, ARTIGAS JM
Dept. d'Òptica. Universitat de València. Dr. Moliner 50. Bujassot (Valencia) SPAIN

Purpose: Orthokeratology (Ortho-K) allows to control the progression of myopia by nonsurgical procedures. The development of reverse geometry contact lenses give a new methodology to orthokeratolgy. Unffortunately, there are only a few exahustive clinical studys about this new technique. The aim of this work is to develope a complete clinical study fo the accelerated ortho-K method.

Methods: 42 subjects participated in the study. 21 of them were a control-group and 21 were fitted with reverse geometry contact lenses (RGCL), with different kinds of retaining technique: daily, nocturne and prolongated. A complete study of ocular parameters was carried out, including corneal topography, biometry, IOP, refractometry, CSF, MTF and VA.

Results: Our results shows a reduction in the corneal dioptric power lower than the total myopia reduction, suggesting a variation of the anteroposterior axis of the eye.

Conclusions: Our study provides a methodological protocol for accelerated orthokeratology and a complete statistical study of the variation of ocular parameters.

376

The Study of Keratotopography in Children in the Assessment of Contact Correction Intolerance

AZNABAYEV M.T., BIKBOV M.M., BAKHTIAROVA G.Z.
Pediatric Dept., Ufa Eye Research Institute (Russia)

Purpose: To study soft contact lens (SCL) intolerance depending on corneal topography with the absence of obvious objective causes in aphakic children during longterm periods following congenital cataract extraction.
Method: Corneal topography in 32 eyes of 25 children aged 6-14 years was studied using a laser computer videokeratoscope TMS-II (USA).
Results: In group I children with good SCL tolerance a difference of corneal refractive power in 5 and 7 mm zones compared with a 3 mm zone was 0,05 D and 0,55 D. The same indices of 0,42 D and 1,04 D were noted in group II children who wore SCLs unregularly because of numerous complications, including repeated episodes of redness. Group III consisted of children with developing SCL intolerance (0,22D and 0,65 D). In children of group III despite a slight overfall of corneal refractive power in absolute values from the centre to periphery, the difference between astigmatism degree (4,46±0,55D, 4,99±0,42D and 5,02±0,99 D in 3, 5 and 7 mm zones) compared with the same reading of group I (1,62±0,57D, 1,82±0,69D and 2,18±0,72D, respectively).
Conclusions: We suppose that one of intolerance possible causes is the corneal refractive power overfall from the centre to periphery. Meanwlile, both its value change along the meridian and astigmatism degree within each zone of great importance.

377

TREND IN PATIENT INTERESTS IN PRK/LASIK AND CONTACT LENSES

BERNICE K. GLOVER, CHRIS O IMAFIDON, AND JOE E. IMAFIDON

PURPOSE : To determine the level of interest shown by contact lenses and spectacle wearers towards Photo-ablative refractive surgery (PRK) after more than six years of commercial availability and LASIK after one year

METHODS: 115 Ametropes self-administered a questionnaire after watching a 30minute video and reading The Royal college of Ophthalmologists (UK) patient information booklet on PRK. All respondents met the requirements for the procedure.

RESULTS: 55% of the respondents would consider having the procedure in the future. The most common reason for wanting surgery was inconveniences of contact lenses (65%). Possible side effects was the most important reason for refusing the procedure. The second reason was cost of the procedure and the third was satisfaction with spectacles or contact lenses. Age range was 21- 60, and gender ratio of 1:2 in favour of females.

CONCLUSIONS The level of interest in LASIK/PRK in current wearers of different corrective modalities is most affected by the fear of possible post-operative complications.

378

VEPs IN THE NEUROTIC PATIENTS DEMONSTRATING VISUAL SYMPTOMS.

JANOCHA A,[1] BORODULIN-NADZIEJA L,[1] PILECKI W,[2] SALOMON E[1] and URBAN E[1].
1.Dep.Physiology, Medical University, Wroclaw (Poland)
2.Dep.Pathophysiology, Medical University Wroclaw (Poland)

Purpose The investigations were undertaken to assess the course of visual evoked potentials (VEPs) in the patients demonstrating various kind of somatoform disorders.
Methods The group examined comprised of 20 subjects reporting symptoms, like diminished visual acuity (11 cases), narrowing of visual field (10), photophobia (4), photopsia (3) and diplopia (2) that mostly occurred periodically showing a clear time causal relationship with stress events.
Results The results of VEPs registrations revealed interhemispheric symmetry and peak P_{100} latency was within the normal limits in all of 20 tested patients, which proved the functional integrity of visual pathways.
Conclusions The presented findings suggest that there were no organic underlying factors responsible for the subjective complaints noted in the examined individuals.

379

RESPONSE ANALYSIS OF THE MULTIFOCAL ERG IN CONE DYSTROPHY

Parks S[1,2], Keating D[1,2], Evans A. L[1], Elliott A. T[1], Hammer H. M [2]
1. Department of Clinical Physics and Bio-Engineering, University of Glasgow, (Scotland)
2. Tennent Institute of Ophthalmology, Western Infirmary, Glasgow, (Scotland).

Purpose. To investigate features of local electroretinogram responses obtained using a Multifocal Technique in a condition with diffuse cone photoreceptor loss.
Methods. Multifocal ERGs and custom photopic (cone) visual field tests were obtained from patients with cone dystrophy.
Results. The results from the static visual field tests reflected diffuse loss of cone photoreceptors with marked losses in sensitivity of central function. MFERG responses also reflected gross amplitude losses in central retinal function. In areas with reduced function (where timings could be obtained) little change in the temporal response could be found.
Conclusions Although these findings are from a limited data set, they suggest that the Multifocal ERG can be used to detect local cone dysfunction in patients with retinal disease but that these changes may not be reflected in the temporal features of the standard multifocal response.

380

CORRELATION BETWEEN ERG AND NEUROPATHOLOGICAL RETINAL FINDINGS IN CREUTZFELDT-JAKOB DISEASE

J.de Seze, CF.Arndt, CA.Maurage, P.Vermersch, S.Defoort-Dhellemmes, F.Pasquier, MM.Ruchoux, A.Destée, JC.Hache
Departments of Neuro-ophthalmology, Neurology and Neuropathology, Lille (France)

Purpose: Examination of retina had been performed in a very few cases of Creutzfeldt-Jakob disease (CJD).
Methods: In 3 patients with definite CJD and abnormal ERG we studied retinal neuropathological findings.
Results: Inner and outer photoreceptor segments were well preserved. Vacuolizations were located in the outer plexiform layer and Muller cells appeared to be swollen.
Conclusion: The ERG abnormalities are well correlated to the neuropathological findings. The vacuolization of the outer plexiform layer without photoreceptor destruction confirms the importance of the neuroretinal impairment in CJD as well showed by the b-wave decrease and a-wave preservation.

381

MULTIFOCAL ELECTRORETINOGRAPHY IN UVEITIC MACULAR EDEMA

BESCH D, SOBOTTKA B, SCHLOTE T, ZIERHUT M, and ZRENNER E.
University Eye Clinic Tübingen (Germany)

Purpose To investigate the diagnostic value of multifocal ERG in the follow up of uveitic macular edema.
Methods Nine eyes of five patients (4 female, 1 male, age ranged from 11 to 62 years) with chronic anterior or intermediate uveitis and macular edema were examined several times (3-6x) during the course of their disease using the multifocal ERG technique.
Results In all nine eyes, macular dysfunction resulted in a reduced amplitude of the multifocal ERG. Even after successful treatment of macular edema (increased visual acuity, no metamorphopsia), macular dysfunction was detectable by reduced ERG activity. The implicit time was prolonged in severe cases of recurrent macular edema including secondary changes. ERG activity only gradually improved after successful treatment and remained decreased in severe cases of recurrent macular edema.
Conclusions Multifocal electroretinography represents an efficient method for the objective measurement and follow up of macular dysfunction in recurrent uveitic macular edema. While amplitude abnormilities could be observed in all eyes with macular edema, the implicit time seems to be affected in progressed cases of chronic macular edema.

382

A THEORETICAL CONSIDERATION ABOUT CORRECTED SHORT AND CONVENTIONAL LONG M-SEQUENCES IN MULTIFOCAL ERG

HARRER M, HORN FK, LANGENBUCHER A and KORTH M.
Dep. of Ophthalmol., Univ. Erlangen-Nürnberg, Germany.

Purpose. At pesent the two commercial systems for multifocal ERG-measurement, VERIS (EDI, San Mateo, CA) and RETIScan (Roland Consult, Wiesbaden, Germany), use slightly different methods to decorrelate the single ERGs (first order kernels, FOK) form the raw signal. VERIS utilizes one cyclic shifted m-sequence with a length of $2^n - 1$ (n=15 or 16) for one measurement. With RETIScan the result is obtained from averaging several partial measurements with corrected sequences (length 2^n, n=7). For a better estimation of the result plots the effects of the two methods are compared. Methods. For both procedures error calculations were made, which characterize the influence on one single ERG from all other hexagons. A simulation was programmed in MATLAB (The MathWorks, Natick, MA) to proof the error calculation and to display the mutual influence. Results. The decorrelation method in VERIS includes a systematic error, which converges for increasing length of the m-sequence and for decreasing hexagon numbers. The RETIScan method doesn't include a systematic error. Conclusions. RETIScan provides an exact decorrelation because of the use of corrected m-sequences. Therefore the result can be obtained from several short m-sequences. VERIS uses coventional m-sequences long enough, so the systematic error is converged. From a mathematical point of view the results of the two systems should not differ. Supported by DFG (SFB 539).

383

AGE-RELATED MACULAR DEGENERATION: CORRELATION BETWEEN ELECTROPHYSIOLOGY AND SERUM VITAMIN E

BELDA-SANCHIS JI[1]; VILELA C[2]; PUERTAS J[2]; VALLET M[2]; DIAZ-LLOPIS M[3]; ROMERO B[1]; ROMERO FJ.[1]
1. Experimental Toxicology and Neurotoxicology Unit. Dept. Physiology. University of Valencia. Valencia. (Spain).
2. Dept. Neurophysiology. Univ. Hospital La Fe. Valencia. (Spain).
3. Dept. of Ophthalmology. University of the Basque Country. Leioa. Vizcaya. (Spain)

Purpose: To observe the characteristics of pattern electroretinogram (PERG) in normal subjects and patients with age-related macular degeneration (AMD), and to evaluate the applied worth of PERG and pattern visual evoked potential (PVEP) in AMD. Finally, to correlate these findings with serum levels of vitamin E.

Methods: The vitamin E serum levels of a total of 40 patients, distributed in a AMD group (25 patients) and a control group (15 patients without ocular affectation) were studied, correlating the biochemical findings with the PERG and PEVP of these patients.

Results: Both PERG and PEVP correlate with best corrected visual acuity in each eye. There were a significant correlation between PERG and serum vitamin E ($r=0.418$; $p<0.001$) and PEVP with serum vitamin E ($r= -0.423$; $p<0.05$).

Conclusions: Our results show that electrophysiological methods are appropriate for evaluating the degree and progression of AMD. The correlation of these methods with serum levels of vitamin E suggest a possible role of this natural antioxidant in the pathogenesis of the disease.

384

THE INFLUENCE OF STIMULUS SIZE ON FUNDUS PERIMETRIC DETECTION OF SMALL SCOTOMATA

Bültmann S, Rohrschneider K, Glück R, Völcker HE
Department of Ophthalmology, University of Heidelberg (Germany)

Purpose To investigate the influence of stimulus size on the detection of the physiological blind spot with fundus perimetry.

Methods Using the Scanning Laser Ophthalmoscope we performed kinetic as well as static threshold fundus perimetry with documentation of fixation in 10 healthy eyes. Stimulus size was changed from Goldmann I to Goldmann V during the kinetic procedure while threshold was determined using Goldmann I, III, and V stimuli. The stimuli during static perimetry were located in a rectangular grid with 2 degrees distance.

Results As expected, the size of the blind spot enlarged with stimuli of decreasing size. Also, no blind spots were detected using Goldmann V stimuli. All probands reported a diffuse brightening. Threshold perimetry revealed a dense scotoma for small stimuli while testing with Goldmann V showed a relative scotoma of 1-4 dB

Conclusion It has been reported earlier using conventional perimetry that the delineation of the blind spot strongly depends on stimulus size. Also, during fundus perimetry, which allows for an exact correction of fixation movements, there is an effect of light scattering with large stimuli. Therefore the absolute scotoma might not be found with a stimulus such as Goldmann V (1.8 deg diameter) which is small in relation to the diameter of the disc (5-7 deg).

385

Phosphen-electrotherapy in patients with partial optic nerve atrophy

Drozhenko V.
Filatov Institute of Eye Diseases and Tissue Therapy, Ukraine.

Purpose. Optic nerve atrophy is one of the most serious eye diseases. For treating partial optic nerve atrophy (PONA) eyes one uses a great number of various pathogenic grounded methods of treatment and symptomatic remedies.

Methods. We have made the generalization of the results obtained in order to find out of increasing the effectiveness of treatment for PONA of various genesis by applying a new method of electrostimulation : phosphen-electrostimulation (PHES).

Results. Visual acuity constituting 0,17±0,02 on the average before PHES rose by 0,12±0,02 and became 0,29±0,02 after therapy (p<0,01). After treatment course the electric sensibility of visual analyzer improved from (127±6)mcA to (88±5)mcA (p<0,01). The electric liability of visual analyzer in conditions of threefold increase of electric sensibility threshold bettered from (38,6±2) Hz till (43,7±2) Hz (p<0,01). Peripheral visual field widened by 65°±6° from 214°±7° till 279°±8° on the sum 8 meridians (p<0,02).

Conclusions. The therapeutic result achieved under PHES affords a good opportunity to enrich data about the mechanisms of functioning of optic nerve electrostimulation discribed before with those of the mechanism of "frequency swinging" which our method is beside on.

386

THE ACCOMMODATION AND CONE LIGHT SENSIBILITY IN PATIENTS WITH NON-COMPLICATED MYOPIA AFTER THE ELECTRICAL STIMULATION TREATMENT

PONOMARCHUK V., SLOBODYANIK S.,
Filatov Institute of Eye Diseases, Odessa (Ukraine)

Purpose .To determine the changes of functional state of visual system in patients with non-complicated acquired myopia after the phosphen-electrical stimulation treatment.
Methods. There was examined 218 patients ages 8-18 years with non-complicated myopia from 0.5 D to 8.0 D. We were determined the binocular and monocular accommodation, cone light sensibility. The treatment was carried out by impulse electric current (20-30 Gz) with the threshold power producing a phosphen phenomenon
Results. Before the treatment there were determined the gradually decrease of cone light sensibility during the increase of myopia degree and the monocular and binocular accommodation decrease beginning from myopia 4.0 D ($p<0.01$). The electrical stimulation was increased of all studying indexes in myopia patients by 28-55% compared with pretreatment level ($p<0.05$) that were depended on myopia degree.
Conclusions. The non-complicated acquired myopia is accompanied by accommodation and cone light sensibility disturbances that are decreased after electrical stimulation therapy.

387

PHOTORECEPTION AS A SEMICONDUCTOR-OPTOELECTRONIC PROCESS

DEMIRCHOGLYAN G

Department of computer video training, All Russian Research Institute of Psysical Culture Moscow

By researches of retina photo conductivity, its volt-ampere, kinetic, lux-ampere, spectral, optical and temperature characteristics it became possible to define several physical parameters. Two components of photo current were found long-time and short-time, connected evidently with existence of adhesion centres of carriers. A lateral square electrooptical effect in retina was found as well as its connection with rodopsin. The hypothesis of photo semiconductor nature of the primary sight processes was confirmed. A proposal was suggested that the information coming from the retina to the brain is not only of the bioelectrical but also optical nature. It was possible to watch the electrical activity of brain using direct influence on it by light stimuli. The mechanisms of photoelectrical effects, discovered in the retina can bring new possibilities to design more effective biolike TV receivers.

388

CORNEAL INCISION AND STITCHING IN THE PIGMENTED RABBIT: A MODEL OF SURGERY-INDUCED OCULAR INFLAMMATION

Bizec JC, Debon C.
Ciba-Vision, Ophtha Research Unit, Basel (Switzerland)

Purpose: In order to assess for drug activity, we set up a surgical inflammation model in the Chinchilla rabbit eye where the protein level in aqueous humor was reaching a similar level as in human cataract surgery, i.e. a flare level from 30 to 60 photons/ms one day after the surgery. **Methods**: Following a corneal pre-incision (sagital) at 1 mm from the limbus, a 2 mm incision (axial) was performed. One stitch closed the eye. This eye surgery was also compared to either a 5 mm incision with 4 stitches or a 150 µl-aqueous humor puncture. *In vivo* measurement of flare intensity in the anterior chamber was performed prior to the surgery and for 6 hours after the surgery by using a laser cell flare meter (LCFM). Voltaren Ophthalmic® (0.1% diclofenac) activity was compared to saline. 30 µl were instilled into the left eye every 15 minutes one hour before the surgery as commonly performed in human. **Results**: The highest flare levels were observed after the 5 mm incision and 4 stitches (600 photons/ms average) out of the linear range of flare measurement. After saline and 2 mm incision + 1 stitch, flare increased up to 220 photons/ms (in average). As regards paracentesis, the maximum flare reached a similar level. The flare picked at about 60 min then decreased slowly. After a day, the flare level returned to a lower level (8-30 photons/ms). A significant inhibition was evidenced after treatment with Voltaren Ophthalmic® (max. 30 photons/ms). **Conclusion**: A new ocular model of inflammation induced during anterior segment surgery was developed with a 2 mm incision, free release of aqueous humor and one stitch. The flare response without anti-inflammatory treatment ranged into the linear part of LCFM measurement. Voltaren Ophthalmic® given prior to the surgery inhibited the inflammatory process in this model.

389

DEVELOPMENT OF A SPRAGUE DAWLEY RAT MODEL OF CHRONIC *ACANTHAMOEBA* KERATITIS.

WATT L[1], AIMARD L[2], FAVENNEC L[2], OLLE P[1], BRASSEUR P[2], BRASSEUR G[1].
1. Service d'Ophtalmologie, Hôpital C. Nicolle, Rouen (France)
2. Service de Parasitologie, Hôpital C. Nicolle, Rouen (France)

Purpose : *Acanthamoeba* keratitis is a rare but severe infection which occurs in contact lens wearers. The aim of this work was to develop an animal model of chronic *Acanthamoeba* keratitis.
Methods : On day 0 (D0), 24 Sprague Dawley rats were inoculated into the cornea with 10^3 *Acanthamoeba* (strain ATCC 50495) associated with a subconjunctival injection of betamethasone. In a first experiment, 15 infected and 5 control rats received 0.57 mg betamethasone at D0, D7 and D14. In a second experiment, 9 infected rats and 9 control rats received 0.285 mg betamethasone at D0, D14 and D21. Results : In the first experiment, 4 control rats exhibited bacterial superinfection while in contrast, no superinfection occured in control rats during the second experiment. All parasited rats developped corneal abcess and no healing was observed on D35. Histological study and culture of cornea confirm that the lesions were due to *Acanthamoeba*.
Conclusion : This model of *Acanthamoeba* keratitis would be useful for physiopathology study and therapeutic agents evaluation.

390

EVALUATION OF DESENSITIZATION BY SUBLINGUAL ROUTE WITH CONJUNCTIVAL CHALLENGE IN ALLERGIC CONJUNCTIVITIS SECONDARY TO DERMATOPHAGOIDES PTERONYSSUNUS

Vérin Ph., Mortemousque B., Bertel F., Barac'h D., De Casamayor J.

Purpose : Immunotherapy raises the threshold for development of severe clinical symptoms. Employment of immunotherapy was restricted to symptoms not adequately controlled by simpler means because of the risk of potentially life threatening systemic reactions. We evaluated the efficacy of immunotherapy by sublingual route using a conjunctival challenge test during desensitization.
Methods : We controlled 50 patients during at least 18 months. All had an allergic conjunctivitis to mite identified using skin patch testings and RASTS. We gave a desensitization by oral route. Conjunctival provocation test (CPT) using standardized extracts of Dermatophagoides pteronyssinus was performed in one eye at the day of the patients recruitment, 6 months and one year later. Ocular response was evaluated by the cumulative clinical score of Abelson Chambers and Smith.
Results : All patients treated by sublingual immunotherapy had a reduction of hypersensitivity reactions (reactivity index) with a close relation to the duration of desensitization time.
Conclusion : Immunotherapy by sublingual route has a good efficacy in house dust, mite allergic conjunctivitis ; the CPT allows to control immunotherapy. It could be helpful to obtain a good compliance of patients who are able to understand the beneficial effect of immunotherapy.

391

COMPARATIVE STUDY OF THE EFFICACY OF TWO ANTI-ALLERGIC EYEDROPS IN A CONJUNCTIVAL PROVOCATION TEST: MEQUITAZINE VERSUS DISODIUM CROMOGLYCATE

DUPIN O.[1], ROBERT F.[2], TRINQUAND C.[1], PERSI L.[3], ARNAUD B.[2]
1 Laboratoire Chauvin, Montpellier (France)
2 Service d'ophtalmologie, Hôpital Gui de Chauliac, Montpellier (France)
3 Clinique des Maladies Respiratoires, Hôpital Arnaud de Villeneuve, Montpellier (France)

Purpose : In order to evaluate the efficacy and the onset of action of a 0.05% mequitazine-based antihistaminic ophthalmic solution versus 2% disodium cromoglycate, a comparative, randomised, double-masked trial was initiated in the allergic conjunctivitis induced by a specific conjunctival provocation test (CPT). 22 asymptomatic subjects presenting with history of allergic conjunctivitis to grass pollens were included in the trial.
Methods : On D1, a first CPT permitted to define the threshold concentration inducing allergic response. On D4, subjects were given 2% disodium cromoglycate ophthalmic solution to instil in one eye 4 times daily for 4 days, and mequitazine vehicle ophthalmic solution in the fellow eye, at the same regimen, except for the last instillation which comprised one single drop of mequitazine ophthalmic solution. 15 minutes after, a CPT was performed using the threshold concentration defined by the CPT on D1. The allergic reaction was then assessed by the sum of the score hyperhaemia and itching, 5 minutes after the CPT. In the case of no positive reaction in one eye, the next higher concentration was instilled successively in the same eye to measure the threshold concentration in this eye.
Results : One instillation of 0.05% mequitazine reduces significantly the allergic response (hyperhaemia + itching: $p< 0.0001$) compared with 2% disodium cromoglycate administered previously for 4 days. Furthermore, the threshold concentration was significantly higher in the group pre treated by mequitazine ($p< 0.001$).
Conclusion : In this model, a single drop of 0.05% mequitazine ophthalmic solution reduces significantly the intensity of the allergic response compared with 2% disodium cromoglycate ophthalmic solution administered for 4 days.

392

CELLS WITH M-CELL CHARACTERISTICS IN THE FOLLICLE ASSOCIATED EPITHELIUM OF THE RABBIT CONJUNCTIVA

KNOP N, and KNOP E
Lab. for Cell Biology, Medical School Hannover (FRG)

Purpose: In the rabbit conjunctiva prominent lymphoid follicles were reported on the light microscopical level. There is no information as yet on the presence of epithelial M cells, supposed to present luminal antigens to lymphatic cells.
Methods: Conjunctival sacs were obtained from rabbits, prepared as whole mount flat preparations and investigated by light, scanning and transmission electron microscopy.
Results: The conjunctiva showed prominent secondary follicles accumulated towards the lacrimal punctum. In the covering follicle associated epithelium there were plenty of lymphocytes, frequently arranged into groups and separated from the lumen only by narrow cytoplasmic sheets that contained frequent vesicles in TEM. In SEM flat cells were seen at the surface with roundish cellular elements detected underneath if the surface was artificially opened. Occasionally the surface cells were occurred as thin shell like structures covering larger hollow rooms containing some roundish cells. TEM revealed the groups of roundish cells to consist of lymphocytes and occasional plasma cells. They were wrapped by a narrow cytoplasmic layer of relatively electron lucent cells leaving only basolateral openings.
Conclusions: The follicle associated epithelium of the rabbit conjunctiva contains epithelial cells with characteristics of M cells as found in other lymphoid tissues.

393

APOPTOSIS IN HUMAN HSV-1 STROMAL KERATITIS

HEILIGENHAUS A, MRZYK S, BAUER D, ANASTASSIOU G, STEUHL KP.
Dept. of Ophthalmology, University, Essen (Germany)

Purpose The pathogenesis of HSV-1 stromal keratitis is poorly understood. Recently, it has been recognized that many viruses induce apoptosis of the infected cells. Keratocyte apoptosis has been found in response to experimental HSV-1 epithelial infection. This study now investigated apoptotic cell death in keratectomy specimens from patients with HSV-1 stromal keratitis.
Methods The keratectomy specimens from patients with active HSV-1 nonulcerative (n=5) or ulcerative (n=10) necrotizing stromal keratitis were studied. Paraffin sections were analyzed histologically and by immunoperoxidase technique for the presence of HSV-1 antigens. The TUNEL-assay (TdT-mediated dUTP nick-end labeling) was used to detect apoptosis.
Results All keratectomy specimens displayed inflammatory cell infiltrations. HSV-1 antigens were detected in 9 specimens from patients with ulcerative keratitis, and in 3 specimens from patients with nonulcerative stromal keratitis. Many cells within the inflammatory infiltrations were TUNEL positive. Numerous TUNEL positive epithelial cells and keratocytes were found adjacent to the ulcer. In the specimens with nonulcerative keratitis, TUNEL positive cells were present in epithelial cells, keratocytes and endothelial cells adjacent to foci of inflammatory reactions. Several corneas with epithelial lesions suggestive of HSV-1 infection had TUNEL-positive keratocytes beneath the areas of infection.
Conclusions Apoptosis was identified in human HSV-1 stromal keratitis. Programmed cell death was detected in the epithelium, keratocytes and endothelium. HSV-1 epithelial infection induces apoptosis of epithelial cells and of the underlying keratocytes. The epithelial and stromal apoptosis may limit the extension of viral replication to the deeper layers of the cornea. Apoptosis could play a role in maintaining corneal transparency in HSV-1 stromal keratitis.

Supported by DFG grant He 1877/7-1.

394

MACROPHAGE DEPLETION INFLUENCES HSV-1 KERATITIS IN MICE

BAUER D,[1] MRZYK S,[1] ROOIJEN N,[2] STEUHL KP,[1] HEILIGENHAUS A.[1]
1. Dept of Ophthalmology, University, Essen (Germany)
2. Dept of Cell Biology & Immunology, University, Amsterdam (Netherlands)

Purpose Herpes-simplex type 1 (HSV-1) infections of the cornea induce an immune-mediated keratitis. The role of macrophages in this inflammatory disease has not been defined. The authors studied the influence of a selective macrophage depletion by dichloromethylen diphosphonate liposomes (Cl_2MDP-LIP) on the course of HSV-1 keratitis.
Methods BALB/c mice were corneally infected with 10^5 PFU of HSV-1 (KOS strain). For macrophage depletion, mice received subconjunctival injections of Cl_2MDP-LIP on days 7 and 2 prior to HSV-1 infection. Groups of mice were: (1) only HSV-1 infection; (2) Cl_2MDP-LIP prior to HSV-1 infection; (3) Cl_2MDP-LIP prior to corneal scratching; (4) PBS-LIP prior to corneal scratching; (5) only corneal scratching. The clinical course of epithelial and stromal keratitis was analyzed. The eyes were studied histologically and immunohistochemically (F40/80 and CD11b mAbs).
Results After Cl_2MDP-LIP treatment, epithelial keratitis was more severe and the healing was delayed. Healing of scrape wounds was not influenced by Cl_2MDP-LIP injections. The clearance of the virus from the infected eyes was delayed by the macrophage depletion. Necrotizing stromal keratitis developed in 78.6% of HSV-1 infected control mice by day 14 after inoculation. By subconjunctival Cl_2MDP-LIP treatment, the incidence of stromal keratitis was reduced to 43% and the keratitis was less severe ($p<0.05$). After Cl_2MDP-LIP treatment, the HSV infected eyes had decreased stromal infiltration with lymphocytes, granulocytes, CD11b+ and F4/80+ cells as compared to the HSV-1 infected control group.
Conclusions These results indicate that macrophage depletion influences the course of HSV-1 induced keratitis in mice. Macrophage functions are involved during the acute epithelial keratitis. Macrophages play a role in the immune-mediated process of stromal keratitis that finally leads to corneal damage.

Supported by DFG grant He 1877/7-1.

395

REDUCTION OF bFGF-INDUCED NEOVASCULARIZATION IN RAT CORNEAS, AFTER TREATMENT WITH A CYCLIC RGD PEPTIDE ANTAGONIST TO αvß3-INTEGRIN, IS ASSOCIATED WITH DOWNREGULATION OF NO ACCUMULATION, TNF PRODUCTION AND IL-8/CINC GENE EXPRESSION.

PRADA J, BAATZ H, KLOTZ O, PLEYER U, and HARTMANN C.
Department of Ophthalmology, Charite/Virchow University Hospital, Humboldt University, Berlin (Germany).

Purpose: We have recently described that the cyclic RGD-peptide cRGDfV is able to inhibit bFGF-induced corneal neovascularization in rats. In order to further elucidate the mechanisms of action of cRGDfV, we have investigated the possible variation of immunological markers related to the expression of adhesion molecules during the observed reduction of bFGF-induced corneal neovascularization.
Methods: Corneal neovascularization was induced by implantation of Hydron pellets containing 400 ng of bFGF in the eyes of Wistar rats. The animals were further treated with s.c. injections of cRGDfV (15 mg/Kg body wt) twice daily for 4 days or received a saline injection. At day 5 after the bFGF-induction, the animals were sacrified and the eyes and plasma samples were collected for further analysis of immunological markers. Nitrite and TNF were measured in plasma by a compensated Griess reaction and a combined ELISA kit/WEHI164 Bioassay, respectively. The IL-8/CINC gene expression was studied by non-radioactive in situ hybridizations with a specific DIG-labelled gene probe in paraffin sections of the corresponding corneal tissue samples.
Results: The systemic application of cRGDfV in bFGF-treated rats resulted in a significant reduction of the vessels surface in corneas, when compared to the corresponding controlls, and this effect was found to be associated with significant decreases in the concentration of nitrite (41.35 $\pm$ 1,55 vs. 32.22 $\pm$ 4,00 mnol/ml) and TNF in plasma (47,11 $\pm$ 6,64 vs. 31.10 $\pm$ 4.37 pg/ml in ELISA, or 37.03 $\pm$ 6.78 vs. 23.76 $\pm$ 1.78 units/ml in Bioassay). In addition, the IL-8/CINC gene expression in corneal cells was found to be reduced by more than 50% after cRGDfV treatment.
Conclusions: Our results indicate that the observed reduction of bFGF-induced neovascularization in rat corneas by systemic treatment with cRGDfV is not only due to a direct blocking effect on αvß3-integrins, but also to a more extended action including downregulation of the production of NO and cytokines.

396

NEW-FORMED LYMPHATIC VESSELS

Mazhdrakova I.[1], Anguelov B.[1] and Nikolaeva S.[2]
1.Dept. of Ophthalmology, Medical University, Sofia (Bulgaria)
2.Dept. of Pathology, Medical University, Sofia (Bulgaria)

<u>Purpose</u>: In normal cornea there are neihter lymphatic, nor blood vessels. The aim of this study is to be checked whether during the sprouting of neo-blood vessels, there are new-formed lymphatic vessels.
<u>Methods</u>: We made a lymphography to five patients with corneal vascularisations, using Patentblau V. Biomycroscopic photodocumentation and transversal electronic mycroscopy (TEM) was performed.
<u>Results</u>: In three of the cases with lymphography the dye entered the conjunctival lymphatic vessels and after that moved into the corneal lymphatic vessels. A corneal lymphatic vessel went slantwise to the blood vessels in the cornea. At one site it crossed them and went more superficially to the corneal blood vessels. The TEM of this lymphatic vessel was characterized with dense matrix of the endothelial cells, many ribosomes, electronical dense mitochondria. A fragment from the valve of the vessel was found.
<u>Conclusions</u>: It was proved that the formation of neolymphatic vessels in vascularized corneas i.e. in inflamatory and other diseases of the cornea, a new direct way was created, through which the corneal antigens may reach the regional lymphatic knots and than to contact the immune system of the human organism.

397

***IN VIVO* CONFOCAL MICROSCOPY IN EVALUATING CORNEAL NERVE REGENERATION AFTER PRK.**

MASTROPASQUA L, CARPINETO P, CIANCAGLINI M, ZUPPARDI E, DORONZO E, GALLENGA PE
Inst. Ophthalmology, University of Chieti (Italy)

<u>Purpose</u> We investigated the potential of confocal microscopy (CM) to verify neural regeneration in human corneas *in vivo* after PRK.
<u>Methods</u> Ten corneas of 10 patients undergoing PRK for myopia were examined preoperatively and at different times postoperatively (7, 14 days, 1, 6 months). Healthy preoperative corneas served as controls to define the normal morphology of epithelial and anterior stromal nerves. A confocal microscope was used to generate real-time images of the corneas on a VHS videotape.
<u>Results</u> Seven days post-PRK in vivo CM 5 eyes revealed delicate nerve fibers beneath the epithelium and above the wounded anterior stroma. After 14 days linear stromal nerve fibers were perceived in all patients. One month control revealed clearly abnormal subepithelial/basal epithelial nerves, whereas the deeper stromal nerves looked normal. After 6 months the degree of regeneration of the subepithelial/basal epithelial nerves was variable and incomplete in all corneas examined. The subepithelial/basal epithelial nerve densities was clearly lower in eyes presenting postoperative haze ≥ 2+.
<u>Conclusions</u> CM clinically confirms the histological data on nerve regeneration after PRK. Low numbers of subepithelial/basal epithelial nerves early appear, but the degree of regeneration is still incomplete for months especially in presence of post-PRK haze.

398

ANALYSIS OF ASTIGMATIC CHANGES AFTER EXCIMER LASER ABLATION FOR ASTIGMATISM USING BIVARIATE STATISTICAL METHODS

HJORTDAL J.Ø.[1], NAESER K.[2], & EHLERS N.[1]
1. Dept. of Ophthalmology, Århus University Hospital,
2. Dept. of Ophthalmology, Ålborg Sygehus, (Denmark).

<u>Purpose:</u> To develop methods for bivariate statistical analysis of changes in regular astigmatism.
<u>Methods:</u> 26 eyes of 19 subjects undergoing PARK for myopia and astigmatism (average attempt 2.5 D) were included in the study. Subjective refraction was measured before and after surgery. Achieved changes in astigmatism were calculated after Fourier transformation of the data. Bivariate statistical analysis was performed by Hotellings T^2.
<u>Results:</u> On average, the achieved change in regular astigmatism was 1.8 D in an axis 4° different than that attempted. The astigmatic treatment error (paired bivariate differences between achieved and attempted changes) was significantly different from zero (Hotellings T^2; $p << 0.01$). Univariate statistical analysis revealed that the flattening error as well as the rotation error were different from zero.
<u>Conclusions:</u> In this study, excimer laser ablation for astigmatism was associated with significant undercorrection and with a systematic rotation of the axis of the error cylinder. The bivariate analysis approach in the analysis of surgically induced astigmatism is essential when changes in cylinder magnitude and axis are to be evaluated.

399

CORNEAL ARGON LASER PHOTOCOAGULATION FOR TREATMENT OF NEOVASCULARIZATION

KULJAČA Z, JOJIĆ Ž.
Department of Ophthalmology, University of Belgrade (Yugoslavia)

<u>Purpose</u> To study the effect of corneal argon laser photocoagulation (CALPH) in the treatment of corneal neovascularization.
<u>Methods</u> Corneal argon laser photocoagulation was used in eight patients to treat deep corneal neovascularization who were candidate for penetrating keratoplasty. Area of neovascularization and clinical outcome were monitored. Potency of the blood vessels was judged clinical, using direct slit-lamp observation. A standard treatment protocol was used.
<u>Results</u> After CALPH, there was marked regression of the neovascularization in all patients. Penetrating keratoplasty was performed a mean of 1,2 months after CALPH. In seven of eight patients no graft rejection occurred over a mean of 4,5 months follow up after keratoplasty.
<u>Conclusions</u> CALPH may be a useful adjunct in the treatment of corneal neovascularization and also may favorably alter the clinical outcome in high-risk keratoplasty patients.

400

MESOPIC VISION IN PHOTOREFRACTIVE KERATECTOMY (PRK)

SCHLOTE T, DERSE M, WANKE B, THIEL H-J, JEAN B
University Eye Clinic Tübingen (Germany)

Purpose To investigate mesopic function after PRK.
Methods In a prospective study mesopic function was investigated in 41 myopic patients, who were interested in PRK. 26 patients made the descision to underwent surgery (Summit ExciMed UV200LA, optical zone 5mm), which was performed in 30 eyes. Mesopic function (glare sensitivity, contrast vision) was measured by using the Mesoptometer II.
Results There was a statistically significant reduction of contrast vision and increase of glare sensitivity after 6 to 9 and 12 to 15 months. The Mesoptometer II contrast level of 1:5 (with and without glare) was used as a critical parameter for the descision, whether mesopic function is markedly reduced or not. Before surgery, contrast level of 1:5 without glare was not recognized in 30%, with glare in 40%. After 6 to 9 months, this contrast level was not recognized in 73% without glare, with glare in 80%. Out of these 30 eyes, 21 eyes were followed over 12 to 15 months. Whereas 38% did not recognize the critical contrast level before sugery, this rate increased to 67% (with glare 81%) after 12 to 15 months
Conclusions Impairment of mesopic function has to be considered as a possible side effect of PRK (optical zone 5 mm). The indication for PRK in special professions (e.g. pilots) should be critical discussed.

401

A PATHOLOGICAL STUDY ON RABBIT CORNEAS AFTER LASER IN SITU KERATOMILEUSIS (LASIK)

HOSODA Y, NAKAYASU K, WATANABE Y and KANAI A.
Dept. Ophthalmology, Juntendo University School of Medicine (JAPAN)

Purpose : To investigate pathological changes on rabbit corneas received laser in situ keratomileusis (LASIK).
Methods : We performed LASIK on rabbit corneas to theoretically correct 10.0 diopters of myopia using the MicroPrecision microkeratome manufactured by Eye Technolgy, Inc. and NIDEK EC－5000 excimer laser. Rabbit corneas were studied pathologically at 3 days, 1 week, 3 weeks and 4 months after LASIK.
Results : At 3 days after LASIK, keratocytes in the ablated area changed morphologically to be fibroblastic cells. And there was the disorder of the structure of collagen fibers in the stroma. But at 4 months after LASIK, these changes almost disappeared. There were not any proliferative changes in the stroma of the ablated cornea for 4 months after LASIK. No significant changes were observed in the endothelium.
Conclusions : The damage on rabbit corneas induced by LASIK was not so severe. Because LASIK caused no proliferative change of the corneal stroma, we think that LASIK offer greater predictability and stability than photorefractive keratectomy (PRK).

402

CORNEAL IN VITRO TOPOMETRY AFTER EXCIMER LASER TREATMENT BY FRINGE PROJECTION OF SILICONE MODELS

SCHRÜNDER S, DANKERT A, MÜLLER B, HARTMANN CHR
Augenklinik Charité, Humboldt Universität, Berlin (Germany)

Purpose: An assessment of the ablation profile as induced by pulses of an excimer laser is vital for the quality of the refractive result. Calibration of the laser source is currently achieved using non organic materials like PMMA. Influences of the tissue (e.g. hydration state) cannot be accounted for in this model. In our experiments we used an in vitro model resembling the characteristics of the human cornea avoiding the limitations of the aforementioned model.
Methods: Silicone models of freshly enucleated pig eyes were produced before and after treatment. Topometry was done using a fringe projection technique that gives the result within several seconds with an accuracy of a few microns. The outcome after different refractions as well as the dependency of the ablation rate on the depth inside the cornea was evaluated.
Results: We found a dependency of the ablation rate on the depth inside the corneal stroma in contradiction to the constant value given by the software of our system. We also confirmed the development of central islands during refractive procedures with our large area ablation system.
Conclusion: Our procedure can serve as a tool to calibrate excimer lasers relying on the characteristics of the cornea rather than on those of artificial models like PMMA.

403

LASIK for High Myopia

TCHAH H and MOON CS
Department of Ophthalmology, Asan Medical Center, University of Ulsan, Seoul, Korea

Purpose : To evaluate the efficacy, safety and predictability of LASIK in the treatment of high myopia
Methods : A prospective study of LASIK for the myopia of -13D to -28.5D and astigmatism up to -3.75D was performed using Visx 20/20 laser and Chiron automatic corneal shaper. Changes in refraction, uncorrected and corrected vision and contrast sensitivity were compared before and after LASIK procedure.
Results : Preoperatively mean spherical equivalent(S.E.) was -17.4D and 35% had corrected visual acuity 0.5 or better and 61% had 0.8 or better. At 1 week postoperatively, mean S.E was -0.06D with 40% between ±1.00D of emmetropia. At 6 month postoperatively, mean S.E. was -1.77D with 46% between ±1.00D of emmetropia. 57% were 0.5 or better and 14% were 0.8 or better. 10% had decreased best corrected visual acuity(BCVA) 2 lines or more. No change in contract sensitivity was identified.
Conclusion : LASIK for high myopia with astigmatism appears to be safe and effective without complications such as decreased BCVA and myopic regression.

404

COMPLICATION AFTER LASIK IN VERY HIGH MYOPIA: LACQUER CRACKS OF FLAP

L.Scorolli., Lg.Scorolli., S.Z. Scalinci., S.Meconi., R.Ricci., R.Meduri.
Department of Ottica Physioopathologic, University of Bologna, (Italy)

Purpose: to report complicatios never described in literature that occurred 1 month after lasik, analyzing risk factors.
Methods: 15 eyes treated with lasik technique, using chirow trephine and chirow lif planoscan with eyetracker for myopia included between -15- 21 D (130-160 n flap 0.5-6 mm optical zone).
Results: emmetropy (+/-1D) achieved in 33,3% (5/15) at the first attempt, 66.6% (10/15) after second treatment.After 1-2 months from treatment 3 cases showed, 2 cases within 1 month after treatment linear cracks of flap without any serious changes in refraction, except for one case (increased hyperopia +3D) found with preoperative corneal thicknes, but all the cases had 130 n flap.
Conclusions:
we recommend not performing lasik in high myopia with thin flaps, for the risk of permanent cracks in optical zone.

405

Effect of topical NSAID and/or anesthetics in pain control and epithelial wound healing after PRK

TCHAH H, LIM HT, KIM YS, and KIM YJ
Department of Ophthalmology, Asan Medical Center, University of Ulsan, Seoul, Korea

Purpose : To find out the topical agent which is the most effective in reducing post-PRK pain and has the least side effects.
Methods : One hudred and five patients were devided into 6 groups. Patients in each invidual group received 1% suprofen, 0.1% diclofenac, 0.05% proparacaine, 0.05% proparacaine +0.1% diclofenac, 0.1% fluorometholone or artificial tears as a control after PRK for 3 days. Degree of pain and epithelial healing rate were evaluated.
Results : Diclofenac reduced the pain after PRK significantly. There was no additive effect of proparacaine when combined to diclofenac. Although diclofenac induced delayed epithelial healing compared to artificial tear, epithelial healing was completed within 3 days after PRK in almost all patients with diclofenac.
Conclusion : Diclofenac is the best in reducing pain after PRK without significant side effects among our tested eyedrops. Addition of proparacaine to diclofenac had no beneficial effect.

406

FLASH PHOTOGRAPHY OF PLUME AND PARTICLES PRODUCED BY ER:YAG LASER PULSES APPLIED TO THE IN VITRO CORNEA

SCHRÜNDER S, KASING V, DANKERT A, HARTMANN CHR
Augenklinik Charité, Humboldt Universität, Berlin (Germany)

Purpose: As the Er:YAG Laser is gaining importance for experimental refractive surgery due to several advantages compared to the established excimer laser its ablation behaviour needs to be investigated. We used triggered flash photography to visualise different states of plume development during the ablation process.
Methods: Pulses of a free running Er:YAG laser were applied to freshly enucleated pig corneas. The pulse duration of the laser was varied via the excitation lamp and an additional external absorber. The output of the power supply of the laser was used to trigger a high intensity Xenon flashlamp. Images were taken with a triggered high resolution digital camera.
Results: The development of a plume cloud extending to more than 10 mm at 1 J/cm² energy density was observed. Its amplitude and form depended on the energy density and the pulse length. The particle density and size differs from the findings of excimer laser ablation products.
Conclusion: The plume and the particles as induced by the treatment of the cornea with an Er:YAG laser were visualised and its extension was measured. This might lead to a better understanding of the ablation process allowing for an optimisation of treatment parameters for this potentially upcoming technique.

407

TREATMENT OF PTERYGIUM WITH HIGH-FREQUENCY RADIO WAVE ELECTROSURGERY

RICCI AL, SBORDONE GB, IGNAGNI S, LO SCHIAVO ELIA R, FIORE C
Dept. Ophthalmology, University of Perugia, Italy

Purpose We describe a new technique for the surgical treatment of pterygium using a high frequency radio-wave electrosection.
Methods We treated 30 eyes (10 eyes was a recurrent pterigia) using a radio surgical instrument that employs radio wave technology along whit a surgical electrode as a surgery cautery The excised tissues were sent for pathological assessment to examine the margins of the cut. The patients was seen one week post-operatively and one month after. One-year follow up was performed.
Results The collapses of the elastic fiber of the lesion permit a rapid and meticulous excision of all abnormal tissue, including cleaning the limbal site and polishing the corneal surface, without surgical blade. The pathological assessment demonstrated a clean incision. Clinical observation of the incision suggested that there was less bleeding during the surgery, probably because of the small coagulative effect of the waveform. All patients have a satisfactory one-week follow up
Conclusions The high frequency radio-wave electrosection has a good compliance and the minimal pain. The advantage of less recurrence, minimal time for surgery and post-operative care seams to indicate this treatment as choose treatment of pterygium.

408

THE EFFECT OF PREGNANCY ON GRAFT REJECTION IN LOW RISK KERATOPLASTY

SCHÖNHERR U; HÄNDEL A, MÜLLER K AND NAUMANN GOH
Department of Ophthalmology, University Erlangen-Nürnberg, Erlangen (Germany)

Purpose A worse graft survival rate has been shown in unselected series for women who have been pregnant. The aim of our study is to determine the effect of pregnancy on the endothelial graft rejection rate in the absence of other risk factors.
Methods Between 1980 and 1994 270 keratoplasties were performed with mechanical trephination for Fuchs dystrophy in 78 male and 192 female patients consecutively. The mean follow-up time was 35 months.
Results In female patients there was no history of pregnancy in 22 keratoplasties, 1 pregnancy in 17, 2 in 39, 3 in 41 and more than 3 in 24 cases. In 49 cases the history of pregnancy was not available. Endothelial graft reaction was seen in 33 of the 270 eyes (12,2 %). There was no significant influence of pregnancy or the number of pregnancies on the endothelial graft rejection rate.
Conclusion Our results indicates, that pregnancy is no major risk factor for immun reaction in the absence of other risk factors. It can be speculated, that a diminished presentation of the graft antigen due to non-vascularization diminish the effect of host pre-sensitization by pregnancy.

409

MORPHOLOGICAL INVESTIGATION OF RABBIT CORNEA WITH UNREJECTED (15 – 67 WEEKS) INTRACORNEAL ALUMINIUM-OXIDE CERAMIC IMPLANTS

ANGUELOV B.[1], NIKOLAEVA S.[2] and YORDANOVA M[3].
1. Dept. Ophthalmology, Medical University, Sofia, Bulgaria
2. Dept. Pathology, Medical University, Sofia, Bulgaria
3. Dept. Orthopaedics, Medical University, Sofia, Bulgaria

Purpose: The aim of the present work is investigation of the morphological changes in rabbit cornea with unrejected (15–67 weeks) intracorneal aluminium-oxide ceramic implants in order to use this material in the keratoprosthesing.
Methods: The experimental investigation is performed on 7 rabbits – NZ (7 eyes). The intrastromal corneal implants are with 4,5 mm of diameter and a central hole. The histologic preparations for light microscopy are stained with HE.
Results: The mean stay of the intracorneal implants is 32 weeks. The morphological investigation of the cornea defined 1 to 2 layers of epithelial cells anterior to the implant with 4 to 6 cell layers in front of the zone of the implant's hole. The layers in front of the implant possess relatively less keratocytes, while those lying anterior to the implant hole are with hypercellularity and keratoblastic transformation. The central implant's hole is filled by vascular and collagenized tissue. The contact tissue surfaces are rough with collagenized prickles along with capillaries. The vascularization in the zone of the implant is anterior, posterior and on the edges.
Conclusion: By a histological view of point the corneal changes present biointegration upon the aluminium-oxide ceramic implant.

410

CORNEAL GRAFTING WITH DONOR TISSUE KEPT IN ORGAN CULTURE FOR 7 WEEKS

Ehlers H, Ehlers N, Hjortdal J, Kristensen E, Olesen, B.
Department of Ophthalmology, Århus University Hospital, DK-8000 Århus C, Denmark.

Purpose: To study the fate of corneal grafts after extended organ culture (7 weeks).
Methods: Six patients with symmetrical eye diseases were grafted bilaterally, in one eye with a cornea prepared by routine organ culture (mean 16 days), in the other with a donor cornea kept for 7 weeks (mean 49 days) in organ culture. The outcome was evaluated by biomicroscopy, graft thickness, endothelial cell density and visual performance after an observation time of at least 1 year.
Results: Penetrating 7-8 mm grafting was uncomplicated in all cases. The endothelial densities were in both groups in the range 1000-2000 cells/mm2, and visual acuity 0.2-0.9 in cases with no other ocular pathology. Postoperative graft thickness and deswelling did not differ between 2 and 7 weeks cultured corneas. At final examination the thicknesses were 0.50 mm and 0.49 mm for 2 and 7 weeks cultured corneas.
Conclusion: Seven-week cultured corneas give clinical results comparable to those obtained using shorter culture periods. An extended culture period may be used to improve other qualities of the graft (compatibility, cell number, cell metabolism) and microbiological control.

411

CORNEAL GRAFT INFECTIOUS QUERATITIS ASSOCIATED TO THERAPEUTIC CONTACT LENS : MICROBIOLOGICAL STUDY.

SANCHEZ A, BRITO C, PUEYO M, FERNANDEZ FJ, MELCÓN B, BADA T, HONRUBIA FM.
[1]Ophthalmology Department. Health National Institute. Miguel Servet Hospital. Zaragoza. Spain.

Purpose: This retrospective study was conducted to identify the microbiologic spectrum and risk factors of microbial keratitis (MK) in therapeutic contact lens (CL) users after penetrating keratoplasty (PK).
Methods: Medical records of 246 PK (17-years period, 1980-1997) were reviewed to identify MK. Criterion for inclusion was MK in PK and positive corneal culture or smear Gram stain.
Results: The incidence reported was 4.8%, 12 cases in 246 PK performed (4.8%). Potential risk factors have been categorized in local ocular (graft descompensation, CL user and suture-related), topical medications (corticosteroids) and systemic causes (diabetes mellitus). Time interval between PK-MK was 27.1 $\pm$ 25.7 months, corneal descompensation and CL were the main late associated risk factor. Microbial spectrum: eight cases were bacterial and four cases were fungal (Candida). Gram positive organisms were predominantly involved -58.3%- (Staphylococci Aureus and Coagulase (-) and Streptococcus species), only one Gram negative involved (Pseudomona). There was one case of infectious crystalline keratopathy due to Streptococcus Mitis.
Conclusion: This study shows a major association of MK in PK to therapeutic contact lens user and Gram positive and fungal organisms predominantly involved.

412

Keratotopography in Epikeratoplasty in Patients with Keratoconus

BIKBOV M.M., KARIMOVA R.A.
Ufa Eye Research Institute (Russia)

Purpose: The aim of the investigation was to evaluate the effectiveness of epikeratoplasty using biolenses from nonfrozen donor tissue in a change of corneal topography and keratoconus stabilization.
Method: Sixteen patients (18 eyes) aged 10-39 years with stage III keratoconus were operated on. The mean follow-up period was 2,75±1,34 years. Corneal topography investigation was performed using a laser computer videokeratoscope TMS-2 (USA).
Results: Visual acuity without correction in preoperative examination of patients was mean 0,03±0,01, corneal refraction in the optic centre was 49,25±2,87D. The surgical results obtained indicated flattening of the cornea with a decrease in its optic centre refraction to 43,38±1,12D and an increase in uncorrected visual acuity to 0,32±1,85. Surface regularity index (SRI) and surface asymmetry index (SAI) decreased to 1,78±0,13 and 3,17±0,86, respectively in the early postoperative period and during the follow-up period up to 2 years they decreased to 0,37±0,09 and 0,62±0,12. With the follow-up period up to 4 years the corneal refractive power indices of the cornea were stable.
Conclusions: Thus, performing epikeratoplasty using nonfrozen donor material on patients with keratoconus contributes to the corneal shape stabilization and restoration of its sphericity.

413

LOOSENING OF SINGLE VERSUS DOUBLE RUNNING SUTURES IN PENETRATING KERATOPLASTY FOR KERATOKONUS

BUDDE WM, JONAS JB
Dept. Ophthalmology, University of Erlangen (Germany)

Purpose To evaluate single versus double running suture in penetrating keratoplasty for keratokonus with respect to suture loosening.
Patients Eighty-eight patients were consecutively operated for keratokonus by the same surgeon. For the first 45 patients, a single running 10-0 nylon suture was used. For the remaining 43 patients, a double running 10-0 nylon suture was taken. Minimal follow-up was one year.
Results Suture loosening was observed significantly ($p<0.001$; Chi-Square-test) more often with single running suture (12/45 patients (27%)) than with double running suture (0/43 patients (0%)). Suture loosening occurred 6.2 ± 3.6 months after keratoplasty (median: 5.6 months; 1.9 to 15 months). Within the subgroup with single running suture, the patients with suture loosening and the patients with tight sutures did not differ significantly in gender or age of patients and donors respectively, time of the corneal graft in the corneal storage medium, size of the corneal graft, and diameter of the patient cornea trephination.
Conclusions Double running suture in comparison to single running suture can effectively prevent suture loosening in penetrating keratoplasty for keratokonus.

414

THE AACHEN-KERATOPROSTHESIS.
FIRST SHORT TERM APPLICATIONS

KOMPA S, NUMAN C J, LANGEFELD S, VON FISCHERN T, VOELCKER N, REIM M, KIRCHHOF B and SCHRAGE N.
Interdisciplinary Center of Clinical Research "Biomat", Technical University, Aachen, Germany

Purpose: Design and product development of the Aachen-Keratoprosthesis are established. The authorisation of ethical commission for first human application has been received. Now the technical realisation of a temporary keratoprosthesis has to be performed before a permanent implantation can be considered. We want to present the results and photographs of the first temporary uses.
Methods: Patients with simultaneous vitreoretinal and corneal disease underwent vitreoretinal surgery using the Aachen-Keratoprosthesis as a temporary keratoprosthesis. After surgery KPL was performed.
Results: The handling and surgery of the keratoprosthesis did not cause any serious problems. Leakage out of the sutures occurred during vitreoretinal surgery but could be stopped. Optical qualities were very satisfying and comparable to the Eckardt-Keratoprosthesis.
Conclusions: The first temporary implantations of the Aachen-Keratoprosthesis were successful. This encourages us to try a permanent implantation.

415

RECURRENCE OF CORNEAL GRANULAR DYSTROPHY AFTER PTK OR CORNEAL GRAFT. RETROSPECTIVE STUDY OF 40 PATIENTS.

ELLIES P, DIGHIERO P, WERNER L, SARAGOUSSI JJ, D'HERMIES F, LEGEAIS JM and RENARD G.
Department of Ophthalmology, Hôtel-Dieu Hospital, Paris, France.

Purpose. The goal of the current study was to compare the recurrence of corneal granular dystrophy (CGD) -Groenouw I- after corneal graft (CG) or after phototherapeutickeratectomy (PTK) in forty patients.
Methods : In this study recurrence was defined as a need for a second treatment. A retrospective study compares the recurrence in two groups of patients with CGD. Two groups were analysed. The first treatment in one group was PTK (group A), and CG in the other group (group B). Indications for a retreatment were defined by a severe loss of best corrected visual acuity and/or painful recurrent erosions. All patients, in both groups had a similar superficial form of CGD at the moment of the first treatment.
Results : The 20 patients of group A have a similar delay of recurrence than the 20 patients of group B.
Conclusions :. CGD had the same delay of recurrence after treatment by PTK or by CG. As PTK is a non invasive procedure with a faster recovery of visual acuity and as it can be repeated and doesn't forbid to turn to a corneal graft. We consider that PTK should be the first step of the surgical treatment of CDG.

416

CONFOCAL MICROSCOPY OF DEPOSITS IN GRANULAR CORNEAL DYSTROPHY

WERNER LP, WERNER LP, DIGHIERO P, SAVOLDELLI M, LEGEAIS JM, RENARD G.
Dept. of Ophthalmology, Hôtel-Dieu de Paris (France)

Purpose: Deposits are found in Granular Corneal Dystrophy mainly in the superficial layers in early stages, whereas additional deeper deposits are a sign of long-standing disease. Confocal microscopy has been used as an imaging method to study corneal layers *in vivo* in real time. The aim of this study was to perform a confocal examination of patients with Granular Dystrophy to evaluate the corneal deposits.
Methods: Ten patients (20 eyes) were selected after agreement. After topical anesthesia (Novesine, MSD) a confocal examination (ConfoScan, TOMEY) was performed in each eye using two different water-immersion objectives (40/0.75 and 63/0.90). Images were recorded, digitized, processed, and photographed.
Results: Deposits were seen as fine and diffuse, round-shaped, trapezoidal-shaped or breadcrumb-shaped reflective structures. Deposits in the superficial layers were flat, while in the deeper layers they were more threedimensional. In the cases of recurrences, deposits were found mostly in the vicinity of the Bowman's layer.
Conclusion: Confocal microscopy is an useful tool to evaluate the deposits in Granular Corneal Dystrophy. The possibility of studying corneal microstructures without any preparational or staining artifacts adds further information to corneal dystrophies.

417

CONFOCAL MICROSCOPY FINDINGS IN LATTICE CORNEAL DYSTROPHY

DIGHIERO P, WERNER LP, WERNER LP, SAVOLDELLI M, LEGEAIS JM, RENARD G.
Dept. of Ophthalmology, Hôtel-Dieu de Paris (France)

Purpose: Lattice Corneal Dystrophy is characterized by subepithelial and stromal accumulations of amyloid material, with symptoms of recurrent erosion or visual disturbances. Confocal microscopy has been used as an imaging method to study corneal layers *in vivo* in real time. The aim of our study was to perform a confocal examination of patients with Lattice Corneal Dystrophy.
Methods: Six patients (12 eyes) were selected after agreement. After topical anesthesia (Novesine, MSD) a confocal examination (ConfoScan, TOMEY) was performed in each eye using two different water-immersion objectives (40/0.75 and 63/0.90). Images were recorded, digitized, processed, and photographed.
Results: Reflective large filaments with a diameter of 50-80 µm were found beside keratocytes nuclei in the anterior stroma. More delicate filaments, together with diffuse central opacities were observed near the Bowman's membrane. Basal epithelial cells showed punctiform reflective structures in 2 eyes. Deep stroma, Descemet's membrane and endothelium were found normal in all cases.
Conclusion: Confocal microscopy is an useful tool to evaluate the deposits in Lattice Corneal Dystrophy. Further investigations should be performed in order to elucidate some aspects of this pathology.

418

EXCIMER PHOTOTHERAPEUTIC KERATECTOMY (PTK) FOR RECURRENT GRANULAR DYSTROPHY.

DIGHIERO P[1], ELLIES P[1], D'HERMIES F[1], WERNER L[1], LEGEAIS JM[1] and G. RENARD G[1]

1. Dept. of Ophthalmology, Hôpital Hôtel-Dieu, Paris, (France)

Purpose : Corneal grafting is a standard treatment for visually disabling granular dystrophy. The visual results of this procedure are generally good, but can be marred by recurrences of granular deposits some years later.

Methods : The records of nineteen patients (twenty-three eyes) treated with excimer PTK (Excimed UV 200 LA, Summit Technology, Inc) for recurrent granular deposits on the donor cornea were reviewed.

Results : In all cases visual acuity was improved and repeat corneal grafting avoided. No significant complications occurred although four eyes had further recurrence of granular deposits which was also successfully retreated with excimer PTK. Follow-up on these cases varies between eleven months and four years.

Conclusions : We believe that excimer PTK offers a simple, safe and repeatable way of restoring visual acuity to most cases of recurrent granular dystrophy. Visual recovery is fast and all the incumbent problems of repeat grafting are avoided.

419

HISTOPATHOLOGICAL AND GENETIC INVESTIGATIONS IN GRANULAR CORNEAL DYSTROPHY (GROENOUW I) WITH UNCOMMONLY EARLY ONSET

C. Meyer[1], M. Meins[2,3], A. Gal[2], F. Meyer[4], H.J. Meyer[4]
1. Dept. of Ophthalmology, Medical University Luebeck, Germany
2. Institute of Human Genetics, UKE, University Hamburg,
3. Dept. of Molecular Genetics, Institute of Ophthalmology, University College London, UK; 4. Eye Hospital Osnabrück.

Purpose. A german family with autosomal dominant granular dystrophy (Groenouw type I) was first characterised as macular dystrophy due to the uncommon early onset and the clinical pattern of the opacification. We investigated the relationship between phenotype, histopathology and a mutation in the ß-IG-h3 gene on chromosome 5q31 encoding for the kerato-epithelin protein.
Methods. A three generation pedigree was obtained and clinically examined. In one case histopathological analysis of a corneal button was performed. Blood samples for genetic analysis were taken following informed consent. Mutation analysis in the ß-IG-h3 gene was performed by PCR and ABI cycle sequencing.
Results. Discrete grey dots were seen in the anterior stroma. Histopathologic study revealed eosinophilic PSA-negative deposits in the axial region of the anterior stroma confirming Groenouw type I. The genetic analysis identified the 1710C->T (R555W) mutation in heterozygous form in affected family members.
Conclusions. This case suggests that considerable variation of phenotype, age of onset and progression can occur in Groenouw type I corneal dystrophy. Molecular genetic analysis as well as histopathological examination can help to make up the diagnosis.
Comm. Rel.ships: None

420

MORPHOMETRIC ALTERATIONS OF THE KERATOCYTE NETWORK IN HUMAN KERATOCONUS

BECKER H-H[1], SOMODI S[1], HAHNEL C[1], WEISS DG[2], GUTHOFF RF[1]
1. Dept. of Ophthalmology, University Rostock (Germany)
2. Dept. of Zoology, Inst. Animal Physiology, Univ. Rostock (Germany)

Purpose: Fluorescence microscopic examinations have shown that keratocyte morphology is altered in keratoconus. The purpose of this study was a morphometric analysis of these alterations.
Methods: After penetrating keratoplasty living recipients' trephanates (n = 4) were stained with the Live/Dead Kit (Molecular Probes, USA) and examined using a confocal laser scanning microscope (Nikon Diaphot 300/ Noran Odyssey XL). High resolution fluorescence images of the keratocyte network were reconstructed three-dimensionally (InterVision® Software). Quantitative data were obtained by computer aided morphometry (VoxelView®).
Results: Differences in cell density, volume density and cell shape were found in the apical region, especially in the posterior stroma, whereas morphometric data of the corneal periphery were comparable with those in the healthy cornea.
Conclusions: The morphometric data allow the analysis of corneal pathology in a quantitative manner. However, further studies are needed to transfer this method to other corneal diseases. In the future it might provide an aquisition technique suitable for examinations in vivo.

421

CULTURED HUMAN KERATOCYTES EXPRESS GLUCOCORTICOID RECEPTOR

BOURCIER T,[1] BORDERIE V,[1] FORGEZ P,[2] LOMBET A,[2] ROSTENE W,[2] and LAROCHE L[1]
[1]Dept of Ophthalmology , [2]INSERM U339, Saint-Antoine Hospital, University of Paris-VI, (France).

Purpose The aim of the study was to investigate whether cultured human keratocytes express the glucocorticoid receptor and to assess the influence of dexamethasone (DXM) on these cells.
Methods Human keratocyte primary cultures were obtained using stromal explants. Third-passage keratocytes were cultured in culture medium (THF) supplemented with various concentrations of DXM (ranging from 10^{-10} to 10^{-4} M). Cell growth and viability were analyzed with a haemocytometer and by means of MTS assay after 2, 4, and 6 days of culture. Some experiments were carried out in the presence of mifepristone (RU38486), an antiglucocorticoid molecule at high concentrations. Early phases of apoptosis were studied by means of keratocytes staining with a fluorescein conjugate of annexin V and propidium iodide and analyzed in flow cytometry. Glucocorticoid receptor mRNA was detected in keratocytes by means of reverse transcriptase polymerase chain reaction (RT-PCR).
Results RT-PCR showed the expression of the glucocorticoid receptor in keratocytes. DXM significantly increased keratocyte proliferation and viability with concentrations ranging from 10^{-9} to 10^{-5} M, with a maximum effect at 10^{-7} M ($p < 0.005$). However, 10^{-4} M-DXM had an inhibitory effect on cell growth as of 4 days of culture. Furthermore, DXM-induced cell growth and viability was enhanced by desteroidized serum as compared with untreated serum. DXM proproliferative effect was inhibited by high concentration of RU38486. DXM by itself induced apoptosis of cultured keratocytes, whatever the concentration used.
Conclusions These results indicate that cultured human keratocytes express mRNA for glucocorticoid receptor and proliferate in response to DXM stimulation (10^{-9} to 10^{-5} M).

422

DIVISION OF CULTURED CORNEAL EPITHELIAL CELLS WAS ORIENTATED BY SMALL APPLIED ELECTRIC FIELDS

ZHAO M, FORRESTER JV, MCCAIG CD
Dept. Biomedical Sciences and Ophthalmology, University of Aberdeen (Scotland)

Purpose To determine whether a small applied electric field orients the plane of epithelial cell division.
Methods The orientation of dividing cells with respect to the EF was defined as a function of $\cos 2\theta$, where θ is the angle formed by the intersection of a line drawn through the dividing plane with a line drawn perpendicular to the field lines. This polarisation index varies from -1 to 1. A dividing cell with its dividing plane to the vector of EF will have a polarisation of -1, and a cell with its dividing plane exactly perpendicular to the EF vector will have a polarisation of 1. A randomly oriented population of dividing cells will have an average polarisation (defined by Σ n cos 2 θ /n) of 0.
Results Significantly more dividing cells of a human corneal epithelial cell line were orientated in the direction of electric fields when cultured in electric fields overnight. Average polarisation is 0.002±0.048 (n=226) for cells cultured without applied fields (P=0.278, not significantly different from random orientation). For the dividing cells cultured in small applied electric fields of 150mV/mm for 20 hours, the average polarisation is 0.560±0.080 (n=46) (P=3.8E-7, significantly different from random orientation).
Conclusion Small applied electric fields oriente the direction of corneal epithelial cell dividing, which may be one of the physiological guidance cues for tissue construction, maintenance and injury repair.

423

ENDOTHELIAL SURVIVAL AFTER A FREEZE-THAW-CULTURE CYCLE IN HUMAN CORNEAS

CANALS M[1], MIRALLES A[2], POTAU JM[1], COSTA J[1], GARCIA J[2].
1. Ocular Morphology Unit. University of Barcelona (Spain).
2. Department of Cryobiology. Cancer Research Institute. Barcelona (Spain).

Purpose
To assess the survival of endothelial cells in human corneas cryopreserved with a previously designed protocol.
Methods
8 human donor corneas were cryopreserved at 1°C/min in a solution cryoprotected with 10% Me2SO or 10% PROH. After storage, corneas were thawed in a water bath at 37°C and then cultured at 37°C for 24 hours. Endothelial cell survival was assessed by double vital staining and scanning electron microscopy.
Results
After the complete freeze-thaw-culture cycle, endothelial cell densities were 1015 cells/mm2 with 24% dead cells (Me2SO) and 790 cells/mm2 with 94% dead cells (PROH). Control corneas had in all cases cell densities greater than 2000 cells/mm2 and less than 17% dead cells.
Conclusions
Cryopreservation of human corneas causes a significative cell loss after post-thawing culturing that exceeds predictions derived from the results observed in rabbit corneas.

424

MECHANIC OF CORNEAL WOUND HEALING

PAGLIARA MM[1], LEPORE D[1], ANTICO L[1], COPPOLA G[1], MINICUCCI G[1], D'AMICO G[1], DE SANTIS R[2], NICOLAIS L[2], AMBROSIO L[2], SCULLICA L[1],
1.Dpt Ophthalmology, Catholic University[1], Rome - Italy;
2.Dpt Materials & Production Engineering, University "Federico II" Naples - Italy

Purpose: The aim of this study is to evaluate the mechanical behaviour of rabbit corneal wound healing and the effect of topical steroid and NSAIDs on stromal and full-thickness incision. **Materials and Methods:** an electromechanical INSTRON 4204 digitally controlled material testing system, able to apply either high or low loads strains at different rates was used. 72 rabbits (144 eyes) underwent a 6mm- full thickness or stromal (450nm deep) incision in the central cornea. After incision, 18 rabbits were left untreated and 18 treated 3 times a day with dexamethasone Na-phosphate 0.1%. Remaining 9 rabbits submitted to stromal incision were treated with 0,1% HA solution. 3 animals per group were sacrificed at day 7th, 3 at day 14th and remaining 3 at day 21st. A 7mm corneal strip, perpendicular to the incision was cut and tested at the INSTRON 4204, with a strain rate of 5mm/min. A stress-strain ($\sigma-\varepsilon$) profile was plotted for each strip to calculate elastic modulus, yield stress and strain, break stress and strain. **Results:** graph shows Elastic modulus (Mpa) 14 days after incision. Stromal incision seems to slightly decrease corneal strength. Corneas treated with HA solution have better mechanical behaviour at day 14th.

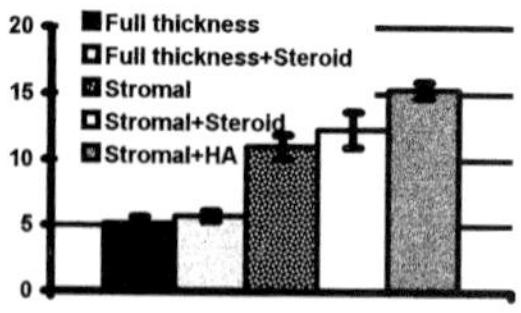

Conclusions: regional and fiber orientation differences, dose-related drug effects, can explain unpredictability of many surgical procedures (KR, LASIK...). The engineering approach to natural tissue mechanical properties we apply seems to be sensible and reproducible enough to allows mechanical measurement of corneal tissue in different experimental conditions. Our data coupled with necessary structural studies will be the basis of a new corneal model for the interpretation of wound healing variability after refractive surgery.

425

EXPERIMENTAL INVESTIGATION OF CORNEA WITH TITANIUM SUPERFICIAL OXIDE-CERAMIC PROCESSED IMPLANTS

ANGUELOV B.
Dept. Ophthalmology, Medical University, Sofia (Bulgaria)

Purpose: The aim of the present work is to investigate the rabbit cornea with intracorneal titanium superficial oxide-ceramic processed implants in order to use this material in the keratoprosthesing.
Methods: The experimental investigation is performed on 7 rabbits-NZ (7 eyes). The intrastromal corneal implants are with 3,0 mm of diameter and a central hole. The implantation is created by a certain operative method in the central cornea. The clinical follow up was done by a biomycroscopy and still is going on.
Results: The clinical follow up period was 1 to 21 weeks. During that time there was no rejection of the corneal implant. The corneal layers in front of the implantn were transparent. In some cases new-formed vessels reached the zone of the implant.
Conclusions: By a clinical view of point we observed good biocompatibility of the cornea to the intracorneal titanium superficial oxide-ceramic processed implants.

426

EYELID, CONJUNCTIVAL, AND CORNEAL FINDINGS IN PATIENTS WITH SLEEP-APNEA SYNDROME

MOJON DS,[1] HESS CW,[2] GOLDBLUM D,[1] FLEISCH-HAUER J,[1] FRUEH BE,[1] KOERNER F,[1] MATHIS J.[2]
1. Dept. of Ophthalmology, 2. Dept. of Neurology, University of Bern, Switzerland

Purpose: To determine the prevalence of eyelid, conjunctival, and corneal findings in sleep apnea syndrome (SAS), an entity characterized by repetitive upper airway obstructions during sleep, inducing hypoxia with the risk of cardiovascular and neurological sequelae.
Methods: 72 caucasian patients referred for evaluation of suspected SAS had complete masked examination of eyelids, conjunctiva, and cornea, including computerized keratometry.
Results: According to the respiratory disturbance index during night sleep (RDI), a value used to diagnose and to grade SAS, 42 of the 72 patients had SAS (60%). The RDI correlated significantly with break-up time, mean eyelid distraction distance, presence or absence of easily evertable eyelids, and lacrimal gland prolapse (Spearman correlation coefficiants). All correlations but the mean eyelid distraction distance remained significant when controlling for age and body-mass index. Other rare findings in SAS patients included: keratoconus, papillary conjunctivitis, blepharoptosis, endothelial dystrophy, and punctate keratopathy.
Conclusions: SAS was significantly associated with reduced break-up time, floppy eyelids, and lacrimal gland prolapse. Severe corneal involvement was rare.

427

LAYER-BY-LAYER CLINICAL OBSERVATION OF THE NORMAL HUMAN CORNEA BY CONFOCAL MICROSCOPY

CHRIS O IMAFIDON, BERNICE K. GLOVER, AND JOE E. IMAFIDON

PURPOSE: To generate clinical images of the human cornea in-vivo and the relative intensity of various layers. The regional pachometry of each part of the cornea was also determined.

METHODS: A new confocal microscope was used to photograph and record the human cornea. All observation was carried out by clinician.

RESULTS: The corneal profile measurement ranged from a relative intensity of 20% at the Tear/Epithelium interface to 90% at the Endothelium/Anterior chamber interface. The mean corneal thickness was 545microns. The Epithelium profile measurement was highest at the basal lamina/stroma interface (95%) but lowest when the epithelium was 42 microns thick (37%). The overall thickness of the epithelium was 50um. Superficial cells of the epithelium; Basal layer of the epithelium; Bowman's membrane; Anterior and posterior stroma; were also observed and photographed.

CONCLUSIONS: Clinical recording of the individual layer of the cornea is possible and will assist in both the selection and post-operative follow-up of the treated or diseased cornea. The exact changes in corneal thickness during wound healing can be monitored. The wider implications of this findings for the aetiology, location and management of corneal haze and other post-ablative procedures will be discussed.

428

OCULAR INFLAMMATION AND CORNEAL DAMAGE VERSUS LENS OPACITIES AFTER ULTRAVIOLET IRRADIATION

MICHAEL R, LÖFGREN S, AYALA M, SÖDERBERG P G
Karolinska Institutet, St. Erik's Eye Hospital, Stockholm, Sweden

Purpose. To study ocular inflammation and corneal damage after short-term exposure to ultraviolet radiation (UVR) in vivo. **Method.** Unpigmented (Fischer) rats and pigmented (Brown-Norway) rats received 5 kJ/m^2 UVR (λ_{MAX} = 300 nm, $\lambda_{0.5}$ = 9 nm) unilaterally during 15 min in vivo. Prior to the UVR exposure, the rats received either mydriatic drops (tropicamide) or miotic drops (pilokarpine). Ocular inflammation (eyelid, conjunctiva, anterior chamber) and corneal damage (haze, opacification, erosion) was recorded subjectively and correlated to measured light scattering in the lens. **Results.** No difference were found in corneal damage between pigmented and unpigmented rats. UVR exposure together with pilokarpine induced less corneal damage than together with tropicamide. Brown-Norway rats had less ocular inflammation than Fisher rats after UVR. **Conclusion.** Unpigmented rats have more ocular inflammation after UVR exposure as compared with pigmented rats. However, the pigmentation has no influence on corneal damage. Tropicamide and pilokarpine influence corneal damage after UVR exposure. Lens damage after UVR seems to be correlated with ocular inflammation, but not with corneal damage.

Supported by: Anders Otto Swärds Stiftelse, Carmen och Bertil Regnérs Stiftelse.

429

PRIMARY OPEN ANGLE GLAUCOMA AND OCULAR HYPERTENSION: NEURAL CONDUCTION IN THE VISUAL PATHWAYS

RADOVIC N., NESHER R.
Institute for Eye Diseases, Belgrade
St.John Ophthalmic Hospital, Jerusalem
Hadassah University Hospital, Jerusalem

Purpose - to evaluate quality of neural conduction in visual pathways in primary open angle glaucoma (POAG) and ocular hypertension (OHT) subjects.
Methods - 57 subjects, including healthy controls (HC) - 26 POAG + 15 OHT + 16 HC - were submitted to visual evoked potentials (VEP) and pattern electroretinogram (PERG) recording. The checkboard patterns used as visual stimuli had size of 20 min/arc, contrast 93%, at reverse rate of 3 per second
Results - POAG and OHT group showed significantly longer PERG and VEP latencies, compared with controls. The PERG amplitudes P50-N95 appeared significantly reduced in POAG and OHT group. In records of VEP amplitudes, OHT subjects data showed no significant differences, comparing with controls, and POAG patients expressed significantly reduced values. Retinocortical time (RT) was prolonged only in POAG eyes, inverse to their PERG amplitudes.
Conclusion - It seems that innermost retinal layers damage, present in POAG, can cause slower neural conduction, in the visual pathways.

430

DISSOCIATION BETWEEN THE SURROGATE ENDPOINT AND THE FINAL ENDPOINT IN POAG

PRZYDRYGA, J

Alcon Laboratories, Inc., Fort Worth, Texas, USA

In recent years a number of studies have been published where, with pharmacological therapy, a dissociation between the surrogate endpoint, IOP and the final endpoint, visual field survival was observed. This phenomena suggests that other factors besides IOP or additional pharmacological properties are involved in the outcome of POAG therapy. Vasodilatation or neuroprotection through Ca^{++} channel blocking activity could explain at least partly this dissociation. An overview of the clinical studies with endpoint dissociation will be given and possible explanations of the phamacological mechanisms behind this phenomena will be discussed.

431

COMPARISON BETWEEN THE G1-TOP AND G1-STANDARD PERIMETRIC PROGRAMS

((M. Losada , M. Abraldes, A. Abreu, M. González de la Rosa)). University of La Laguna. Spain

Purpose: The purpose of this study was to compare the results obtained with the Standard G1 program versus those from the G1-TOP rapid strategy. The original TOP program sub-divides a regular 32 matrix of examination points into four regular sub-matrixes which are tested sequentially. Each patient's response is utilized to modify that particular point and the surrounding points from the sub-matrixes remaining, in a way that each point is tested only once. With program G1-TOP, a similar strategy is utilized with this irregular matrix by subdividing it into four sub-matrixes and applying the responses to the nearest points, bearing in mind the distance to them. Methods: This study consisted of 46 patients (67 eyes) with a mean age of 54.1±17.2 years. The sample consisted of 8 subjects with a normal eye exam, 10 with early glaucoma , 34 with advanced glaucoma , 9 patients with visual fields originated in neurological disorders and 6 with abnormal fields from chorioretinal lesions. All subjects were examined consecutively with the G1-standard and G1-TOP programs using the Octopus 1-2-3 perimeter. Results: The results of the G1 version of the TOP algorithm were similar to the ones obtained previously with the 32 version. Excellent correlation was found between the indices in the two examinations. G1-TOP produces, on average, a mean sensitivity which is 0.75dB thresholds higher than G1-standard. Mean duration of the test for G1-TOP was 2:21±0:26 min. while G1-STANDARD took 11:22±1:19 min. (relation G1TOP/G1standard : 1/4.8, or a net reduction of 79.3%). Conclusions:G1-TOP program produces very similar results to G1-STANDARD in a much smaller fraction of the time utilized by the traditional strategy.

r = correl. coeffic.	Total MD		MD (SN)		MD (IN)		MD (ST)		MD (IT)		sLV		Thresh.	
s.e. = est. error YX (dB)	r	s.e.	r	s.e.	r	s.e.	r	s.e.	r	s.e.	r	s.e.	r	s.e.
G1-TOP Vs G1-STAND.	0.97	1.53	0.96	2.12	0.96	2.20	0.96	2.01	0.96	1.93	0.87	1.25	0.85	4.33

432

SHORT WAVELENGHT AUTOMATED PERIMETRY: ABNORMAL PERIMETRIC CRITERIA.

POLO V, LARROSA JM, PABLO L, PINILLA I, ROJO A, CUEVAS R, RUIZ O, HONRUBIA FM.
Dept Ophthalmology. Hospital "Miguel Servet". Zaragoza. Spain.

Purpose: To determine the sensitivity and specificity of different perimetric algorithms and their combination in short-wavelength automated perimetry (SWAP) to detect early glaucomatous damage.
Methods: 160 eyes of 83 glaucoma suspects were studied (intraocular pressure above 21 mm Hg and normal conventional automated perimetry). SWAP and retinal nerve fiber layer (RNFL) assessment were performed. Perimetric abnormality criteria were presence of clusters of points with significant sensitivity losses and/or criteria based on Global visual field indexes (GI).
Results: 102 eyes out of 160 (63.75%) showed normal SWAP while 58 (36.25%) were pathologic. Fifteen eyes met the GI criteria while 54 met the clusters of points criteria. The distribution of each criteria with the RNFL assessment showed a statistically significant association of both parameters ($p<0.001$).
Conclusions: The presence of clusters of altered points showed higher sensitivity than the GI criteria in detecting early glaucomatous changes. SWAP abnormalities were associated to diffuse or mixed RNFL atrophies.

433

NORMAL VARIABILITY OF SHORT-WAVELENGTH AUTOMATED PERIMETRY (SWAP) THRESHOLDS VALUES ACROSS CENTRAL VISUAL FIELD.

PABLO L, POLO V, LARROSA JM, PINILLA I, FERNANDEZ FJ, MARCUELLO B, HONRUBIA FM,.
Dept Ophthalmology. Hospital "Miguel Servet". Zaragoza. Spain.

Purpose: To determine the distribution of sensitivity thresholds of short-wavelength automated perimetry (SWAP) in the central visual field, analyzing their variability depending on the eccentricity, in normal subjects.
Methods: 128 eyes of 128 normal subjects were analyzed. They underwent a SWAP examination. A lineal regression model was used to establish a "standard visual field" (SVF). The SVF determines the threshold distribution and its variability.
Results: The regression analysis obtained a SVF, age-corrected, which considers the influence of age in the different points of the visual field. The threshold distribution showed higher inter-subject deviations as eccentricity increased (p<0,001).
Conclusions: The determination of variability of the threshold sensitivity deviations in the different points of the central visual field allows future development of perimetric algorithms for SWAP.

434

EXTENSION AND DEPTH PERIMETRIC DEFECTS: SWAP VERSUS CONVENTIONAL AUTOMATED PERIMETRY.

GOMEZ ML, POLO V, LARROSA JM, PABLO L, PINILLA I, FERNANDEZ FJ, RUIZ O, HONRUBIA FM.
Dept Ophthalmology. Hospital "Miguel Servet". Zaragoza. Spain.

Purpose: To compare the amount and distribution of visual field defects in conventional automated perimetry (CAP) and short-wavelength automated perimetry (SWAP) in glaucomatous subjects.
Methods: 22 eyes of 22 subjects were considered for the study (intraocular pressures higher than 21 mm Hg and pathologic CAP). SWAP was performed with a modified Humphrey visual field analyzer. Differential location maps were used to assess the depth and distribution of the visual field defects.
Results: The extension of the defects in the standard and total deviation maps was more important in the SWAP than in the CAP test for all the probability levels (p<0,001). Although there was a significative association (p<0,05) between the amount of CAP and SWAP defects the correlation was weak (r= 0,2865). Conclusions: Visual field defects in SWAP are more extensive and deep than the defects revealed with CAP. This fact can be explained by the special sensitivity of the short-wavelength mechanisms of the visual pathway.

435

PREDICTIVE VALUE OF THE PATTERN-ELECTRORETINOGRAM IN GLAUCOMA

FERNANDEZ FJ[1], GONZALVO FJ[1], ALMARCEGUI C[2], SANCHEZ A[1], BADA T[1], MELCON B[1], POLO V[1], LARROSA JM[1], HONRUBIA FM[1].
1 Dept. of Ophthalmolgy, Zaragoza (Spain).
2 Dept. of Neurophysiology, Zaragoza (Spain).

Purpose: To determine the ability of Pattern-electroretinogram (PERG) to discriminate the individual evolution of glaucomatous visual field losses in glaucoma suspects (GS).
Methods: We studied 151 eyes of 78 GS, classified depending on their risk to develop glaucomatous damage. The initial visual field (VF) was normal. The eyes with 2 reduced amplitudes (P50, N95 or NP) in the PERG were considered pathologic. The mean follow-up was 30 months (range, 13-50 months); the VF was evaluated at the end of the study.
Results: At the begining of the sthdy the PERG was pathologic in 65 eyes (43 %), 45 of these eyes (69 %) the VF was pathologic at the end of the study. The positive predictive value of the PERG of visual field glaucomatous changes was 69 % and the negative predictive value was 80 %. The N95 amplitude showed the best predicitve value.
Conclusions: The PERG study can discriminate the glaucoma suspects subjects that will develop visual field gluacomatous losses.

436

OCULAR HYPERTENSION - REFINING A DIAGNOSIS

ANSARI EA [1] and BUCKINGHAM TJ [2]
1. Dept. Ophthalmology, St James's University Hospital
2. Dept. Optometry, Bradford University (U.K.)

Purpose Ocular hypertension (OH) presents a continuing clinical challenge because of its relative frequency and the increased risk of developing POAG. In OH the incidence of developing POAG over a 5-year interval is 3-5% compared to 0.5-1.25% in a normotensive population. OH management remains controversial. Prophylaxis may prevent optic neuropathy before visual field changes are detected. Conversely, many with OH never develop glaucoma and neither surgical nor medical treatment is free of risk.
Methods Oscillatory movement displacement thresholds (OMDT) have been demonstrated to detect early neural loss in many conditions including POAG and optic neuritis OMDT of 29 normotensive individuals and 44 untreated age-matched OH eyes (20 male and 24 female) were obtained and compared.
Results About one third of OH patients who were dismissed without treatment exhibited abnormal OMDT. Mean OMDT for OH (37.1 arc sec) were significantly different (t=2.734, p 0.007) from the mean obtained from normotensives (22.2 arc sec).
Conclusions Initial results emphasise the need for more vigorous differentiation of OH using appropriate psychophysical techniques which indicate early neural damage.

437

OCULAR HYPERTENSION (OHT): THE INFLUENCE OF OPEN ANGLE GLAUCOMA IN THE CONTRALALERAL EYE.

JÜNEMANN A, HORN F, KORTH M
Dep. Ophthalmology, University Erlangen-Nürnberg, Erlangen (Germany)

Purpose: to evaluate, if eyes with OHT show differences in morphology and function, depending on the diagnosis of the contralateral eye with OHT or open angle glaucoma (OAG). Method: 58 patients with bilateral OHT and 29 patients with OHT in one eye and OAG in the contralateral eye were included. Critera for OHT: normal optic disc (stereo color slides), normal visual field (Octopus G1 program, MD, CLV, Bebié-curve) and IOP>21. Critera for OAG: glaucomatous optic disc and IOP > 21 mmHg. Groups were matched concerning age and IOP. Quantitative evaluation of optic disc by planimetry of stereo color photographs. Sensory tests: spatio-temporal constrast sensitivity, temporal contrast sensitivity, blue-on-yellow VEP, pattern ERG. Visual fields analysis: pointwise and by using 10 clusters of retinal nerve fiber bundles. Statistics: nonparametric test (Mann-Whitney). Results: No significant (p>0.1) differences in the quantitative analysis of optic disc and no significant differences (p>0.1) in the sensory tests or visual field analysis between both groups. Conclusion: The diagnosis of OAG in the contralateral eye showed no influence on morphology and function of OHT. This may indicate that eyes with OHT can be included in cross sectional studies, despite of early glaucoma in the contralateral eye. Supported by DFG grant (SFB 539)

438

FULL-FIELD FLICKER SENSITIVITY IN LOW-TENSION AND OPEN-ANGLE GLAUCOMAS.

HORN FK, VELTEN IM, JÜNEMANN A, and KORTH M.
Dep. of Ophthalmol., Univ. Erlangen-Nürnberg, Germany.

Purpose of this study was to evaluate whether temporal contrast sensitivity (TCS) is reduced in low tension glaucoma (LTG) as well as in open angle glaucomas (OAG). Methods. TCS (37.1 Hz) was measured in a full-field bowl. Subjects: 89 LTG and 484 OAG with previously elevated intraocular pressure were classified into five subgroups taking into account the depth of their perimetric losses (Octopus G1, mean defect, Bebié curve); 257 controls for correlation with actual intraocular pressure at the time of flicker testing. Results. No significant correlation between TCS and actual intraocular pressure in normals or patients. TCS is highly significantly (p<0.0001) correlated with perimetric defects. The slope of the regression line is slightly steeper in OAG (Y=1.35 - 0.032 X) than in LTG (Y=1.35 - 0.024 X), but the loss of TCS is similar in both patient groups if field-loss matched subgroups were compared. Conclusions. The similarity of TCS results in OAG and LTG indicates that TCS measured in a full-field bowl is determined by the actual pattern and amount of the patient's visual field loss rather than by the pathogenesis of the perimetric defect. Considering the high correlation with perimetry and its other advantages (low influence of actual intraocular pressure, photopic conditions, quickness) the test may be a supplement in glaucoma screening.

Supported by DFG (SFB 539)

439

CORRELATION OF FUNCIONAL AND STRUCTURAL MEASUREMENTS IN THE EARLY STAGES OF GLAUCOMA.

POLO V, LARROSA JM, PABLO L, PINILLA I, ROJO A, CUEVAS R, FERNANDEZ FJ, HONRUBIA FM.
Dept Ophthalmology. Hospital "Miguel Servet". Zaragoza. Spain.

Purpose: To determine the correlation between the structural changes in the Retinal Nerve Fiber Layer (RNFL) and functional losses detected with Short-Wavelength Automated Perimetry (SWAP) in a population of patients with suspected glaucoma.

Methods: 49 eyes of 49 ocular hypertensive subjects who met the selection criteria (intraocular pressure greater than 21 mm of Hg and normal standard visual fields) were studied. SWAP was performed with a modified Humphrey Field Analyzer. Visual field indexes (MD, CPSD) were calculated for SWAP. Semiquantitative RNFL scores were given separately to diffuse and localized defects of the RNFL.

Results: The MD increased significantly (p<0,001) with higher Diffuse and Total RNFL scores, with good correlation coefficients. A small correlation was found between the CPSD and the RNFR scores (Diffuse, Total and Localized RNFL scores).

Conclusions: Diffuse retinal nerve fiber layer losses are associated with diffuse field loss (MD) while focal structural damage showed no correlation with visual field losses.

440

CORRELATION BETWEEN SHORT-WAVELENGTH AUTOMATED PERIMETRY AND NEURORETINAL RIM AREA

LARROSA JM, POLO V, PABLO L, PINILLA I, ROJO A, FERNANDEZ FJ, HONRUBIA FM
Dept Ophthalmology. Hospital "Miguel Servet". Zaragoza. Spain.

Purpose: To determine the correlation between the planimetric optic nerve head parameters (neuroretinal rim) and functional losses detected with Short-Wavelength Automated Perimetry (SWAP) in a population of patients with suspected glaucoma.

Methods: 42 eyes of 42 ocular hypertensive subjects who met the selection criteria (intraocular pressure greater than 21 mm of Hg and normal standard visual fields) were studied. A planimetric optic nerve head study was performed, determining the total and sectorized neuroretinal rim areas. Also, a short-wavelength automated perimetry was performed with a modified Humphrey Field Analyzer.

Results: There were no statistically significant correlations between the neuroretinal rim areas and the global perimetric parameters. However, the corrrelations between the inferotemporal neuroretinal rim area and some superonasal visual field regions were statistically significant.

Conclusions: Some short-wavelength perimetric defects are topographically correlated to determined neuroretinal rim areas.

441

ANALYSIS OF THE STRUCTURE AND VISUAL FUNCTION IN THE EARLY DIAGNOSIS OF GLAUCOMA.

HONRUBIA FM, GOMEZ ML, LARROSA JM, PABLO L, FERNANDEZ J, POLO V, TORRON C.
Dept Ophthalmology. Hospital "Miguel Servet". Zaragoza. Spain.

Purpose: To evaluate the efficiency of the structural , electrophysiological and psychophysical tests in the early diagnosis of glaucoma.

Methods: 60 eyes with suspected glaucoma, without visual field defects, were underwent a retinal nerve fiber layer evaluation, a pattern-electroretinogram and a short-wavelength automated perimetry.

Results: The follow-up ranged from 27 to 97 months. At the end of this time, 11 eyes showed glaucomatous visual field defects. Eight of these eyes had the 3 tests pathological at the beginning of the study, and 3 eyes had 2 test abnormal. The patients with glaucomatous changes were older and the follow-up longer than the suspected cases.

Conclusions: The use of different stuructural, electrophysiological and psychophysical tests increases tour ability to detect early glaucomatous damage.

442

THE USE OF OPTICAL COHERENCE TOMOGRAPHY IN THE DIAGNOSIS OF GLAUCOMA.

CARBONEZ G., STALMANS P., GOETHALS M., LEYS A., SPILEERS W.
Dept. of Ophthalmology, KU Leuven, Belgium

Purpose: Optical Coherence Tomography (OCT) enables the measurement of the retinal fiber layer (NFL) thickness. A circular scan around the optic disc allows the measurement of the NFL thickness in different regions around the disc. Repeated assessments of the NFL thickness were performed in normal and glaucomatous eyes and the reproducibility of the measurements was evaluated. **Methods:** We studied 20 eyes of 20 subjects using OCT: 10 normal control subjects and 10 glaucoma patients. Normal patients underwent two series of scans, each consisting of two scans around the optic disc. Glaucoma patients were submitted to one session consisting of two scans. Each scan was performed by using internal fixation (fixation with the same eye was used). The circular scan could be divided in 4 quadrants (superior, inferior, temporal and nasal). For each quadrant an integrated NFL thickness was computed. Reproducibility was defined as the extent to which the measurement could be reproduced (expressed in %). **Results**: Reproducibility was higher in normal eyes compared to glaucomatous eyes (93% versus 76%). Inter-visit measurements provided a slightly higher degree of reproducibility than intra-visit measurements (97% versus 93%). Nasal quadrant measurements are significantly more difficult to reproduce than the three other quadrants. **Conclusion:** Measurement of the NFL thickness provided by OCT combined with automated image analysis promises to be an objective and reproducible assessment of glaucoma onset and progression.

443

REPRODUCIBILITY OF PLANIMETRIC OPTIC NERVE HEAD ANALYSIS WITH SCANNING LASER OPHTHALMOSCOPE

LARROSA JM, POLO V, PABLO LE, GOMEZ ML, HONRUBIA FM.
Dept Ophthalmology. Hospital "Miguel Servet". Zaragoza. Spain.

Purpose: To determine the variability of disc and cup area measurements in digital images obtained with scanning laser ophthalmoscope.

Methods: 10 sets of images of 4 optic discs (normal, myopic, ocular hypertensive and glaucomatous) were obtained with the Rodenstock scanning laser ophthalmoscope. Images focussed at different depths were used by 2 operators (with and without experience in planimetry) to determine the disc and cup areas by means of an image analysis program. This study was performed in 10 images obtained from the same optic nerve (inter-image analysis) and 10 times in the same image of each optic nerve (intra-image analysis).

Results: The variability of all the measurements was under 5%. Disc area measurements were lower than cup area determination. The experienced operator obtained lower variability. The myopic optic disc images were less reproducible than the other groups of images.

Conclusions: The planimetric analysis of optic nerve head digital images obtained with scanning laser ophthalmoscope is reproducible and allows quantification of optic nerve head areas.

444

GDX NEW PARAMETERS TO DETECT PRECOX GLAUCOMATOUS DAMAGE

SCOROLLI LG., SCOROLLI L., SCALINCI S.Z., MECONI S., MEDURI R..
Department of Physiopathologic Ottica, University of Bologna, Bologna (Italy)

Purpose: to confirm the difference in "retardation" between glaucomatous and not glaucomatous eyes, and to search other parameters of predictability.

Methods: 30 healthy eyes (mean age 59+-8) and 30 glaucomatous eyes (mean age 65+-) were studied (mean of 3 acquisitions).

Fifteen eyes with a confirmed nasal defect (humphrey 30-2 treshold) were examined with GDX undercompared with normal group.

Results: all the glaucomatous eyes showed a grater retardation, expecially in sup/inf quadrants. The more significative statistic resulted "simmetry"; "ratios" and the " number"; disputable all the others parameters all the nasal defects found confirmation in our personal analysis of morphology of the retardation histogram. The stadiation of the risk is under study.

Conclusions: the GDX offers a moltitude of informations that need a standardization.

We believe that an accurate observation of the retardation curv could avoid contradictory diagnosis.

445

RISK FACTORS FOR OPEN ANGLE GLAUCOMA: A NESTED CASE CONTROL STUDY

KAIMBO WA KAIMBO D[1], BUNTINX F[2], MISSOTTEN L[3]

1 Dept of ophthalmology, University of Kinshasa (D.R. Congo)
2 Clinical Epidemiology Unit, KULeuven (Belgium)
3 Dept of Ophthalmology, KULeuven.(Belgium)

Purpose: to identify possible risk factors associated with open-angle glaucoma (OAG). Design: a case-control study nested within a cohort of consecutive patients seen at an eye clinic. Data on demographic, anthropometric and, diet habits as well as medical characteristics were collected from 142 patients by medical examination and interview.

Patients and Methods: 40 consecutive patients with OAG and 104 controls chosen randomly between all consecutive non OAG patients seen at the University Department of Ophthalmology and general private practice of ophthalmology, both in the city of Kinshasa. Odds ratio for the relation between OAG and age, sex, ethnicity, family history of Glaucoma, the length of stay in Kinshasa, body mass index, hypertension, diabetes mellitus, smoking, alcohol,and diet habits were calculated. Adjusted odds ratio resulting from stepwise logistic regression.

Results: Family history of glaucoma, age, body mass index, hyperopia, Mongo ethnic group and consumption of rice conferred a significantly greater risk of OAG.

Conclusions: this study seems confirm that Mongo ethnic group is associated with an increased risk of OAG.

446

OCULAR BLOOD FLOW AFTER TOPICAL BRIMONIDINE THERAPY. A COLOR DOPPLER STUDY

CELLINI M, PELLE D, ROSSI A, MORETTI M.
Institute of Ophthalmology - University of Bologna (Italy)

Purpose: To assess the effects of brimonidine an alpha 2-agonist on intraocular pressure and blood circulation in normal eyes.
Methods: The effects of topical brimonidine 0.2% on intraocular pressure and ophthalmic and posterior ciliary arteries blood speed were measured in a group of 30 healthy volunteers. The patients underwent IOP evaluation with pneumotonometry and color Doppler imaging (CDI) of the ophthalmic artery, central retinal artery and posterior ciliary arteries with peak systolic velocity (PSV) and resistent index (RI) evaluation.
Results: The intraocular pressure was reduced of 12% in brimonidine 0.2%-treated eyes and of 2% in placebo-treated eyes ($p<0.005$).
Before and after treatment with brimonidine 0.2% the ophthalmic artery data were as follows: PSV 38.580±1.627 cm/sec vs 38.680±1.640 cm/sec ($p<0.168$); RI 0.0.646±0.010 vs 0.643±0.008 ($p<0.111$). The results for the central retinal artery were PSV 14.100±1.235 vs 14.300±1.520 cm/sec ($p<0.210$); RI 0.623±0.010 vs 0.630±0.009 ($p<0.175$) and in posterior ciliary arteries were PSV 14.260±0.435 cm/sec vs 14.570±0.519 cm/sec ($p<0.017$); RI 0.654±0.14 vs 0.643±0.012 ($p<0.001$).
Conclusion: Topical administration of brimonidine 0.2%, an alpha 2-agonist drug which acts at a vascular and neuronal level, in normal eyes reduces the IOP and improves the blood flow in the posterior ciliary arteries.

447

A STUDY COMPARING PRESSION OCULAR MEASURES WITH TONOPEN AND MANOMETRY IN RABBITS

A Lauretti F; E Romão; MLV Rodrigues, CR Lauretti;
Dep. Ophthalmology, Ribeirão. Preto- USP (Brazil)

Purpose: Evaluation of Tonopen in measures of ocular pressure in rabbits.
Methods: 5 rabbits were anesthetized with 0.5% ketamine IV, the randomized eye was cannulated, and connected to a polygraph, registering the IOP continuously. The system was connected to a bottle with saline and heparin with a mercury manometer and air insuflator. The intraocular pressure was elevated to different values (5mmHg to 40mmHg) by manometry and measured with Tonopen each interval of 5mmHg.
Results .The values of measures with Tonopen were always below the manometric values , (media of -2.7 mmHg)
Conclusions The data suggest that Tonopen underestimates the values of intraocular pressure in rabbits.

448

PROPOFOL DECREASES THE RABBIT INTRAOCULAR PRESSURE IN A BIPHASIC DOSE-RELATED WAY

CR Lauretti; A Lauretti F; E Romão, GR Lauretti; MLV Rodrigues
Dep. Ophthalmology, Ribeirão. Preto- USP (Brazil)

Purpose :In our previous study, a low dose propofol infusion resulted in decrease in ocular pressure, quick in onset and unrelated to the blood pressure and heart rate in outpatients. This study was conducted to examine the effect of intravenous (IV) propofol (PPF) on the IOP in rabbits.
Methods: 12 rabbits were anesthetized with 0.5% ketamine IV, the eye and the carotid were cannulated, and connected to a polygraph, registering the IOP continuously. The IOP was increased to 30 mmHg and the descending IOP curve registered after drug, injection at 7-minute interval, in the order: 1) IV saline; 2) 0.1 mg/kg IV PPF; 3) 0.3 mg/kg IV PPF; 4) 0.9 mg/kg IV PPF; and 5) 2.7 mg/kg IV PPF.
Results.: IV propofol decreased the IOP in a biphasic dose-related way ($p<0.001$). In the first 10 seconds, there was a correspondent decrease in the mean arterial blood pressure (MAP) ($p<0.01$). In the following period (10-70 seconds), the MAP returned to initial values ($p>0.05$), but the IOP kept a constant decrease.
Conclusions: The data suggest that in the first 10 seconds, propofol has decreased the IOP through venodilatation, causing an increase of the aqueous humour coefficient outflow by increasing the ratio of the vase at forth potency, according to Poiseuille 's law.

449

NYCTOHEMERAL VARIATIONS OF INTRA-OCULAR PRESSURE IN 11 NORMOTENSIVE GLAUCOMATOUS PATIENTS

MAURENT K[1], BRU M[1], ROMANET JP[1], MASELLA JJ[1], MOUILLON M[1], BUGUET A[2]
1 - Service d'Ophtalmologie, CHU de Grenoble (France)
2 - Centre de Recherche du Service de Santé des Armées (la Tronche - France)

Purpose: The authors present the analysis of eleven nycthohemeral curves of intra-ocular pressure (IOP) over 24 hours in a population of 11 patients suffering from a normotensive glaucoma, in order to analyse the circadian rhythm of IOP in these patients, and the relationship between IOP, sleep stages, and blood pressure.
Methods: 11 caucasian patients (8 females, 3 males) ranged in age from 50-75 years. All patients presented a normotensive glaucoma, with normal values of daytime IOP (IOP < 21 mmHg 8:00 am, noon, 6:00 pm). IOP measures were performed hourly during 24 hours with a Tonopen XL® Sleep stages and blood pressure were recorded by polyhypnography (Medilog® 9000 II) and holter.
Results: The IOP's curves showed two peaks in the morning, and at the beginning of sleep, with a circadian rhythm of IOP.
Conclusions: As high IOP glaucomatous patients, normotensive glaucomatous patients had change of their circadian rhythm of IOP, but they kept a nocturnal acrophase as healthy subjects.

450

CLINICAL EVALUATION OF DEEP SCLERECTOMY.

HONRUBIA FM, GOMEZ ML, PABLO LE, POLO V, LARROSA JM, TORRON C.
Dept Ophthalmology. Hospital "Miguel Servet". Zaragoza. Spain.

Purpose: To evaluate the outcome, complications and short-term results of deep sclerectomy for open-angle glaucoma treatment.
Methods: 21 glaucomatous eyes underwent a deep sclerectomy procedure. The mean age was 68,72 years old. The surgical technique was described by Koslov et al, using collagen material to help the aqueous outflow. The preoperative mean intraocular pressure (IOP) was higher than 25 mm Hg in all the cases.
Results: 3 months after surgery 16 eyes had an IOP < 19 mmHg (84%), although only 9 eyes did not require medical treatment, 4 eyes required YAG application on the filtration area and, in 3 eyes the surgical procedure failed to control the IOP, and the patient had to be programmed for a new surgical procedure.
Conclusions: Although these preliminary results are promising, in our experience, the outcome is not better than tradicional trabeculectomy procedures, although the complications are minimal.

451

NON PENETRATING DEEP SCLERECTOMY IN PRIMARY OPEN-ANGLE GLAUCOMA

SANCHEZ-SALORIO M[1,2], PEREZ V[1], CAPEANS C[1], RODRIGUEZ-ARES MT[1], PAZOS B[2],
1. Dpto. Ophthalmology. University of Santiago de Compostela. Complejo Hospitalario Universitario de Santiago (Spain)
2. Fundación Instituto Gallego de Oftalmología. Santiago de Compostela (Spain)

Purpose
The aim of this study to evaluate the middle-term results in basis of intraocular pressure of patients who undergo non-penetrating deep sclerectomy, a new filtering surgery technique which is presented as an alternative to classic trabeculectomy in the management of primary open-angle glaucoma.
Methods
After marking a conjunctival flap based in limbus and a superficial scleral flap we realize ablation of the underlying sclera taking away the external wall of Schlemm´s channel chamber to the remaining descemet layout can be seen. Topical mytomicin-A is then applied with the help of a surgical sponge. 18 eyes from 15 patients presenting primary open-angle glaucoma and whose intraocular pressure was not under control even with the maximal topical visual acuity determination, slit-lamp examination, gonioscopy and intraocular pressure determination were performed days 1,4 and 7 and months 1,2,3,6,9 and 12 after surgery. All surgical procedures were performed by the same surgeon.
Results
The postoperative values of intraocular pressure were 30,5 ± 8,5 mmHG. The mean follow-up was 7,03 ± 2,3 months. Mean age was 70,5 ± 8,5 years. Intraocular presure values at the end of evaluation was about 16,5 ± 4,7 mmHg. Best-corrected visual acuity does not become medified. There werw no inflammatory signs in anterior chamber. At the end of the study 69,2% of the patients remain well controlled without pharmacological therapy and 7,7% receive therapy with one drug. During the realization of the surgical procedure we experimented 5 perforations (27,7%). In any case we were able no observe those complications typical of trabeculectomy (chronie hypotomy, hypotonic maculopathy, flat anterior chamber, hypema, cataract or choroidal detachment).
Conclusion
Non penetrating deep sclerectomy can be a alternative to trabeculectomy in primary open-angle glaucoma.

452

NON PENETRATING DEEP SCLERECTOMY: USE OF A CORNEAL COLLAGEN SHIELD AS A NEW DRAINAGE DEVICE

SANCHEZ-SALORIO M[1,2], CAPEANS C[1], PAZOS B[2], RODRIGUEZ-ARES MT[1], PEREZ V[1]
1. Dpto. Ophthalmology. University of Santiago de Compostela. Complejo Hospitalario Universitario de Santiago (Spain)
2. Fundación Instituto Gallego de Oftalmología. Santiago de Compostela (Spain)

Purpose
To report the use of a fragment of corneal collagen shield as a drainage device in deep sclerectomy (DS)
Methods
Ten eyes with open angle glaucoma were operated on DS. A fragment of the shield was placed under the scleral flap. Clinical and ultrasound biomicroscopy evaluations were performed 15, 30 and 90 days after surgery.
Results
Postoperative IOP decreased significantly in all ten cases from a preoperative mean value of 35 ± 8,5 mmHg to postoperative (3 months) of 16,2 ± 4,2 mmHg. In all six cases ultrasound biomicroscopy showed clearly the separation of the scleral flap from the floor of the sclerectomy. The height of the cavity depend of the quantity of the material used. Initial images showed ECOS that corresponded to the collagen strip. In later controls these ecos disappeared leaving a empty cavity. In one case in which the space was totaly occupied by the implant the ECOS could be seen still two months after surgery.
Conclusion
The device is safe, cheap and has no adverse side effects.

453

EARLY HISTOLOGICAL CHANGES IN DIODE LASER SCLEROSTOMY

B.MELCON, A. SANCHEZ, FJ. FERNANDEZ, R. ALVAREZ, M. PUEYO, FM. HONRUBIA.
DEPARTMENT OF OPHTHALMOLOGY. MIGUEL SERVET HOSPITAL. ZARAGOZA. SPAIN.

Purpose: To assess early histological changes following ab externo diode laser sclersotomy in the rabbit eye.

Material and method: Twelve New Zealand albino rabbits underwent ab externo sclerostomy in one eye (right eye). The energy source employed was a diode laser. Two sclerostomies were performed in every case in the temporal superior quadrant. Three animals were sacrified with an intravenous Pentobarbital inyection on days 2, 4, 7 and 11 after surgery. Treated eyes were enucleated and submitted for light microscopic processing.

Results: Two days after surgery all the eyes showed patent transscleral fistulas. The sclerostomy is at that moment sorrounded by two distinct layers: a layer of highly damaged colagenous tissue, representing an area of severe thermal insult (average: 28 μm) and another characterized by a marked swelling and moderate colagenous damage (average: 558 μm). On day 4 the two areas are still present. Fibroblasts are observed in the margins of the sclerostomy. On days 7 and 11 fibroblasts invade the treated area. The layer of highly damaged collagen is reduced and fragmented. Two sclerostomies were patent on day 7 and one on day11.

Conclusion: Diode laser sclerostomy induces the presence of two distinct areas of collateral thermal damage. The layer of intensely heat-damaged tissue is removed in the early phases after surgery.

This project was supported by the FIS (Fondos Investigación Sanidad) (grant FIS 98/1494)

454

AB EXTERNO DIODE LASER SCLEROSTOMY:LONG TERM IOP EVOLUTION.

B.MELCON, A. SANCHEZ, FJ. FERNANDEZ, T. BADA, I. GONZALEZ, FM. HONRUBIA.
DEPARTMENT OF OPHTHALMOLOGY.MIGUEL SERVET HOSPITAL. ZARAGOZA. SPAIN.

Purpose: Proliferation of fibroblast has proven to be a principal mechanism in conventional filtering surgery failure. The aim of laser sclerostomy is to reduce scarring and to prolong filter function. The purpose of this work was to evaluate the efficacy of diode laser in ab externo sclerostomy in an experimental animal model.

Methods: Thirty-four New Zealand albino rabbits underwent diode laser ab externo laser sclerostomy in one eye remaining the fellow eye as unoperated control. The laser was set at 2500 mW and 500 ms. Intraocular pressure was monitored for 60 days after surgery.

Results: In all cases 2 adyacent full-thickness sclerostomies were achieved. IOP was reduce in treated eyes more than a 20% of control values during 15,5 days after the procedure althought filtering blebs disappeared within 7 days. Corneal thermal damage was the main intraoperative complication.

Conclusion: Diode laser is an effective energy source in ab externo sclerostomy. More studies are necessary to improve the efficacy of the procedure with the association of substances to delay scar formation or by modifications of the technique.

This project was supported by the FIS (Fondos Investigación Sanidad) (grant FIS 98/1494).

455

CILIARY ABLATION. COMPLICATIONS.

Pueyo M, Honrubia FM, Melcon B, Gonzalez I, Sanchez A, Fernandez J, Albalad E.
Department of Ophthalmology. Hospital Miguel Servet. Zaragoza. Spain.

Purpose: This study carries out and clinical and histological analysis of the complications observed after transscleral contact cyclophotocoagulation by diode laser.

Methods: Sixty pigmented rabbits underwent transscleral contact cyclophotocoagulation by diode laser in one eye, and then they were divided randomly into three groups. The rabbits received 15 applications of laser at 270° at a distance of 0.5 mm from the limbus. 0.9, 1.8, and 2.7 J were used according to group. The study lasted 80 days.

Results: We noticed an increase in the number and intensity of the anterior chamber inflammatory signs and the hypertensive crisis as the energy level applied increased. In addition, it is noteworthy that there were two scleral perforations in the group treated with 2,7 J.

Conclusions: There is a relationship between the application of higher energy levels and a higher incidence of complications both in quantitative and qualitative terms. Further research on diode cyclophotocoagulation is necessary to determine the optimum technique for producing as few undesirable effects as possible.

456

REFRACTORY GLAUCOMA. TREATMENT.

Pueyo M, Honrubia FM, Pablo LE, Gomez ML, Melcon B, Sanchez A, Fernandez J.
Department of Ophthalmology. Hospital Miguel Servet. Zaragoza. Spain.

Purpose: To evaluate the clinical effectiveness of contact transscleral cyclophotocoagulation with diode laser.

Methods: Twenty-one eyes with glaucoma refractory were treated with the IRIS OcuLight SLx diode laser system and the IRIS G-Probe (600 μm optic fiber). All eyes were treated with 15 spots over 270ª, 1 mm posterior to the limbus, using 3.0 J (1.0 W X 3.0 sg). The mean follow-up was 22,24 ± 9,89 months (from 12-45 months).

Results: Intra-ocular pressure was controlled at 21 mmHg or below in 47,62 % of the patients. 75 % of the painful glaucoma were painless after the laser treatment. Visual acuity decreased in 5 eyes (23,81 %). Chronic uveitis occurred in two eyes (9,52 %). No case of scleral perforation, or hypotony were observed.

Conclusions: The contact transscleral cyclophotocoagulation with diode laser is efficient to reduce intraocular pressure in refractory glaucoma.

457

AB EXTERNO LASER DIODE SCLEROSTOMY AND SILICONE TUBE IMPLANT FOR GLAUCOMA SURGERY

SANCHEZ A, MELCÓN B, PUEYO M, FERNANDEZ FJ, BADA T, HONRUBIA FM.
[1]Ophthalmology Department. Miguel Servet Hospital. Zaragoza. Spain.

Purpose : Aim of this study is to produce a permanent opening at the limbus by laser diode to allow aqueus humor flow to subconjunctival space. Silicone tube-shunt have been implanted to prevent fistula scar closure or iris incarceration.
Methods: Diode laser ab externo sclerostomy by Iris Medical Instruments, Oculight SLX , operating 2500 mW and 500 ms parameters, were carried out in five rabbits. Multiple laser pulses are applied until full thickness and wide (>200 μm) opening is achieved. Subsequently were implanted an open silicon tube (Silastic 200 μm diameter) with an adhering hydrophilic contact lens material to final open end and finally covered by conjunctiva. This device are designed to produce a posterior or equatorial bleb.
Results: Short-term efficacy (two weeks) is documented, It creates a fistula with minimal surgically induced trauma and minimum postoperative inflammation. Significantly intraocular pressure lowering versus control eye (>20%) were obtain in all cases. Transient peripheral corneal and iris burns, tube-shunt displacement and conjunctiva perforation were complications.
Conclusions : Ab externo laser diode sclerostomy and silicone tube implant for glaucoma surgery is a simple procedure for to create a subconjuntival fistula. Long term follow up experimental studies are needed to further evaluation. It would be a glaucoma surgical option for high risk eyes.

458

TRANSILLUMINATION IN TRANSSCLERAL CYCLOPHOTOCOAGULATION

SCHLOTE T, VÖLKER M, JEAN B and THIEL H-J.
University Eye Clinic Tübingen (Germany)

Purpose To study placement of laser spots in transscleral contact cyclophotocoagulation (TCC) by transillumination.
Methods TCC using a diode laser was performed in fresh, enucleated porcine eyes using different procedures: 1. A standard procedure without visualization of the ciliary body. 2. Laser application into the middle part of the ciliary body after visualization by transillumination. 3. Laser application into the anterior part of the ciliary body.
Results In all groups 110 laser applications were performed. Without visualization, macroscopically visible ciliary body lesions were created in 54.5 % (8.1 % displaced into the iris root). Using transillumination and placement of laser spots into the middle part of the ciliary body, lesions were induced in 40.9% (16.4 % displaced posterior to the ciliary body). Applications into the anterior part of the ciliary body during transillumination resulted in a success rate of 68.2 % (6.5 % posterior to the ciliary body). There was no statistical significant difference between the groups.
Conclusions Transillumination does not increase the efficacy of TCC in normal structured eyes. In the treatment of glaucoma associated with anatomical abnormilities of the eye (e.g.; buphthalmus) transillumination may be a simple, but probably superior method for the application of laser spots.

459

STRUCTURAL CHANGES IN THE CILIARY BODY AFTER DIODE LASER TRANSSCLERAL CYCLOPHOTOCOAGULATION (TSCPC) IN AN EXPERIMENTAL ANIMAL MODEL.

RAMÍREZ AI[1], SHAFIK M[2], SALAZAR[1] JJ, RAMÍREZ[1] JM, TRIVIÑO A[1]
1. Inst. Invest. Oftalmol Ramon Castroviejo. UCM. Madrid (España)
2. Dept. Ophthalmology. Alexandria University (Egypt)

Purpose To study tissue changes and the therapeutic effect after the TSCPC in an experimental model imitating refractory glaucoma, and to try to explain the mechanism of action of this therapeutic method.
Methods 40 pigmentd hybrid rabbits were used in this study. A unilateral experimental glaucoma was induced in 30 rabbits using an enzymatic model of α-chemotrypsin. 10 animales were used as normal control. 20 glaucomatous eyes were treated with diode laser TSCP(Oculolight SLX, IRIS Medical Instr.), applying 16 equidestant impacts at energy level of 1,15 J at 0,5 mm from the limbus.The same treatment was applied unilaterally in the normal control animals. The IOP was monitored daily. Animals were sacrificed at 1 day, 3 days, 1 week, 3 weeks and one month for gross and histological study.
Results The glaucomatous eyes demonstrated significany lowering of the IOP during all the follow up month. The ciliary body demonstrated marked coagulative necrosis and destuction of the ciliary epithelium with extensive intravascular thrombosis. The process of healing strarted from the 2nd week. After one month, the ciliary body demonstrated marked fibrosis and contraction with regeneration of the ciliary epithelium The used energy level produced milder lesions in normal eyes.
Conclusions Diode laser TSCPC is an effective method to control IOP in refractory glaucoma. The energy levels used should be adjusted to suit the glaucomatous eyes. Ciliary epithelium destruction is the main mechanism of this technique. Other secondry mechanisms seem to fortify its action.

460

EVALUATION OF THE BLOOD-AQUEOUS BARRIER ALTERATION AFTER DEEP SCLERECTOMY AND TRABECULECTOMY

PISELLA PJ[1], HAMARD P[2], BOURGES JL[1], SCHEER S[1], LIMON S[1]
1.Dept. Ophthalmology IV. Quinze-Vingts National Ophthalmology Center, Paris (France)
2.Glaucoma Center. Quinze-Vingts National Ophthalmology Center, Paris (France)

PurposeTo evaluate and compare postoperative inflammation after glaucoma surgery as trabeculectomy (Tr) and non penetrating deep sclerectomy (NPDS) with a laser flare meter (LFM). This clinical, non invasive technique studed the alteration of the blood-aqueous barrier by quantifying the aqueous flare *in vivo.*
Methods Measurements with the LFM (Kowa, FM 500) were done before and at 1, 7 and 21 days following surgery in 28 patients (28 eyes). The patients were randomized in 3 groups. Group1 (n=7) was the Tr group, group 2 (n=14) was NPDS group and group 3 (n=7) included patients with combinated surgery, phacoemulsification with NPDS, and served as control.
Results Mean flare values increased significantly at D1 in the 3 groups (respectively, 16.4 ph/ms, 18.6 ph/ms, 32.4 ph/ms) but only in group 1 and 3 at D7 (respectively, 22.8 ph/ms, 9.1 ph/ms, 19.1 ph/ms). At day 21, flare values returned to baseline in the 3 groups. Conclusions Blood-aqueous barrier is altered in all the procedures but NPDS seems to be the less aggressive technique.

461

ARC-SHAPED SCLERAL FLAP IN TRABECULECTOMY AS A SINGLE TECHNIQUE OR AS A COMBINATION WITH IOL IN THE POSTERIOR CHAMBER

TANEV V., KOEV K.
Dept. Ophthalmology, Medical University, Sofia (Bulgaria)

Purpose. An arc-shaped scleral flap is proposed for trabeculectomy as a separate technique and as a part of the triple procedure (TE+ECCE+PC IOL).
Methods. 61 patients (66 eyes), separated in two groups, were operated. On 34 eyes (I group) TE with arc-shaped scleral flap was performed and on 32 eyes (II group) - the triple procedure.
Results. After the trabeculectomy, the measured intraocular pressure was mean 19.21±0.53 mm Hg 1 week after the procedure and 19.05±0 mm Hg 1 year after the procedure, and the visual acuity was mean 6/36 1 week after the procedure and 6/30 1 year after the procedure. After the triple procedure, the measured intraocular pressure was mean 18.77±0.48 mm Hg 1 week after the procedure and 18.66±0.44 mm Hg 1 year after the procedure, and the visual acuity was mean 6/18 1 week after the procedure and 6/15 1 year after the procedure.
Conclusions. The advantages of the arc-shaped flap are: more easier performance, especially of the triple procedure; better adaptation due to the lack of angles in the incision and less astigmatism in the triple procedure.

462

SUBCONJUCTIVAL INJECTION OF TAXOL VS MITOMYCIN-C IN EXPERIMENTAL FILTERING SURGERY.HISTOPATHOLOGICAL FINDINGS

PABLO L[1], ROJO A[2], RAMIREZ T[2], POLO V[1], CUEVAS R[3], LARROSA JM[1], GÓMEZ ML[1]
1. Dept. Ophthalmology. Miguel Servet Hospital. Zaragoza, Spain.
2. Dept. Ophthalmology. Hospital General Soria. Spain.
3 Dept. Ophthalmol. Hospital Reina Sofia. Tudela, Spain.

Purpose: To determine the dosage of Taxol (Tx) with similar histological pattern of action in filtering surgery than Mitomycin-C (MMC).
Methods: the right eyes of 42 pigmented rabbits underwent filtering surgery and a postoperative injection of 0.4 ml containing: 34 micrograms (µgr) of Tx Group I, 68 µgr of Tx Group II, 0.16 mg of MMC Group III. Histological parameters were compared after 58 days, including fistula and optically patent area presence in all the treatment groups (Fisher exact test), A $p<0.05$ was considered as significant for all the analyses.
Results: No significant differences were found between MMC group and Tx groups neither between both Tx groups.
Conclusion: Regarding histological parameters no differences were found among the different study groups.

463

TAXOL AS AN ALTERNATIVE OF MITOMYCIN-C IN EXPERIMENTAL FILTERING SURGERY

ROJO A[2], PABLO L[1], RAMIREZ T[2], POLO V[1], CUEVAS R[3], LARROSA JM[1], HONRUBIA FM[1]
1. Dept. Ophthalmology. Miguel Servet Hospital. Zaragoza, Spain.
2. Dept. Ophthalmology. Hospital General Soria, Spain.
3 Dept. Ophthalmol. Hospital Reina Sofia Tudela, Spain.

Purpose: To determine the dosage of Taxol (Tx) with similar clinical outcome in filtering surgery and less incidence of side-effects than Mitomycin-C (MMC).
Methods: The right eyes of 42 pigmented rabbits underwent filtering surgery and a postoperative injection of 0.4 ml containing: 34 micrograms (µgr) of Tx Group I, 68 µgr of Tx Group II, 0.16 mg of MMC Group III. Clinical parameters were evaluated during 58 days. Clinical signs, intraocular pressure and bleb presence were statistically significant compared in all the treatment groups (Mann-Withney U test), A $p<0.05$ was considered as significant for all the analyses.
Results: Significant differences were found between MMC group and Tx groups mainly during the last explorations regarding intraocular pressure and bleb prominence with a better control in the eyes treated with the antimicrotubular agent. Relevant complications included inflammatory reaction in several eyes of Tx groups.
Conclusion: 34 µgr Tx dosage could be a good alternative to MMC in filtering surgery.

464

MITOMYCIN C-PRAE-INTRA-POSTOPERATIVE ?

SIAROV N, APOSTOLOV V.
GLAUCOMA CLINIC,SOFIA,MEDICAL UNIVERSITY (BULGARIA)

As an alternative to the traditional method of intra-operative application of Mitomycin C, a low dose of this drug was injected subconjunctivally before or after a trabeculectomy in human eyes with end-stage glaucoma. Seventeen patients with failing filters (Group III) were given an injection with 0.01 mg of Mitomycin C (0.25 ml of 0.04 mg/ml solution) into the area of the filtering bleb. In 8 of the cases this procedure alone resulted in restoration of the bleb and in the remaining 9 a subsequent needle revision was required to achieve adequate IOP control. Twelve additional patients (Group I) received 0.02 mg of Mitomycin C (0.25 ml of 0.08 mg/ml solution) into the region of the intended filter 1 week before the operation. The results were compared with the control Group II of 25 consecutive patients who underwent a trabeculectomy with intraoperative application of Mitomycin C 0.04 mg/ml. No conjunctival, corneal, scleral or uveal complications were experienced in neither group. Subconjunctival injection of Mitomycin C appears to be an effective method of administration. These low concentrations seem to be safe for use in human eyes.

ORAL PRESENTATIONS

1111

COATING AND COLONIZATION OF ePTFE POLYMER USED FOR KERATOPROSTHESIS.

MURAINE M[1], LEGEAIS JM[2], DELPECH A[3], DELPECH B[3], SAITER JM[4], DRUBAIX I[2], VANNIER JP[3] and BRASSEUR G[1].
1. Service d'Ophthalmologie, Hôpital C. Nicolle, Rouen (France)
2. Service d'Ophthalmologie, Hôtel DIEU, Paris (France)
3. Laboratoire DIFEMA, Faculté de Médecine, Rouen (France)
4. LECAP, Faculté des Sciences, Mont-Saint-Aignan (France)

Purpose : To define the optimal pre-treatment of hydrophobic polymer ePTFE used for keratoprosthesis in order to promote its colonisation by stromal fibroblasts *in vitro*. This should improve the elaboration of an hybrid-artificial cornea.
Methods : ePTFE was treated *in vitro* either by hyaluronic acid, fibronectin, Albumin or foetal calf serum. Modification of wettability was evaluated using contact angle measurement. Distribution in the polymer was investigated using immunochemistry. Uncoated and coated PTFE were seeded with human keratocytes. Histological observations were performed after 2 or 7 days to evaluate colonisation.
Results : Immersion in ethanol before coating allows tested molecules to enter and deposit into the PTFE. PTFE becomes slightly hydrophilic after coating, specially with fibronectin and reaches 3.5 mJ/m² of surface tension. Coating of PTFE with albumin and hyaluronan induced small adhesion and proliferation. Coating with fibronectin and serum improved strong attachment and proliferation on the PTFE. Unfortunately, colonisation was not evidenced in the thickness of the polymer.
Conclusion : Coating and culture conditions need to be improved to allow better *in vitro* colonisation.

1112

ARE THERE ANY CHANGES IN THE TEAR FILM AFTER UV-EXPOSURE?

Zlateva V.[1], Toncheva R.[1], Tsukahara, Sh.[2], Chen L.[2]
1. Dept. Ophthalmology, Med. University, Sofia, Bulgaria
2. University Eye Clinic, Jamanashi, Japan

Purpose: Electron-microscopic study to try to visualise the tear film along with the corneal epithelium after UV-exposure using freeze-substitition technique.
Methods: The experimental animals (albino "Wistar" rats) were exposed to 280 and 320 nm UV light with different power (30 and 10W) and exposure time. For the freezing technique, the corneas were cut into small pieces in liquefied nitrogen, treated afterwards with 2% osmium tetroxide, absolute acetone and condensed carbon monoxide at t° up to -80°C for 20 h. The samples were afterwards kept at -20°C for 2 h., at -4°C for 2 h. and at room t°. They were included in epoxy resin, cut by an ultramicrotome and observed conventionally.
Results: With the implemented experimental method, certain changes in the microvilli of the corneal epithelium and the glucocalyx are observed. Due to the intimate connection between the corneal surface and the tear film, the change in the normal corneal epithelium morphology after UV-exposure, recorded on all electronograms, produce an unstable tear film.
Conclusions: Numerous surface-active agents and physical factors as UV-rays could alter the tear film morphology and thus produce a chronically unstable tear film.

1113

THE FOURTH SUBTYP OF KERATOCYTES IN HUMAN DONOR CORNEAS

HARTMANN U[1], EHLERS N[2] and WINTER R[1]
[1]Dept. Ophthalmology, Medical School Hannover (Germany)
[2]Dept. Opthalmology, University Eye Clinic Arhus (Denmark)

Purpose To evaluate morphology, variety of types, function, and distribution of keratocytes in fresh and cultured human donor corneas. Methods Twenty human donor corneas were examined directly after enucleation using confocal microscopy. 72 human corneas were evaluated after 3 weeks of incubation in different basal media. Additionally, three-dimensional cultures of keratocytes were established for studies on morphology and molecular mechanisms. Results In cultured corneas there were three subtypes of keratocytes: underneath Bowman's membrane, small keratocytes created a dense, three-dimensional cell network. In the central stroma, mostly pyramidal and star-shaped keratocytes were arranged in parallel layers. The third subtype was observed near Descemet's membrane, where large cells built a tight cell network. In all fresh corneas, a fourth subtype of keratocytes could be identified: long, fusiform-shaped cells perilimbal in all stromal layers. These cells showed a simple structure with small cell bodies and elongated cellular processes, terminating in fine cell cobwebs. This fourth subtype of keratocytes was only observed in fresh corneas, but not in cultured corneas. In the peripher regions, the 3D-cultures presented a cell type very similar to the fourth subtype. Conclusions In the periphery of fresh human donor corneas, a fourth type of keratocytes is existing. This subtype was not observed in cultured corneas and is supposed to work as a kind of stem-cell with the capability to differentiate into other types.

1114

PROTEOGLYCANS AND THE REGULAR PATTERN OF COLLAGEN FIBERS IN THE HUMAN CORNEA

MULLER LJ,[1] PELS E,[1] SCHURMANS L[2] AND VRENSEN G[1]
1)Dept. Morphology, The Netherlands Ophthalmic Research Institute, Amsterdam 2)Dept Ophthalmology,University Leiden, Leiden (The Netherlands)

Purpose: The regular arrangement of collagen fibers in the corneal stroma is thought to be controlled by proteoglycans (PG's). To study this in detail the pattern of PG's in the human cornea was investigated ultrastructurally using quinolinic phtalocyanin (QP) as a selective PG staining.
Methods: After short paraformaldehyde/glutaraldehyde fixation, one half of four corneas of eyes, enucleated because of melanoma, were stained according to Scott with or without 50% E-PTA (to enhance contrast) before processing for light and electron microscopy. The other halves were osmicated and served as controls.
Results: The overall contrast of QP/E-PTA stained tissue is low, but sufficient to study PG's. In cross-sections (anterior-posterior) PG's connecting collagen fibers are arranged in an oblique pattern. In contrast in tangential sections, parallel to the surface, PG's are mainly arranged perpendicularly to the collagen fibers.
Conclusions: The arrangement of PG's in different planes of the stroma suggests that higher forces are needed to move collagen fibers in the central-peripheral than in the anterior-posterior direction. This may explain why corneas swell in the anterior-posterior direction without changing the curvature.

Scott JE and Haig M. J Anatomy 158: 95-108, 1988.

1115

STABILITY OF CORNEAL THICKNESS IN SUBJECTS MORE THAN 45 YEARS OF AGE

ASTIN CLK.
Dept. Vision Sciences, Aston University, Birmingham (UK).
Dept. Ophthalmology, Birmingham Heartlands Hospital (UK).

Purpose To assess corneal thickness variations over time in two groups of subjects more than 45 years of age.

Methods Optical pachymetry was performed on 5 corneal regions (superior, central, inferior, nasal, temporal) every 2 weeks for 14 weeks. Group A (n=13) subjects were awaiting cataract extraction on the fellow eye. Group B (n=10) subjects had good visual acuity. All had good general health.

Results The central cornea had a thickness value significantly less than that in other regions ($F=9.17$, $df=4,60$, $p=0.01$).
One way ANOVA on changes from original value showed time effect was not significant ($p<0.05$) for both groups. Further analysis using ANOVA indicated apparent overall thickness changes in the superior and central regions of group A ($p=0.004$). This change was suspected to be due to less accurate fixation related to mild lens opacities.

Conclusions In these groups corneal thickness values remained stable over 14 weeks. The results act as a baseline for comparison in further studies of similar subjects undergoing treatments. Good fixation during measurements is important.

1116

A NEW APPROACH TO OPTIMISED CORNEAL CRYOPRESERVATION

CANALS M[1], MIRALLES A[2], POTAU JM[1], COSTA J[1] and GARCIA J[2].
1.Ocular Morphology Unit. University of Barcelona (Spain).
2. Department of Cryobiology. Cancer Research Institute. Barcelona (Spain)

Purpose
To set up an improved cryopreservation protocol that should be suitable for human corneas.

Methods
Endothelial viability was tested in 264 New Zealand rabbit corneas after using different cryopreservation solutions in combination with different cooling rates and different thawing speeds. Endothelial viability was assessed by tissue culturing, vital staining and scanning electron microscopy after all steps involved in the cryopreservation process.

Results
Maximum cell survival was achieved when using Me2SO or PROH at a 10% concentration, with direct addition and dilution of the cryoprotectant, a 1°C/min cooling rate and thawing at 37°C. After the complete cryopreservation process, endothelial cell densities were 1951 cells/mm^2 with no dead cells (Me2SO) and 1553 cells/mm^2 and 1% dead cells when using PROH.

Conclusions
Cryopreservation of rabbit corneas with the protocol designed shows endothelial viability close to acceptable limits.

1121

TRANSGENES AND MUTANTS EXPRESSED IN LENS: TOOLS FOR THE STUDY OF CATARACT

BLOEMENDAL H,[1] BENEDETTI E.L[2] and DUNIA I.[2]
1. Dept. of Biochemistry, University of Nijmegen (The Netherlands)
2. Institut Monod du CNRS, Universit́e de Paris VII (France)

Since a long time many different conditions that lead to cataract have been known. One of the causes of the initiation of lens opacification, discovered about a decade ago, is the overexpression of transgenes in lens. It seems that the nature of the coding part of a transgene does not matter as long as the promoter of a gene construct drives the gene into the lens. Common features of the consequences of overexpression are: inhibition of the dencucleation process and interference with lens fiber cell differentiation. A survey of typical examples from the literature and our own investigations will be given.

1122

COMMON PATHWAY OF CATARACT FORMATION BY MUTANT GAMMA CRYSTALLINS WITH TRUNCATED FOURTH GREEK KEY MOTIFS.

R.A.QUINLAN[1], A.SANDILANDS[1], A. M. HUTCHESON[1], S. MASAKI[2], J. GRAW[3], G.F.J.M. VRENSEN[4] AND A.R.PRESCOTT[1].
1. Dept of Biochemistry, The University of Dundee (Scotland)
2. Dept. of Biochemistry, Institute for Developmental Research, Kasugai. (Japan)
3. Genetics, GSF-National Research Center for Environment and Health. (Germany)
4. Morphology Dept., Netherlands Ophthalmic Research Institute. (The Netherlands)

Purpose. Gamma crystallins are structural proteins which are important in lens transparency. Mutations in these proteins cause lens cataract both in mouse and man. In the mouse mutants, Cat2 and Elo, the γ-crystallin mutations resulted in microphthalmia, retardation of lens cell differentiation as well as lens cataract. The underlying mechanism leading to the disruptions caused by such γ-crystallin mutations has yet to be discovered and is the purpose of this study.
Methods. The mouse muatants *Cat2* ^{nop} *, and Cat2* ^{t} were established either on the particular genetic background of (102/E1xC3H/El)F_1 hybrids or were backcrossed to the strain 102/E1. Rabbit polyclonal antibodies to mutant γ-crystallin proteins *Cat2* ^{nop} and *Elo* were raised and used to detect mutant proteins in affected lenses and transfected cells. The transcriptional and translational effects were monitored by RT-PCR, by immunohistochemistry and by immunoblotting.
Results. Both mutant γ-crystallin proteins *Cat2* ^{nop} and *Elo* were detected in the lenses of affected mice during early stages of lens development. The mutant proteins concentrated in the nuclei of the central fibre cells in both *Cat2* ^{nop} and *Elo* lenses. Transcription of some, but not all lens proteins were affected and resulted in reduced protein levels.
Conclusions. Mutations in the fourth Greek key of γB-crystallin (*Cat2* ^{nop}) and γE-crystallin (*Elo*) do not destabilise the proteins. The mutant proteins now occupy a completely different cellular compartment, namely the nucleus. Disruption of nuclear organisation results, leading to the inhibition of the transcription of lens fibre cell specific genes. We propose that it is these effects upon transcription which causes microphthalmia and retardation of lens cell differentiation in these mutants.

1123

IMMUNOCYTOCHEMISTRY OF EYE LENS AND CATARACTOGENESIS

DUNIA, I.[1], GONG, X. H.[2], KUMAR, N.[2], GILULA, N. B.[2], BLOEMENDAL, H.[3] and BENEDETTI, E. L.[1,3]
1. Institute J. Monod CNRS-Paris University, (France).
2. Dept. Cell Biology, The Scripps Research Institute, La Jolla, (USA).
3. Dept. of Biochemistry, Nijmegen University, (The Netherlands).

Ultrastructural and immunocytochemical analyses of eye lens from transgenic mice expressing mutated genes coding for cytoskeletal and membrane constituents indicated that the accumulation of the transgene products generates abnormal cytoskeletal and membrane organization leading to cataract. The targeted deletion of a lens fiber connexin (knock-out mice for connexin α3), was also followed by lens opacification (Gong et al., Cell, **91**, 833-843, 1997). SDS-fracture labeling and confocal microscopy show that the common structural markers present in both transgenic and knock-out mice lenses are the disruption of communicating junctions and the appearence of extensive membrane domains characterized by orthogonal lattice of repeating subunits comprising MP26 and connexins. Our experimental data unequivocally point to the relevance and direct implication of the lens plasma membrane and cytoskeleton abnormalities on cataractogenesis.

1124

GENETIC DISSECTION OF EYE ABNORMALITIES IN THE MOUSE

FAVOR J[1], NEUHÄUSER-KLAUS A[1], SANDULACHE R[1], STAMBOLIAN D[2], GRIMES P[2] and LYON MF[3].
1. GSF-Inst of Mammalian Genetics, Neuherberg (Germany)
2. Dept. Ophthalmology, U Pennsylvania, Philadelphia (USA)
3. MRC-Mammalian Genetics Unit, Harwell (UK)

Purpose To identify genes involved in eye development.

Methods F_1 offspring of mutagenized parental mice were examined by slit lamp biomicroscopy for eye abnormalities. Mutations were mapped relative to microsatellite markers. Based on chromosomal position candidate genes were identified and the mutations characterized by sequencing the corresponding cDNA.

Results We have identified and maintained a total of 170 independent mutations. To date 60 mutations have been mapped to 28 loci. The affected gene has been identified for a number of mutations including *Pax2*, *Pax6*, *Mip*, *Lim2*, *Cx50*.

Conclusions Our collection of mouse eye mutations represents a valuable resource to genetically dissect and study those loci which affect eye development.

1131

CELL PROLIFERATION IN THE HUMAN FETAL VENTRICULAR ZONE AND PIGMENT EPITHELIUM

KOSMIN AS[1], GRIERSON I[2], D van Velzen[3]
Depts. of Experimental Ophthalmology and Fetal Pathology, Liverpool University, (United Kingdom)

Purpose: Comparison of the pattern and duration of cell proliferation in the human fetal pigment epithelium and neuroretinal ventricular zone. **Method:** Sagittal sections of 17 wax embedded normal human fetal eyes and 1 eye from a 3.5 month neonate were cut to include both the optic nerve and retina. Immunohistochemistry was performed on sequential sections using antibodies against the proliferation markers, Ki-67 and proliferating cell nuclear antigen. Sections were assessed using light microscopy and computerised perimetry. **Results:** In early specimens proliferation was found to occur over the whole length of the ventricular zone and pigment epithelium. As gestation progressed, a centrifugal wave of cessation of proliferation was observed in the pigment epithelium which narrowly preceded a similar wave in the ventricular zone. By 31 weeks, proliferation in both layers was restricted to the far retinal periphery and was last detected at 35 weeks. **Conclusions:** This study has shown similar centrifugal trends in proliferative behaviour in the human fetal pigment epithelium and overlying ventricular zone. The close temporo-spatial relationship suggests that cessation of proliferation in the ventricular zone may be regulated by the pigment epithelium.

1132

EZRIN IN THE RETINAL PIGMENT EPITHELIUM OF THE HUMAN AND VERTEBRATE EYE

KIVELÄ T,[1] JÄÄSKELÄINEN J,[2] VAHERI A,[3] CARPEN O[4]
Departments of [1]Ophthalmology, [2]Neurosurgery, [3]Virology, and [4]Pathology, University of Helsinki (Finland)

Purpose: To localize in the RPE ezrin, a phosphoprotein that tethers actin microfilaments to cell membrane proteins, especially in polarised epithelia.
Methods: 7 fetal human eyes (gestational week, 14 to 28), 9 normal adult human eyes, 9 eyes with a uveal melanoma, and eyes from several vertebrates were studied using the avidin-biotinylated peroxidase complex (ABC) method and mAb 3C12 to ezrin.
Results: Ezrin gradually appeared in developing human RPE from the 14th week of gestation onward. The apical cytoplasm and microvilli of the normal adult RPE reacted with mAb 3C12, but its basal cytoplasm was labeled in reactive RPE cells only. Ezrin was also present in the RPE of the baboon, pig, raccoon dog, cow, and rat, and in these species its basal cytoplasm could also be immunoreactive. MAb 3C12 did not label the avian RPE. In most species, ezrin also localised to basket fibers of Müller's cells.
Conclusions: Ezrin is concentrated in the apical cytoplasm and microvilli of the RPE, which participate in turnover of photoreceptors, making it one candidate gene for causing retinal degenerations.

1133

CD95 (Fas/APO-1) MODULATES DAUNOMYCIN INDUCED APOPTOSIS IN RETINAL PIGMENT EPITHELIAL CELLS

Hueber A,[1] Esser P,[1] Kociok N,[1] Bartz-Schmidt KU,[1] Schraermeyer U[1], Heimann K[1] and Weller M.[2]
1. Dept. of Vitreoretinal Surgery, University of Cologne (Germany)
2. Dept. of Neurology, University of Tübingen (Germany)

Purpose In proliferative vitreoretinopathy, the anthracycline derivate daunomycin is used as a chemotherapeutical adjuvant to vitreoretinal surgery. In this study, we investigated a possible synergism between the induction of the endogenous death program by daunomycin and the CD95 receptor ligand system.

Methods Cell culture experiments were performed using human RPE cells treated with different concentrations of daunomycin with or without the addition of CD95 antibody. Apoptotic cell death was confirmed by in situ DNA end labeling (TUNEL) and comet assay. Nuclear morphology was examined by acridine orange fluorescence microscopy. Quantitative determination of apoptosis was performed by a photometric enzyme immunoassay for cytoplasmatic histone associated DNA fragments. Flow cytometry studies were performed to investigate the regulation of the CD95 ligand and receptor in human RPE cells following exposure to daunomycin.

Results RPE cells were inhibited in a dose dependent manner, when incubated with daunomycin. The typical appearance of apoptotic nuclei including nuclear chromatin condensation could be observed. Exposure of the RPE to daunomycin resulted in strong enrichment of histone associated DNA fragments and comets as an indicator of apoptosis. The simultaneous application of the CD95 antibody lead to a synergistic reduction of cellular proliferation. Daunomycin significantly enhanced the expression of CD95 ligand in RPE cells, whereas the corresponding CD95 receptor was not affected.

Conclusion The proapoptotic synergism between antiproliferative agents and CD95 in RPE cells could lead to a possible reduction of daunomycin in the therapy of proliferative vitreoretinopathy.

1134

Erbium:YAG Laser Ablation of Retinal Tissue in a Perflourocarbon Environment. Determination of Laser - Tissue Interaction in Pig Eyes

WESENDAHL TA [1], FRENZ M [2], JANKNECHT P. [1]
[1] Dept. of Ophthalmology, University of Freiburg, Germany
[2] Institute of Applied Physics, University of Berne, Switzerland

Purpose: The ER:YAG laser emitting light at a wavelenght of 2.94µm has been shown to produce precise tissue ablation which makes it a strong candidate for the ablation of epiretinal and vitreo-retinal membranes (laser-peeling). We evaluated the effects of the ER:YAG laser radiation on the pig retina in perfluorocarbon filled eyes.
Method: We used an experimental in vitro setup to apply laser pulses of various energies to the surface of the pig retina in perfluorocarbon filled eyes. Free running (τ=250µs and τ=500µs) ER:YAG laser energy was transmitted through a zirconium fluoride (ZrF_4) fiber guarded by a quarz tip measuring 400µm and 1 mm in diameter. Probe - retina distance was adjusted to 1 mm and energy was applied in a circular pattern at radii of 3,0 and 5,5 mm. Radiant exposures were set to 1, 3, 5, and 10 J/cm^2 .
Results: Tissue ablation increased proportionally with radiant exposure. 1 J/cm^2, caused a maximum tissue ablation depth of 5 µm. Thermal damage was minimal. 3 J/cm^2 produced an ablation depth of 8- 15 µm, 5J/cm^2 resulted in 12 - 20 µm ablation, and 10J/cm^2 produced 20 - 50 µm ablation ot retinal tissue. A 250µs puls caused distortion of outer photoreceptor segments whereas 500µs produced considerable less damage.
Conclusion: Ablation threshold is below 1 J/cm^2. Two major obstacles need to be addressed. First, the pressure gradient causes damage to photoreceptors and second, the distance between the probe and the retina needs to be controlled more precisely in order to achive high precision tissue ablation.

Anatomy: retina and optic disc

1135

Rdy-MICE WITH HEREDITARY DEGENERATION LOSE ACAID WITH AGE

(Th. NEUHARDT[1], U. WELGE-LÜSSEN[1], C. WAGNER[1], C.A. MAY[1], J.W. STREILEIN[2], E. LÜTJEN-DRECOLL[1])
Dept. of Anatomy II, Erlangen, Germany[1]; The Schepens Eye Research Institute, Boston, USA[2].

Purpose: To determine whether immune privilege is lost from mouse eyes with genetically determined retinal degeneration. **Methods** ACAID experiments were performed in three rodent strains with different forms of inherited retinal degeneration and in different age groups (age range 1 -17 months). The data were compared with those of age-matched controls. In old rdy-mice, which had lost ACAID, corrosion cast preparations of the choroidal vasculature were investigated and the area lacking choriocapillaris (CC) determined. In addition, loss of RPE was evaluated in histological serial sections. The aqueous humor of young and old rdy-mice was investigated for the levels of $TGFß_2$ using ELISA methods. **Results:** ACAID was readily induced by injection of Ovalbumin into the anterior chamber of the eyes of young rodents with neuronal retinal degeneration. In rdy-mice of more than 12 months age, loss of ACAID was accompanied by significant reduction in $TGFß_2$ levels in aqueous humor, and both of these changes correlated with loss of RPE and CC of the central retina. **Conclusion:** Degeneration of the neuronal retina in rdy-mice leads indirectly, but inevitably, to loss of ocular immune privilege by a process that involves deterioration of the ocular immunosuppressive microenvironment. Supported by IZKF, Erlangen, Germany.

1136

IMMUNOHISTOCHEMICAL GLUTAMATE RECEPTOR SUBUNIT LOCALIZATION IN THE RAT RETINA

Jan KLOOSTER and Willem KAMPHUIS
Dept. Morphology, The Netherlands Ophthalmic Research Institute (Amsterdam, The Netherlands)

Purpose Glutamate is the major excitatory neurotransmitter in the retina activating different types of glutamate receptors (GluR). Ionotropic glutamate receptors can be subdivided into three types of receptors, the AMPA, kainate (KA), and NMDA type. To find out which cells in the retina express ionotropic GluRs, an immunohistochemical study using subunit specific antibodies was performed.

Methods Male Wistar rats were perfused with buffered 4% paraformaldehyde. Sections of retinas were incubated with antibodies against subclasses of AMPA (GluR1, 2, 4), KA (GluR5-7) and NMDAR1 receptors. An ABC elite kit was used to visualize the primary antibodies.

Results GluR1 was observed in the ganglion cell layer (GCL), GluR2 in the inner nuclear layer (INL) and GluR4 on the dendrites of the Müller cells. The dendrites of Müller cells showed also GluR 5-7 receptor immunoreactivity. NMDA receptor immunoreactivity was detected in GCL, the inner plexiform layer and in the INL.

Conclusions These results show that AMPA and NMDA receptors are differentically involved in processing visual stimuli. The KA receptors on the Müller cells, however, may be involved in the response to increased extracellular glutamate levels released by the other retinal cells.

1137

A NEW TECHNIQUE TO ANALYSE THE NEURAL-VASCULAR RELATIONSHIP OF HUMAN RETINA IN THREE DIMENSIONS

ZHANG Y, IRELAND G and BOULTON M.
Dept. of Ophthalmology, Manchester University (UK)

Purpose: To develop a new technique to assess the relationship of the vascular and neural retina in three dimensions using confocal laser scanning microscopy.

Methods: Central retina centered at macular region was isolated from fixed normal human eyes. The specimens were stained with immunofluorescent staining for collagen type IV (basement membrane of blood vessels) followed by using propidium iodide (PI) staining for nuclei. Confocal laser scanning microscopy was used to obtain images from both staining in two channels.

Results: Immunofluorescent staining for collagen type IV provided smooth and clear images of all size of the blood vessels. PI staining demonstrated the nuclei of ganglion, inner and outer nuclear layer continuously. Images captured in two channels simultaneously illustrated the relationship of the vasculature and neural retina in situ clearly.

Conclusion: Dual staining of flat mount retina with fluorescent staining for the blood vessel components and nuclei in association with confocal laser scanning microscopy provide a convenient and precise method for analysis the relationship of neural and vascular relation of retina.

1138

THE DEVELOPMENT OF AN IMAGE ANALYSIS SYSTEM TO INVESTIGATE OPTIC NERVE HEAD CONNECTIVE TISSUE DEVELOPMENT

WARDROP DRA, BROTCHIE D, NEEDHAM AD, BIRCH M, HOWARD CV and GRIERSON I.
Unit of Ophthalmology, University of Liverpool (U.K.)

Purpose To use a computerised image analysis system to clarify development of connective tissue (CT) in the human optic nerve head.

Methods Twenty-two foetal optic nerve heads of 15 - 42 weeks gestation were sagittally sectioned at 5 µm. CT localised with Picrosirius Red (PSR) staining was analysed using Aequitas software and percentage areas occupied by CT estimated for the choroido-scleral lamina.

Results At 15 weeks little CT was present except near the hyaloid vessel, and around capillaries in the lamina cribrosa. At 24 weeks, CT was seen in the posterior scleral region, at the edges of the optic nerve head and around the hyaloid artery. From 24 - 42 weeks, CT continued being deposited. The optic nerve's diameter increased over this period as did percentage area of optic nerve head occupied by CT.

Conclusions Deposition of CT may replace space previously occupied by axons that are known to degenerate between 16 and 30 weeks gestation. Improved understanding of this deposition may help clarify events in open-angle glaucoma where axonal loss is also accompanied by optic nerve head architectural changes.
(Supported by the Wellcome Trust)

1141

TENASCIN AND FIBRONECTIN DETECION IN SURGICALLY REMOVED SUBFOVEAL CHOROIDAL NEOVASCULAR MEMBRANES.

Cardillo Piccolino F.[1], Nicolò M.[1], ,Giovannini A.[2], Mariotti C.[2], Zardi L.[3].
1. University Eye Clinic of Genoa, Italy
2. University Eye Clinic of Ancona, Italy
3. Advanced Biotechnology Center, Genoa, Italy

Purpose Tenascin (Tn) and fibronectin (Fn) are two extracellular matrix glycoproteins which participate in the regulation of cell proliferation and migration especially during malignant process and tissue repair. Purpose of this study was to evaluate the distribution of different isoforms of Tn and Fn in choroidal neovascular membranes (CNVM).

Methods Eleven CNVMs were surgically removed from 13 patients (6 with age related macular degeneration, 4 with multifocal choroiditis, 1 with degenerative myopia, 1 post-surgery recurrence and 1 idiopathic). Membranes were placed on a nitrocellulose filter and then snap-frozen in liquid nitrogen. One section from each membrane was stained with hematoxylin and eosin. Immunohistochemistry was performed using a streptavidin-biotin horseradish peroxidase complex. The monoclonal antibodies (MAb) used were BC-1 which recognises the B isoform of Fn (B+.Fn); IST-6,which recognises Fn molecules without the ED-B sequence; BC-2, which binds to alternatively spliced A1 and A4 Fn-like repeats and detect only the high-molecular weight isoform of Tn; BC-4, which binds to EGF-like repeats and detect all isoforms of Tn.

Results Both MAbs against Tn isoforms gave a similar pattern staining. ECM amid the proliferating vessels showed a diffuse and strong positive reaction for both Tn isoforms in all the membranes tested . The cellular component amidst the fibrous tissue did not express Tn. A different pattern of distribution and intensity of the immunostaining for Fn isoforms was observed. A focal B+.Fn isoform expression was found around proliferating vessels in 50% of the CNMs. Whereas B-.Fn isoform was able to stain ECM of all CNMs.

Conclusions To our knowledge this is the first study which evaluated Tn and Fn isoforms expression in surgicallly removed CNVMs. Our results suggest that Tn and ED-B Fn may be specific markers of fibrovascular tissue proliferation.

1142

OCULAR HISTOPATHOLOGICAL MANIFESTATIONS IN CICATRICIAL PEMPHIGOID

RIVAS L, SANZ AI, OROZA MA and TOLEDANO A
Dept Ophthalmology. Hospital Rwn6n y Cajal. Madrid. Spain

Purpose: Cicatricial pemphigoid (CP) is a systemic autoimmune disease affecting, mainly, the basement membranes of ocular and oral mucous membranes, and less in skin. Histopathological finding of OCP include squamous metaplasia, obstruction of glandular ducts, and abundant inflammatory cells. Grade 1 of OCP shows a subepithelial fibrosis. Grade 2 has a fornix foreshortening. Grade 3 presents symblepharon formations. And, the hallmark of grade 4 is the ankyloblepharon and surface keratinization.

Methods: We have studied 32 patients with OCP with clinical tests, laboratory tests, impression cytology, conjunctival biopsy, direct immunofluorescence, and immununohistochemistry.

Results: Patients with grade 1 showed a great number of neutrophils and Langerhans cells. Alterated laboratory tests and mild squamous metaplasia with early goblet cells loss were found. In the 2nd grade, cellular infiltration of the substantia propia, inclunding an increased number of plasma and mast cells were observed. Clinical tests alterations have started in this grade. An increase of IgG, IgA and C4 were found in approximately 75% of patients. Grade 3 showed the start of obstruction of main and meibomian glandular ducts, with aquous tear film alterations. IgG circulating deposition were present in up to 50% of patients. Grade 4 had corneal scarring and ulceration and blindness.

Conclusion: Clinical and laboratory tests, and morphological and immunofluorescence techniques could be useful to help in the diagnosis of a systemic disease as the OCP.

1143

TREATMENT OF EXPERIMENTAL RETINOBLASTOMA WITH REPLICATION DEFECTIVE HERPES SIMPLEX VIRUS MUTANTS

Nicolò[1] M., Cardillo Piccolino[1] F., Chiocca[3] E.A., Cilli[2] M., Corte[2] G., Zingirian[1] M. University Eye Clinic[1] and Advanced Biotechnology Center[2] of Genoa, Italy; Massachusetts General Hospital-Harvard Medical School[3] MA. USA.

Purpose. To investigate herpes virus (HSV) mutants ability to kill retinoblastoma (Rb) cells *in vitro* and *in vivo*.

Methods. Three HSV mutants, defective for γ 34.5 (R3616), ribonucleotide reductase (RR) gene (HRR3) and both γ 34.5 and RR (MGH1) were used to infect Y79 cells in vitro at different multiplicity of infection (m.o.i.). Virus mediated oncolysis was determined by the inability of infected cells to exclude trypan blue dye, while virus replication was measured by LacZ gene expression Experimental Rb were obtained by injecting Y79 cells in the vitreous cavity of 6 *Scid* mice (12 eyes). Thirty days later, one animal was sacrificed, four animals received intraocular injection of MGH1 (10^8 pfu/ml) and one animal was injected with saline as a control. Animals were sacrificed at 3, 7 and 14 days post HSV mutant injections.

Results. All HSV mutants were able to infect, replicate in and kill Y79 cells. MGH1 and R3616 were significantly more efficient than HRR3 at an m.o.i. of 0.1. Histologically, treated Rb showed a progressively higher number of tumor cells in necrosis at 3, 7 and 14 days post MGH1 injection when almost all the tumor was necrotic. Necrosis was absent in the animal sacrificed the same day of mutant injections as well as in the control one. No viral cytopathic effects were observed in normal ocular tissues.

Conclusions. HSV mutants due to their neurotropic properties and ability to replicate only in actively proliferating cells are able to induce short-term necrosis in experimental Rb. This study will provide a rationale for further exploitation of oncolytic herpes viruses as a potential treatment of Rb.

1144

CYTOFLUORIMETRY AND LYMPHOCYTE SUBSETS IN UVEAL MELANOMA: PRELIMINARY RESULTS

FOCOSI F., MANGANELLI C., TURCO S., LOCARNO C.M.
Dept. Ophthalmology, Catholic University – Roma (Italy)

Purpose To evaluate the immunologic behaviour in patients affected by uveal melanoma.

Methods Cytofluorimetry was performed in 16 patients with uveal melanoma (mean age, 61.8 years; 12 females, 4 males) and in an age-matched control group (10 subjects). Follow-up lasted 1 year in 14 cases, 3 and 4 years respectively in 2 cases. Blood samples were collected at 11 a.m., after a light breakfast. Immunologic phenotype study included total lymphocytes, CD4/CD8 ratio and CD3 levels.

Results Total lymphocytes were reduced in 3 cases, within normal limits in 11. CD4/CD8 ratio was reduced in 6 cases, increased in 2 cases and normal in 4 cases. CD3 cells were slightly increased in 2 cases and slightly decreased in 2 cases. The patient followed-up for 3 years showed CD4/CD8 ratio and CD3 within normal limits. The patient examined for 4 years presented a clear reduction of the CD4/CD8 ratio over time, being CD3 normal.

Conclusions. Our preliminary results seem to confirm a great variability of the immunologic behaviour in patients with uveal melanoma. Further studies are required in larger numbers of patients and controls to have a good statistical analysis and diurnal variations of the lymphocyte subsets.

1211

CELLULAR MECHANISMS IN CORNEAL GRAFT REJECTION

VAN DER GAAG R, VAN DER VEEN G and SLEGERS TPAM
Dept Ophthalmo-Immunology, The Netherlands Ophthalmic Research Institute (The Netherlands)

Corneal graft rejection is generally thought to be a process in which T-cells play a central role as mediators of delayed type hypersensitivity reactions (DH) or directly as cytotoxic T-lymphocytes (CTL). Orthotopically placed corneal grafts have been shown to induce systemic immunity. Besides T-cells, macrophages also play an important role in corneal graft rejection. In a rat model with 100% rejection of corneal grafts by day 12, depletion of macrophages in the vicinity of the corneal graft by subconjunctival injection of liposomes containing dichloromethylene diphosphonate resulted in survival of all the corneal grafts beyond 100 days. Immunohistochemical investigation of these treated rats showed significantly reduced cellular infiltration in the both the acceptor corneal rim and the donor corneal button as well as a significant reduction of neovascularization around postoperative day 12. It is not clear whether the acceptance of corneal grafts in these rats was caused by interference with the induction of immunization to donor antigens or by interference with the effector mechanism of graft rejection.
In this overview we will attempt to disclose the role macrophages may play in activation of cytotoxic lymphocytes following corneal transplantation.

1212

MUCOSAL TOLERANCE AS A STRATEGY FOR PREVENTING REJECTION OF CORNEAL GRAFT

FILIPEC M[1], KUFFOVÁ L[1,2] , KRULOVÁ M[2], FORRESTER J V[3] AND HOLAN V[2]

1. Dept. Ophthalmology, Charles University, Prague
2. Institute of Mol. Genetics, Academy of Sciences, Prague
3. Dept Ophthalmology, University of Aberdeen, Aberdeen

Purpose: Immunological rejection is one of the leading causes of corneal allograft failure. To prevent graft rejection we are developing new strategies based on mucosal tolerization of graft recipients.
Methods: Corneas were grafted orthotopically in mice in strain combination with genetic disparity at both MHC and non-MHC antigens. The recipients were treated by peroral or intranasal administration of alloantigens (cells or soluble antigens) using different time and dose schedules. Rejection action was evaluated using scoring system according the intensity of infiltration opacity, edema and neo-vascularization. Immune status of the recipients was tested in vitro in tissue cultures.
Results: All corneal grafts in untreated recipients suffered rejection reaction within 3 weeks after transplantation. Intranasal administration of soluble antigens significantly improved survival of allografts and over 60% of the grafts survived permanently. Soluble antigens were more effective in the induction of tolerance than allogenic cells. In vitro study demonstrated shift to Th 2 type of cytokine response in tolerized recipients.
Conclusions: Mucosal tolerization has been shown as an effective and promising approach for suppression of allograft rejection in corneal transplantation

1221

BLOOD LEVELS OF OXIDATIVE METABOLITES IN A.M.D. PATIENTS

BENCHABOUNE M.[1], THEROND P.[2], FAURE P.[2], MALVY D. [2], BLES N. [3], KOENIG F[1].
1. Hôpital de BELLEVUE, Saint-Etienne, France
2. C.H.U., Le Kremlin-Bicêtre, Grenoble, Bordeaux,France
3. Laboratoire des GRANIONS, Monaco

Purpose To compare blood levels of different metabolites and components of oxidative stress in A.M.D. patients and the general population.
Methods 42 patients were enrolled in a prospective double blind pilot study of Selenium preventive action against AMD decompensation. Blood samples taken at inclusion are compared with a cross-matched population.
Results Both populations were statistically identical in term of age, sex and for different components : seric thiol, selenium, ferritin, glutathion peroxydase as well as for vitamins A,C, E and betacaroten. But some metabolites showed a difference with standard levels:

	AMD	Normal	P
malonaldehyde	3,4 ± 0,7	1,42 ± 0,28	< 0,01
free fatty acids	0,29 ± 0,09	0,25-0,80	< 0,01
proteic carboxyls	0,32 ± 0,14	0,74 ± 0,04	< 0,01

Conclusion Perturbation of seric levels for some oxidative stress metabolites could indicate abnormal lipidic peroxidation Follow-up of these abnormalities will demonstrate if normalization occurs under treatment.

1222

SUPEROXID DISMUTASE ISOENZYMES IN THE HUMAN EYE

B SVENSSON , A BENDIG , STEFAN L MARKLUND AND KURT KARLSSON UMEÅ UNIVERSITY

PURPOSE: We have determined the levels of secreted interstitial located extracellular superoxid dismutase (EC-SOD), the cytosolic copper- and zinc- containing SOD(CuZn-SOD), and the mitochondrial manganese - containing SOD(Mn-SOD) in tears, cornea, sclera, aqueous humour, lens, vitreous body, and retina of the human eye.
METHODS: SOD enzymatic activity was determined by the direct spectrofotometric method using KO2. The amounts of EC-SOD and CuZn-SOD protein were also determined using enzyme – linked immuno absorbant assay.
RESULTS: Tears, aqueous humour and vitreous body contained small amounts of SOD-activity.The lens contained the least SOD-activity 15 fold less then that of the average human tissue. The majority came from CuZn-SOD but the lens also contained considerable amounts of inactive enzyme. There was some Mn-SOD, but the EC-SOD content was neglible. The cornea and sclera contained several times more SOD-activity than the lens, and the EC-SOD contents were equal to or larger then that of CuZn-SOD. The retina contained much CuZn-SOD-activity, but the EC-SOD and Mn-SOD activities were low.
CONCLUSIONS: SOD-activity was found to be low in all occular tissues but retina, sclera and cornea.

1223

EFFECT OF EXCITATORY AMINO ACIDS AND ANTAGONISTS ON NITRIC OXIDE RELEASE FROM THE RABBIT RETINA

NEAL MJ, MATTHEWS KL and CUNNINGHAM JR
Dept Pharmacology, St Thomas' Hospital, London SE1

Purpose To study the glutamate receptors involved in the release of nitric oxide (NO) from the retina.
Methods Rabbits were anaesthetised with urethane (1.5g/kg IP) and an eye cup prepared. Krebs bicarbonate medium was placed in the eye cup and replaced every 10min. NO in the resulting samples was measured using nitrate reductase and a nitric oxide meter.
Results When the dark adapted retina was exposed to glutamate (5mM) the release of NO was increased by 40% ($P<0.001$). The non-selective glutamate antagonist, PDA (5mM) did not block the effect of glutamate on NO release. However, APB (100μM) abolished the effect of glutamate and also, itself, significantly increased NO release. In contrast to APB, PDA alone had no effect on NO release. Kainate (20μM) and NMDA (100μM) both significantly increased the resting release of NO.
Conclusions The light evoked release of NO from amacrine cells in the rabbit retina is inhibited by glycine (IOVS, 1998, 39, 850-853). Thus it is possible that exogenous glutamate and APB increase NO release by hyperpolarising the bipolar cells with an input to glycinergic amacrine cells.

1224

BETAXOLOL ATTENUATES NMDA-INDUCED DEATH OF RETINAL GANGLION CELLS BY REDUCING CALCIUM ENTRY

WOOD JPM, NASH MS and OSBORNE NN.
Nuffield Lab. of Ophthalmology, Univ. of Oxford, Oxford (UK).

Purpose
To determine whether the β-adrenoceptor antagonist, Betaxolol, could prevent excitotoxic death of retinal ganglion cells and also how it could affect NMDA-stimulated calcium influx into neurones.
Methods
Intravitreal injections of NMDA (100μM) or NMDA plus betaxolol (both 100μM) were administered to adult rats and after varying times, retinas were analysed for loss of ganglion cell Thy-1 mRNA and protein. The effect of betaxolol on NMDA-stimulated $^{45}Ca^{2+}$ entry into foetal rat cortical neurones was also determined.
Results
A dramatic decrease in both mRNA and protein for Thy-1 was noted up to 8 days after injection of NMDA, indicating a loss of retinal ganglion cells. This could be blocked by betaxolol. In rat cortical cultures, NMDA stimulated a large influx of $^{45}Ca^{2+}$ into neurones and betaxolol significantly attenuated this. Preliminary data further indicates that betaxolol acts by reducing calcium entry at t-type channels.
Conclusions
Betaxolol protects retinal ganglion cells from excitotoxic insults. It appears to achieve this by reducing NMDA-stimulated influx of calcium into these neurones.

1225

TYROSINE HYDROXYLASE ACTIVITY IN THE RAT RETINA AFTER NEONATAL EXPOSURE TO METHAMPHETAMINE

SALGADO-BORGES J,[1] GOMES-DA-SILVA J,[1] DE-MIGUEL R,[2] FERNÁNDEZ-RUIZ J,[2] TAVARES MA.[1]
1.Institute of Anatomy, Medical School of Porto & IBMC, University of Porto (Portugal);
2.Department of Biochemistry, Faculty of Medicine, Universidad Complutense, Madrid, (Spain).

Purpose: Methamphetamine (MA) is a drug of abuse known to interfere with the normal functioning of neuronal circuitries, namely the catecholaminergic pathways, in particular acting upon tyrosine hydroxylase (TH). This experimental model aims to assess effects of neonatal exposure to MA during the first month of life in the rat, both regarding general growth parameters and TH activity in retina.
Methods: Four Wistar rat litters were assigned to each experimental group. Litters were culled to 8 pups (4 males and 4 females, whenever possible), and weighed every two-days. Experimental groups received 10 mg of (+)-MA-HCl/kg body weight/day, sc., from postnatal day (PND) 1 to the day before sacrifice; control groups received isovolumetric doses of saline. Rats were sacrificed at PND 14 and 30, the retinas were quickly removed, frozen and kept at -70°C until assayed. TH activity was measured by HPLC-EC in 2 animals/sex/litter.
Results: At PND 30, the body weight of both males and females exposed to MA was lower than the body weight of respective controls. Males exposed to MA have increased retinal TH activity (expressed as ng L-DOPA/mg protein/h), both at PND14 and 30.
Conclusions: These findings support the view that early exposure to MA affects both overall development parameters as well as biochemical indicators of catecholamine metabolism in the rat retina, namely, affecting the activity of its synthesis rate-limiting enzyme, in a manner that seems to be sex-dependent.

Supported by Project PECS/C/SAU/87/95 and JNICT BD 9279/96.

1226

CHARACTERISATION OF RETINAL PHOSPHODIESTERASE (PDE) ISOZYMES AND THE EFFECTS OF SILDENAFIL IN VITRO.

WALLIS RM, CASEY J, HOWE L, LEISHMAN D, NAPIER CM.
Pfizer Central Research, Sandwich, UK.

Purpose. Sildenafil is a potent inhibitor of PDE5 that is effective in the treatment of erectile dysfunction. Mild, transient, dose-related visual adverse events have been observed in clinical trials. This study investigated the pharmacological basis of these effects.
Methods. PDE activities of human and dog retina were separated using anion exchange chromatography. In dog isolated retina, changes in transretinal potential in response to a 50-ms blue-light pulse were recorded in the absence and presence of sildenafil (0.1-100 μM).
Results. The profile of retinal PDE-dependent cGMP-hydrolytic activity was comparable in both species. Two main chromatographic peaks were resolved, corresponding to cone and rod PDE6. Activity was inhibited by the PDE6-specific antibody ROS-3 and sildenafil (IC_{50} 26.9-58.2 nM). Sildenafil caused a dose-related (threshold 0.3 μM) change in the kinetics of the light response of dog isolated retina, decreasing the rates of hyperpolarisation and depolarisation.
Conclusion. PDE6s of human and dog retina are similar. Functional results are consistent with inhibition of PDE6 by sildenafil and are only observed at higher concentrations than are maximally active on rabbit corpus cavernosum (0.1 μM).

1227

EFFECTS OF HYDROCORTISONE IN PORCINE PIGMENT EPITHELIUM

SARI A[1], ARNDT CF[1,2], HACHE JC[2], MATRAN R[1].
1. Dép.Physiologie (JE 2084&IFR22), Université Lille II
2. Exploration Fonctionnelle de la Vision, CHR&U Lille

Purpose: Corticosteroids appear to intervene in pathogenesis of central serous chorioretinopathy. Steroid induced ion transport changes within the pigment epithelium are not well known.
Methods: The native tissue (porcine pigment epithelium + choroid, n=8) was placed in a Ussing type chamber. After baseline determination of the transepithelial potential (TEP), short circuit current (Isc) and tissular resistance (Rt), the effect of apical hydrocortisone 10-4 M (HC) was assessed.
Results: The mean baseline TEP was 5.2 +/- 6.4 mV, the mean Isc 41+/-49 $\mu A.cm^{-2}$ and Rt 230 $\Omega.cm^2$. When the tissue preparation was exposed to HC 10-4 M in the apical bath, the mean TEP decreased to 1.5 mV ($p<0.01$), the Isc decreased to 36 $\mu A.cm^{-2}$ ($p < 0.001$) and the Rt increased to 265 $\Omega.cm^2$ ($p < 0.001$).
Conclusions: Hydrocortisone appeared to reduce the transepithelial potential and the short current circuit. Further work is necessary to link this finding to reduced apical fluid absorption which could be implicated in central serous chorioretinopathy.

1228

METHYLPREDNISOLNE EFFECT ON Nd:YAG LASER INDUCED RETINAL INJURY

TREISTER G, VIDNE O, SOLBERG Y, DUBINSKI G, TCHIRKOV M, YINON U, BELKIN M and ROSNER M.
Goldschleger Eye Institute, Sheba Medical Center
Tel-Aviv University (Israel)

Purpose: To examine the effect of methylprednisolone (MP) on retinal injury induced by Nd:YAG laser.

Methods: Nd:YAG laser-induced retinal lesions were inflicted in eyes of 48 pigmented rats. The treated group received IP injections of MP in saline at doses of 10 mg/kg, 150 mg/kg or 300 mg/kg. Six injections at intervals of 8 hours were given, starting immediately after exposure. The control group received saline at the same schedule. The rats were sacrificed 20 days after exposure and the lesions were evaluated by light microscopy and morphometric measurements. The most effective dose (300 mg/kg) was evaluated also when treatment was delayed for 8 and 16 hours.

Results: The lesion size was smaller in the test group as compared with control only with immediate treatment of MP 300 mg/kg (p=0.04). No effect was seen when treatment was delayed.

Conclusions: MP treatment showed very mild beneficial effect on Nd:YAG laser induced retinal injuries in the regimens tested, only when started immediately after exposure.

1231

EFFECT OF bFGF ON THE RAT ERG-RESPONSE

CERVETTO L[1], GARGINI C[1], BISTI S[2], BELFIORE MS[1], and STONE J[3].
1. Dip. PNFB, Università di Pisa, Italy
2. Dip. STB, Università de L'Aquila, Italy
3. Dep. Anatomy and Histology, University of Sydney, Australia

Purpose. The neurotrophic factor bFGF protects photoreceptors from injury and delays degeneration, but the mechanism of this action is not understood. We have explored the effects of bFGF on the retinal function by recording the ERG from retinae in which bFGF had been upregulated either by cutting the optic nerve (ON) or by intravitreal injection.
Methods. The ON of the right eye was sectioned, leaving that of left eye intact as a control. The ERG response to flashes of increasing intensity was recorded 20-30 days after the ON section in both dark and light-adapted conditions. In separate experiments 1μl of a solution containing 1μg/μl bFGF was intravitreally injected into one eye while the controlateral eye received 1μl of saline: the ERG was recorded after 3-5 days from both eyes.
Results. Endogenous upregulation and exogenous application of bFGF were associated with changes in the flash ERG in both dark and light adapted conditions. In bFGF upregulated retinae the amplitude of the b-wave was drastically reduced and the time to the peak slightly increased. The amplitude of the a-wave was unmodified or increased in response to bright flashes.
Conclusions. These results show changes in the light response following upregulation of bFGF which suggest that the protection from injury by the neurotrophic factor is associated with reduction of signal transmission from photoreceptor (which generate the a-wave) to the inner layers of the retina.

1232

ON-OFF-CONE'S PATHWAYS IN ERG AND PSYCHOPHYSICAL TESTING.

I.ZOLNIKOVA, T.BERNINGER[1], A.SHAMSHINOVA[2]
1.University Eye Clinic, Ludwig-Maximilian University
2.Helmholtz Institute of Eye Diseases

Purpose: comparison between electrophysiological and psychophysical methods for investigation of ON- and OFF-cone pathways the function of in normal subjects and in Stargardt dystrophy/
Methods and materials: As a electrophysiological method full-field long-flash ERG was used to receive the responses for stimulus onset (ON-response) and for stimulus offset (OFF-response) for L- and M-cones. As a psychophysical method we used topography mapping, presenting achromatic point stimulus darker and brighter than background in 2 and 12 angle degrees of the visual field. Reaction time (RT) was used as evaluation parameter. We examined a group of normal subjects and patients with Stargardt dystrophy.
Results: Normal subjects had demonstrated ON and OFF ERG-responses as b- and d-waves. ON-OFF channels topography produced a symmetric reduction of RT for the stimuli of equal steps darker and brighter then background. All patients with Stargardt dystrophy demonstrated b-wave reduction for green stimuli, ratio b/d being reduced, suggesting ON-channel involvement. RT was increased symmetrically for ON- and OFF-channels in the central 2°, and at 12 ° increased predominantly for brighter stimuli, thus demonstrating a reduction of ON-channel function.
Conclusion: The correlation of electrophysiological and psychophysical methods in ON- and OFF- cone pathways examination may be the new approache to discover the mechanisms of visual loss in Stargardt dystrophy.

1233

MONITORING RETINAL FUNCTION DURING BACKGROUND TRANSITION.

Lachapelle P, Rousseau S, Behn D, Dembinska O, Koenekoop RK, Little JM and Polomeno RC. Department of Ophthalmology McGill University-Montreal Children's Hospital.

Purpose: Monitor, with the electroretinogram (ERG), the recovery of retinal function during background transition. **Method:** ERGs were obtained from normal subjects and patients affected with selected retinal disorders (n=30 total) as the retina recovered from a prolonged exposure to a bright (>500 cd.m^{-2} white, red, green or blue light) photopic environment: 1- in the presence of a dimmer (32 cd.m^{-2}) photopic background (Type 1) or, 2- at the onset of dark-adaptation (DA; Type 2). **Results: Type 1** is characterised by a transient (tau= 30.5 seconds for b-wave measurements) enhancement of all the ERG components (a-wave: 16%, b-wave: 78%, i-wave: 183%, OP_2=46%, OP_3=12%, OP_4=84%); the effect being more pronounced following a bright red background or in CSNB patients (b-wave=150%; tau=20 sec.). **Type 2** yields a rapid (first 20-30 sec of DA) growth of OP_4 (which is absent at onset) and b-wave while the a-wave, OP_2 and OP_3 are minimally affected (except in patients with an unusual form of cone dystrophies). **Conclusion:** The transient nature of the effects would suggests a strong neural component probably at the level of the outer plexiform layer as suggested with results obtained from CSNB (ON-bipolar cell anomaly) and cone dystrophy (OFF-bipolar cell anomaly) as well as differential effect on a- and b-waves and OPs. Animal studies should confirm this impression. Supported MRC MT13353

1234

CLINICAL AND ELECTROPHYSIOLOGICAL FINDINGS IN AUTOSOMAL DOMINANT VITREORETINOCHOROIDOPATHY

LAFAUT B[1], KESTELYN Ph[1], SPILEERS W[2] & DE LAEY JJ[1]
1 Ophthalmology, University Hospital Gent (Belgium)
2 Ophthalmology, Catholic University of Leuven (Belgium)

Purpose To report clinical and electrophysiologic findings in autosomal dominant vitreoretinochoroidopathy which is a rare disorder.
Methods A 3 generation family was examined. Electro-oculography was obtained and electroretinography according to ISCEV standards was performed.
Results Characteristic annular peripheral pigmentary changes were present in all affected members. Additionally variable chorioretinal atrophy, from tigroid aspect to marked chorioretinal atrophy was seen in several patients. Some patients presented a microcornea and shallow anterior chamber without microphthalmia. The electro-oculography was pathological in the affected patients and normal in the unaffected. The electroretinography tended to worsen with age with maintenance of near normal latencies.
Conclusion The clinical presentation of autosomal dominant vitreoretinochoroidopathy is variable. Electro-oculography seems to be a discriminative test. The condition may be associated with anterior segment abnormalities other than presenile cataract.

1235

ELECTROOPHTHALMOLOGICAL CHANGES IN OCCLUSIVE RETINAL VASCULOPATHIES

Henč-Petrinović Lj, Petrinović-Dorešić J and Kuzmanović B
Ophthalmology Dep.G. Hospital "Sv.Duh",Zagreb (Croatia)

Purpose: To find the models of electrophysiological behaviour of the different types of circulatory disturbances depending on the degree and localisation of retinal ischemia.
Methods: Electrooculography (EOG) and electroretinography (ERG), photopic and scotopic were performed in 104 patients with occlusive retinal diseases.
Results: Central retinal artery occlusion (CRAO) in 14 eyes caused reduced EOG ratio, reduced photopic a- and b- wave amplitude, their ratio and oscillatory potentials (OP's). Similar are the changes in 25 eyes with ischemic central venous occlusions (ICVRO) with prolongation of the a- and b-wave latencies and OP's absence. On the contrary, non-ischemic central venous occlusions (n-ICVRO) in 31 eyes caused only slightly prolonged a- and b-wave latencies and OP's reduction. Arterial branch occlusion (BRAO) in13 eyes produced photopic b-wave reduction, but in venous branch occlusions (BRVO) in 21 eyes none of the parameters was changed.
Conclusions: The similarity of the ERG and EOG changes in the CRAO and ICRVO group confirms the presence of ischemia in the latter. The differences in electrophysiological model between the ICRVO and n-ICRVO group make it easier to discern these two groups of occlusions as separate clinical entities.

1236

Influence of microinjection of betaendorphine into the lateral geniculate body (GL) on flash visual evoked cortical response (FVECR) in rats.

Pojda S.M.*, Plech A.R.*, Plech A.**
*Department of Ophthalmology and Eye Clinic in Bytom and ** Department of Pharmacology in Zabrze, Silesian Medical University, Katowice, (Poland).

Purpose : It has been found in our previous study that intracerebroventricular (icv) injections of opioids had distinctly modified FVECR in rats. The aim of present study is to determine an effect of the betaendorphine, a potent opioid peptide, injected into GL on FVECR in rats.
Methods : Experiments were performed on 10 female adult Wistar rats, 250-330g, stereotaxically implanted with guide caniula into right GL, two active electrodes bilaterally on dura above the occipital cortex and one reference electrode on the skull in interorbital level. One week later FVECR were recorded by the 1000 LKC (USA) electrophysiological set, with ganzfield stimulation of both mydriatic eyes under chloral hydrate anesthesia.
Results : Betaendorphine depressed and changed the shape of FVECR : decreased the P2 and P3 and increased N1 waves. This effect was long acting and dose-depended in doses 0,125; 0,25; 0,5; 2 nmols. Intrageniculate injections of Naloxone, an opioid agonist, incompletely reversed betaendorphine effect. Moreover the latency time was prolonged to 110%.
Conclusion : Betaendorphine in GL modulates FVECR similar to one observed after icv injection. In the GL case the effect occurs immediately and after 20-times smaller doses.

1237

THE TOPOGRAPHY VEP IN CORTICAL VISUAL IMPAIRMENT IN CHILDREN

KRIVOSHEEV A., KOPTELOV U., MOSIN I.
Moscow Helmholtz Research Institute of Eye Diseases

Purpose: To determine the functional state of the striate and extrastriate centers of the visual system in children with CNS involvement due to the perinatal asphyxia.
Metods: The transient flash- and reversal pattern-VEP, Brain Mapping, the 3D-localisation of sours of the visual evoked bioelectrical activity were used(BrainLoc, MBN Inc., Russia). 5 healthy subjects, 12 patients, (4-8 years), with the cortical visual impairment (CVI) with the bilateral descending optic nerve atrophy were investigated.
Results: In healthy subjects the latency of the P_2 component of the flash-VEP was normal, the dipole source was localized contralateral to stimulating eye in the occipital and parietal lobes mainly; the dipole sources of the P_{100} component of pattern-VEP were located in parietooccipitale and paraventricular area. In children with CVI the latency of P_2 and P_{100} components was significantly increased. The dipole sources were located in the frontal, central and parietal areas mainl. In the some patients it was impossible to define a position of the virtual dipole source for the P_2 component, which can reflect an absence of the dominanting centres of the bioelectrical activity.
Conclusion: The topographical VEP Brain Mapping with the localisation of the virtual dipole may be helpful for the determination of the functional state of the visual system and the prognosis of the disease in children with CVI.

1238

SLO-m-ERG, SLO-microperimetry and colour ERG of ON-OFF-pathways in the diagnosis of macular dystrophies

Rudolph G[1], Bechmann M[1], Berninger T[1], Arden GB[2], Ehrt O[1] Hogg C[3], Holder G[3], Zolnikova I[4], Boergen KP[1], Kampik A[1]
[1]Augenklinik der Ludwig-Maximilians-Universität, Mathildenstr.8, D-80336 München
[2]City University, Appl. Vis. Res. Center, Goswell Road 321, UK ECV1V7DD London
[3]Moorfields Eye Hospital, City Road, UK-EC1V 2PD London
[4]Helmholtz Inst. of Eye Diseases, Sadovaya-Tchernogriazskaya, RF-119881 Moscow

Purpose: To enhance the possibilities in the diagnosis of juvenile macular dystrophies by using new diagnostic tools, represented by the scanning-laser-ophthalmoscope evoked multifocal-ERG, colour ERG and SLO-microperimetry.
Methods: A confocal scanning laser ophthalmoscope is used to perform a multifocal ERG and SLO-microperimetry. The visual stimulus is generated by a helium-neon laser with a wavelenght of 622.8nm. Visualization of the fundus, of the stimulus matrix and of the perimetry stimuli is guaranteed by using an infrared diode laser (730nm). Colour ERG of ON-, OFF-pathways to a long flash colour stimulus was performed with a 4-channel LED Ganzfeld stimulator.
Results: Patients with juvenile macular dystrophies show a reduction of amplitudes analyzing the first order response. The results are correlated to the data obtained by SLO-microperimetry. Measuring ON-, OFF pathways show reduced responses in early stages of macular dystrophies.
Conclusion: The SLO-m-ERG and SLO-microperimetry offers a new method of mapping of retinal function under simultaneous control of fixation. The colour ERG is helpfull in the early detection of impaired cone function.

1241

THE CLINICAL SIGNIFICANCE OF EYELID BASAL CELL CARCINOMA HISTOPATHOLOGY

ROSNER M,(1) LUKOVETSKY S(2) and ROSEN N.(1)
1. Goldschleger Eye Institute, Sheba Medical Center
2. Dept. of Ophthalmology, Edith Wolfson Medical Center Tel-Aviv University (Israel)

Purpose: Basal cell carcinoma (BCC) is known to have a variety of cellular growth patterns. We evaluated the significance of the histopathologic findings in eyelid BCC.

Methods: Eighty seven eyelid specimens with BCC excised during the last 3 years at the Goldschleger Eye Institute were revised and the histopathologic findings were matched with the clinical data retrieved from the patients' files.

Results: Eyelid BCC was diagnosed in 82 patients. Twenty percent of the lesions were big (>20 mm in longer axis), 42% of intermediate size, and 38% were small (<11 mm). Most (81.6%) specimens showed a mixture of different cellular differentiation types. The solid type was the most common (81.6%) followed by morpheaform (44.8%). Morpheaform features were commonly seen in the big and intermediate lesions, but appeared also in 40% of the small tumors.

Conclusions: As morpheaform features were seen also in very small tumors, the margins of every lesion should be carefully checked during excision for remnants of neoplastic cells. Long-term follow-up should is recommended even for cases with small tumors.

1242

LONG-TERM OUTCOME OF OCULAR ADNEXAL LYMPHOMA

C. AUW-HAEDRICH[1], A. KAPP[1], S. COUPLAND[2], A. SCHMITT-GRAEFF[3], R. BUCHEN[1], H. WITSCHEL[1]

1.University Eye Hospital, Freiburg (Germany)
2.Institute of Pathology, Benjamin Franklin Hospital, Berlin
3.Institute of Pathology, Freiburg (Germany)

Purpose To classify ocular adnexal lymphoma according to the Revised European and American Lymphoma classification and to determine the patients´ outcome.

Methods Immunohistochemistry was performed on representative histological sections of 55 cases of 47 patients (age 32-89.7 y, 28 f, 19 m) with ocular adnexal lymphoma using antibodies for CD20, BCL2, CD21, CD23, CD43, CD3, CD5, Ki67-Ag, p53, Cyclin D1, pan-cytokeratin, κ, λ, IgD and IgM. Data regarding the outcome were obtained from the physicians and hospital files. The Student´s t-test was used for statistical analysis. Results Almost all cases represent B-cell lymphomas: extranodal marginal zone lymphoma (EMZL) (39), diffuse large B-cell lymphoma (8), lymphoplasmocytic lymphoma/immunocytoma (3), mantle cell lymphoma (2) , follicular center lymphoma (2) , plasmocytoma (1). One case of systemic T-cell lymphoma was found. The average follow up time was 85 months. In 19 patients complete remission was achieved, 11 patients died due to lymphoma, 6 patients due to other causes, 6 patients had persistent tumor at final follow up. The lymphoma subtype had a significant correlation to the stage at initial manifestation (p=0.02), but not to the stage at final follow up. A significant correlation was noted between the positivity of Ki67-Ag and the final course (p=0.004). Conclusion 70% of our cases with ocular adnexal lymphoma are of the EMZL-subtype. Ki67-Ag has proven to be an important marker concerning the prognosis.

1243

NEUROENDOCRINE CARCINOMA MIMICKING ADENO- AND BASAL CELL CARCINOMA

C. AUW-HAEDRICH[1], N. BOEHM[2], H. WITSCHEL[1]
1. University Eye Hospital, Freiburg (Germany)
2. Institute of Pathology, Freiburg (Germany)

Purpose To show the histologic patterns of a bronchial neuroendocrine carcinoma, which initially was thought to be an adenocarcinoma, with orbital metastasis in a 47-year-old patient.

Methods Histological sections of a subcutaneous tumour of the right lower lid were stained with HE and PAS. Immunohistochemistry was performed using antibodies for pan-cytokeratin, neuron-specific-enolase (NSE), chromogranin and synaptophysin.

Results The subepidermal tumour showed a basaloid pattern with moderate polymorphy of the nuclei. Small cytoplasm vacuoles were reminiscent of sebaceous cells. So the tentative diagnosis of a basal cell carcinoma with sebaceous differentiation was made. Further resection, however, of this unexpectedly extensive tumour revealed palisading and trabecular growth patterns and rosette formation with high grade-polymorphy of the tumour cells. Immunhistochemistry was positive for epithelial and neuroendocrine markers both in the primary lung tumour and its lid metastasis.

Conclusion A neuroendocrine carcinoma should be considered in carcinomas with atypical adenoid and basaloid growth patterns.

1244

THE EPIDEMIOLOGY OF RETINOBLASTOMA IN JEWISH AND ARAB POPULATIONS IN ISRAEL

PE'ER J,[1] ABDULRAZIK M[1] and ISCOVICH J[2]
1. Dept. of Ophthalmology, Hadassah University Hospital, Jerusalem (Israel)
2. Israel Ministry of Health, Jerusalem (Israel)

Purpose: To evaluate time trend incidence of retinoblastoma in Israel by subpopulation and calendar periods.

Methods: Case-findings diagnosed from 1960 to 1994 were retrieved from the National Cancer Registry. Multiple sources of diagnoses were re-abstracted to ascertain completeness, diagnosis appraisal and demographic parameters. Incidence rates by sub-population, age and gender adjusted, are expressed per person-years or live-born.

Results: Incidence rates of retinoblastoma experienced a stable trend for the whole population, with a non-substantial increase in the last decade. Non-Jews experienced the highest rates. Among Israeli-born Jews, those of Asian parental origin had the lowest relative risk; those of African parental origin had the highest relative risk. Age at diagnosis was higher among non-Jews.

Conclusions: Retinoblastoma incidence rates in Israel are slightly high compared to Western countries with a more homogeneous population, such as the UK, similar to rates from the USA, but lower than rates published from the Middle East. The highest incidence rates and age at diagnosis among non-Jews deserve further consideration.

1245

META-ANALYSIS OF TRILATERAL RETINOBLASTOMA

KIVELÄ T
Department of Ophthalmology, Helsinki University Central Hospital, Helsinki (Finland)

Purpose: To refine clinical characteristics of trilateral retinoblastoma (TRB): retinoblastoma (RB) associated with ectopic intracranial tumour (EIT).
Methods: A systematic review of literature, using Medline and textbooks as starting points. Relevant data from 102 identified unique patients was entered into a database.
Results: TRB showed no sex predilection (M:F 42:50, $P=0.47$). Median age at diagnosis of RB was 5 mo (range, 0-29), and it was lower for the 46 children (49%) who had familial RB than for 48 (51%) children with sporadic RB (2 vs 6 mo, $P<0.0001$). RB was unilateral in 11 children (12%), bilateral in 83 (86%), and 2 had EIT only. Median age at diagnosis of EIT was 26 mo (range, 1-141) and time from RB 24 mo (range 6 mo before to 141 mo after). The 74 (77%) pineal EIT were found later than the 22 (23%) sellar EIT (33 vs 7 mo, $P<0.0001$); similar size (median, 27 vs 30 mm, $P=0.61$) and survival (8.0 vs 9.5 mo, $P=0.45$) suggested that the latter truly arised earlier. Only 3 patients, all detected by screening, are in remission more than 2 years from diagnosis of EIT (30, 108, 168 mo).
Conclusions: Sellar EIT in TRB resembles intraocular RB in time course and may thus have a different cell of origin, perhaps a retinal stem cell in transit, than pineal EIT.

1246

BENZAMIDE-SCINTIGRAPHY IN AN ANIMAL MODEL OF HUMAN UVEAL MELANOMA

Bonicel, P.[1], Bacin, F.[1], Michelot, J.[2], Bonafous, J.[4] Papon, J.[2], Labarre, P.[2], Kemeny, J.-L.[3], Moins, N.[2], Madelmont, J.-C.[2]

[1].Service d'ophtalmologie, CHU Clermont-Ferrand, [2].INSERM U 484 Clermont-Ferrand, [3]. Service d'anatomie pathologique, CHU Clermont-Ferrand, [4]. Service de medecine nucléaire, CHU Clermont-Ferrand.

Purpose: Follow-up of tumoral growth patterns in an animal model of human uveal melanoma using clinical examination, benzamide-scintigraphy, tumor uptake and histopathological analysis.
Methods: Heavily pigmented tumors established in the anterior chamber of ten immunosuppressed New-Zealand rabbits were imaged by scintigraphy six hours after an intravenous injection of 37 MBq of N-(2-diethylaminoethyl)-4-[^{123}I]-iodobenzamide (BZA). After enucleation, the tumor uptake of each globe was determined by NaI scintillation. Histopathological analysis was performed by light and electron microscopy and an evaluation of the melanin content was realized by spectrophotometry. All these analysis were repeated once a week until the end of the experimentation, at day 45.
Results: Diffuse, flat, pigmented tumors appeared 7-9 days after intracamerular implantation. At day 16, the scintigraphy became positive showing an asymmetrical uptake of BZA. This hyperfixation was explicited by the counting of the tumor and its melanin content.
Conclusion:The images obtained in the rabbit eye were very similar to those of uveal melanomas observed in man. The histopathological results confirm the characteristics of human uveal melanoma. This model seems to be of great value for the evaluation of new diagnostic methods in the management of uveal melanoma.

1247

MICROVESSEL DENSITY AND OUTCOME OF CHOROIDAL AND CILIARY BODY MELANOMAS

KIVELÄ T, MÄKITIE T, SUMMANEN P, TARKKANEN A
Department of Ophthalmology, Helsinki University Central Hospital, Helsinki (Finland)

Purpose: To reassess the prognostic significance of microvessel density (MVD) in uveal melanoma.
Methods: A series of 167 patients enucleated in 1972-1981 for a malignant ciliary body or choroidal melanoma was analysed. Sections were immunostained for CD34 epitope with mAb QBEND/10, and bleached with dilute hydrogen peroxide. MVD was counted from three most highly vascularized areas ("hot spots") using a 0,313mm^2 graticule and without knowing the patient's outcome. Before analysis, 34 patients (20%) were excluded: 33 due to necrotic or unrepresentative blocks and 1 due to missing follow-up.
Results: The median MVD in 134 evaluable tumours was 40/0.313mm^2 (range, 5-121). MVD was higher in tumours that had microvascular loops ($P=0.0001$), networks ($P=0.0005$), and epithelioid cells ($P=0.028$). The cumulative 10-y probability of survival declined with increasing MVD being 91%, 71%, 41% and 34% by quartile ($P<0.0001$). In Cox regression, epithelioid cells (HR 2.50), loops (HR 2.68), MVD (HR 1.23), and tumour diameter (HR 1.11) were independent prognostic factors.
Conclusions: Quantitative (MVD) and qualitative (pattern) features of microvessels both influence prognosis.

1248

OPTIMIZATION OF PLAQUE THERAPY OF INTRAOCULAR TUMORS USING MAGNETIC RESONANCE IMAGING .

BACIN F[1], CHIAMBARETTA F[1], KWIATKOWSKI F[2], RAVEL A[3], PEREZ N[3], DALENS H[1], BOYER L[3], DONNARIEIX D[2], ROZAN R[2].
1. Dept. Ophthalmology, 2. Dept. Radiotherapy Centre J.Perrin, 3. Dept. Radiology, CHU Clermont Ferrand (France).

Purpose MR imaging was used to generate models of the affected eye and of the tumor, and to check the geometry of the eye and the tumor location. Methods We obtained MR images of the globe in 22 patients with an intraocular tumor before plaque therapy. Using the software Plaque Simulator 2.15 (Astrahan 1992), the eye and the tumor were reconstructed 3-dimensionally. The echography measurements, the color fundus photomontages and the findings during the surgery were compared with the MRI results. The dosimetry calculated on the COMS standard eye was compared to the dosimetry calculated on the reconstructed eye. Results There was no statistically significant difference in the tumor dimensions on the MRI compared with the other examinations but there were statistically significant differences between the standard eye and the reconstructed eyes. Important differences in the dosimetry to the macula and to the disc were noted, being over 60 Gy in 23% and 10% of the cases respectively. Conclusions By improving the accuracy of dosimetry to the critical points of the eye, MRI seemed very useful to the management of plaque therapy.

1249

EARLY DETECTION OF METASTATIC SPREAD OF UVEAL MELANOMA BY RT-PCR AMPLIFICATION OF THE TYROSINASE GENE: THE RATIONALE FOR A PROJECT PROPOSAL

FREZZOTTI R, MASTRANGELO D
Centro per la Ricerca Interdipartimentale per lo Studio delle Affezioni Tumorali dell'Occhio, University of Siena, Siena (Italy)

This paper will address the background and rationale of the above project proposal, the details of which will be discussed in the Protocol Drafting Committee Meeting of the Ophthalmic Oncology Group.

1250

TUMOUR DOUBLING TIMES IN METASTATIC MALIGNANT UVEAL MELANOMA: UNTREATED AND TREATED PATIENTS

ESKELIN S,[1] SUMMANEN P,[1] PYRHÖNEN S,[2] HAHKA-KEMPPINEN M,[2] KIVELÄ T[1]
Departments of [1]Ophthalmology and [2]Oncology, Helsinki University Central Hospital (Finland)

Purpose: To evaluate screening schedules and efficacy of chemotherapy by estimating tumour doubling times (DT). Methods: Time (t) from latest negative scan and mean diameters (d) of all individual metastases from 23 consecutive patients diagnosed to have metastatic uveal melanoma and participating in annual screening were determined from US and CT scans; 15 patients received chemo- or immunotherapy and their later scans were also evaluated. Doubling times were estimated from DT= t/10*log(d2/d1), presuming that metastases 4 mm or smaller gave negative scans. Results: Estimated mean DTs for untreated metastases ranged from 20 to 120 days, with a median of 36.5 days and a mean of 47.5 (SD 23.8). The larger the metastasis was, the shorter its DT tended to be. DT was 40 days or less for all metastases 50 mm or larger in size. During therapy, mean DTs ranged from 17 to 191 days with a median of 61 days and a mean of 96 (SD 65) days. Conclusions: The estimated mean DTs before treatment suggest that scanning should be done every 2 to 3 months, which is neither practical nor indicated given the rarity of objective responses. However, current treatments do slow down tumour growth.

1251

TREATMENT OF INTRAOCULAR METASTATIC TUMOURS

B.ROMANOWSKA, M.STARZYCKA
Dept. Ophthalmology, CM UJ, Kraków, Poland

Purpose: Analysis of types of intraocular metastatic tumour and estimation of the results of the treatment.
Material and method: In the years 1994 - 1997 metastatic intraocular tumours were diagnosed in 17 patients (22 eyes). The primary tumour in 9 patients developed in the breast, in 5 cases in the lungs, in 2 in the brain, and in 1 case in the kidney. Metastases developed in 10 months to 11 years since the diagnosis and treatment of the primary tumour. In order to confirm the diagnosis of the tumour ultrasonography was always performed, sometimes together with fluorescein angiography. Irradiation with 106Ru plaques was applied in 11 eyes and laser coagulation in 11 eyes. In 5 patients the eye was enucleated. In 4 patients chemotherapy and in 2 cases hormonotherapy were applied.
Results: In 19 cases significant decrease of tumor mass of was obtained. Only in 3 cases the tumor developed further (in 2 cases the eyes ere enucleated and in 1 case irradiation of the tumour was planned). 13 patients are currently observed, the remaining 4 do not come to the control examination, and there is no information as to their fate.
Conclusions: Basing on these preliminary results we consider that brachytherapy could be a method of treatment also in metastatic tumors.

1252

Five years follow up of choroïdal melanoma treated by protonbeam. A serie of 167 patients

L. Desjardins, C. Levy, F. D'Hermies, E. Frau, P. Schlienger, S. Delacroix, A. Mazal, B. Asselain, P. Validire
CPO - INSTITUT CURIE

We have reviewed a serie of 167 patients treated by protonbeam for choroïdal melanoma in Orsay who have a five years follow up.
There were 54,5 % women. The mean age was 59 years. The median follow up was 59 months. There was initial retinal detachment in 25 % of cases and invasion of optic disk in 5 % cases. The mean tumour diameter was 12 mm and the mean tumour thickness was 6,3 mm. The initial visual acuity was 20/50.
Results : 37 patients (22 %) died. Among them, 27 died of metastatic disease, 33 patients have presented metastatic disease (20 % at 5 years). Factors that are statistically significant for survival are largest tumour diameter and tumour volume ($p < 0,0001$) and also location of the tumour and age of the patient.
Local tumour response at five years was as follow :
tumour was stable in 23 cases
regression was observed in 105 cases
The tumour was totally flat in 29 cases
The mean tumour thickness at five years was 3,5 mm
The were 6 local recurrences (3,7 %), 2 of them were treated by enucleation, 1 by I_{125} plaque and 3 by retreatment by protonbeam.
14 patients were enucleated for other causes.
The mean visual acuity at five years is 20/200.
47 % of patients have a visual acuity better than 20/200. The frequency of ocular side effects is related to initial tumour volume.
Conclusion : this study shows a good local tumour control at five years with approximately 10 % of secondary enucleation after protonbeam irradiation of choroïdal melanoma.
Tumour size appear as a major risk factor for metastatic disease and ocular side effects.

1253

Proton Beam Irradiation of Uveal Melanomas with Extraocular Extension

Authors: Zografos L.[1], Egger E.[2], Chamot L.[1], Schalenbourg A.[1], Goitein M.[2]

1) Jules Gonin Eye Hospital, Lausanne, Switzerland
2) Paul Scherrer Institute, Villigen, Switzerland

Purpose: Extraocular extension of uveal melanomas is a statistically significant factor worsening the patients' life expectancy and local tumor control of the extraocular portion of the tumor. This study was performed in order to assess the efficacy of proton beam irradiation for local tumor control.

Methods: We treated with an accelerated proton beam 94 cases of uveal melanomas. Following surgical localization of the tumor, the irradiation was performed with a treatment planning that took into account the shape and volume of the extraocular extension with a security margin of 3 mm. The follow-up period was more than 1 year and less than 14 years in all the cases.

Results: Tumor-related mortality was 56% at 5 years and 82% at 10 years. Local tumor control of the extraocular portion of the tumor was achieved in all the cases except one which presented a massive recurrence in the orbit necessitating orbital exenteration.

Conclusions: Proton beam irradiation of uveal melanomas with extraocular extension is a valuable therapeutic alternative for the local control of the tumor.

1254

LONG-TERM SURVIVAL AFTER RUTHENIUM PLAQUE RADIOTHERAPY FOR UVEAL MELANOMA. A META-ANALYSIS OF STUDIES INCLUDING 1,066 PATIENTS.

SEREGARD S
Ophthalmic Path & Oncol Service, St Eriks Eye Hospital (Stockholm)

Purpose: Case series of patients managed by brachytherapy for uveal melanoma are often comparatively small and survival data show considerable inter-study variation. The aim of this study was to summarise similarly structured case series for meta-analysis.
Methods: A systematic review generated 5 similarly structured case series including survival data for 1,066 patients treated by ruthenium plaque radiotherapy for uveal melanoma. After assessing the inter-study clinical heterogeneity, data were weighed for study size and pooled.
Results: Patient and radiotherapy characteristics were largely homogenous, but tumour size varied considerably between studies. The 5-year melanoma-related mortality rate was 6% for small and medium tumours (T1/T2) and 26% for large (T3) tumours. The 5-year and 10-year melanoma-related mortality rates for a balanced set of tumours with small, medium and large tumours being present in similar proportions were 14% and 22%, respectively
Conclusions: Case series of patients with uveal melanoma managed by brachytherapy may be pooled to increase sample size and study power. The present estimate of survival following plaque radiotherapy compares favourably with previously summarised data of survival after enucleation for similarly sized tumours.

1255

LONG-TERM VISUAL RESULTS AND OCULAR COMPLICATIONS AFTER I-125 BRACHYTHERAPY OF 100 MALIGNANT UVEAL MELANOMAS

SUMMANEN P,[1] HEIKKONEN J,[2] KIVELÄ T,[1] TOMMILA P,[1] IMMONEN I,[1] LAATIKAINEN L,[1] TARKKANEN A[1]
Department of [1]Ophthalmology and [2]Department of Oncology, University of Helsinki, Helsinki (Finland)

Purpose: To assess complications from I-125 brachytherapy (IBT) of large choroidal and ciliary body melanomas. Methods: 100 patients (M:F 45:55; median age, 63 y and range, 31-85) treated with IBT (median top dose, 100 Gy) were analyzed for visual outcome and complications using the life-table method and Cox proportional hazards model (median follow-up, 3 y). 95/100 tumors were large (T3). Results: The cumulative 2- and 3-y probabilities of retaining vision were 29% and 27% for VA 0.3, 36% and 24% for VA 0.1, and 90% and 78% for LP. The most common causes of permanent visual impairment were radiation maculopathy (RMP), optic neuropathy (RONP) and neovascular glaucoma (NVG). Posterior location did not notably decrease the risk of NVG, and no clear cut distance from the macula and optic disc diminished the risk for RMP or RONP. The 2- and 3-y cumulative probabilities of local relapse were 5% and 9%. Conclusions: IBT gives good local tumour control of large melanomas, as compared to Ru-106 therapy, but complications that decrease vision are more frequent than after Ru-106 therapy of small to medium-sized melanomas.

1256

FAILURES OF CONSERVATIVE TREATMENT OF POSTERIOR UVEAL MELANOMA

STARZYCKA M[1], STACHURA J[2] and ROMANOWSKA B[1].
1. Dept. Ophthalmology, CM UJ, Cracow (Poland)
2. Dept. Clin. and Exp. Pathomorphology, CM UJ, Cracow (Poland)

Purpose: Searching for the risk factors responsible for the failure of the treatment of melanoma with episcleral plaque brachytherapy.
Methods: Records of 23 cases of posterior uveal melanoma in which the eyes had to be enucleated after earlier conservative treatment were rewieved. The clinical characteristics of the tumors, dose of radiation and results of histo-pathological examination were analysed.
Results: The direct indications for enucleation were: increase of tumor mass in 15 cases, consecutive glaucoma and increase of tumor mass in 6 and only glaucoma in 2.
Histopathological examination revealed that the great majority (18) of tumors were mixed cell melanomas.
Conclusions: It is very difficult to predict the results of conservative treatment of melanoma basing on their clinical characteristics. Tumor size seemed to be the most valuable among the many risk factors discussed in relation to prognosis for plaque brachytherapy of melanoma.

1257

Lasers of nearest infrared region (Nd:YAG and diode) in treatment of rather massive choroidal melanomas

Volkov V., Kulakov Ya., Marchenko O.
City outpatient ophthalmodiagnostic and laser Center, Military Medical Academy, City Hospital № 2, St. Petersburg, Russia

PURPOSE: To approve efficiency of deeply penetrating laser radiations for rather massive (with size of tumors up to 600 mm^3) choroidal melanomas in posterior part of an eye with the purpose of the extension of possibilities organ-saving treatment of the patients.
METHODS: In experiment was studied volumetric distribution of an absorbed thermal energy of Nd:YAG (1,06 μm) and diode (0,81 μm) lasers depending on parameters of radiation. In clinical practice was estimated possibility of full destruction of melanoma in posterior part of an eye up to 8 mm in height with the help of transpupillary focussing of irradiation of the Nd:YAG laser or by contactly compressive effects of endolaser diode tip during vitreous operation.
RESULTS: Desired effect achieved by means of quasicontinuous mode of exposure by pulse bursts, by each duration about hundreds microseconds for Nd:YAG laser, and with continuous irradiation of diode laser with density of energy created in tissue about 1-2 J/mm^3. With the help of Nd:YAG laser was reached effect of full destruction of tumors in 85 cases among 122. Cataract was developed in 18 cases during the treatment and for prolongation of course at 12 cases it was necessary by a surgical way to remove cataract. Enucleation was required in 19 cases (because of the continued growth of tumor or operational complications). By diode laser it was possible to destroy juxtapapillary melanoma in 14 cases among 16. In a number of cases during treatment was used combination of laser and brachytherapy.
CONCLUSION: Approved lasers of nearest infrared region allow with success to conduct organ-saving treatment for enough massive (with size of tumors up to 600mm^3) choroidal melanoma in posterior part of an eye. For period of observation 5-14 years for Nd:YAG laser and 2-4 years for diode laser prognosis for life of patients does not worsen in comparison with cases when enucleation has been made.

1311

MECHANISM OF MMP-2 ACTIVATION IN KERATOCONIC CORNEAS.

SMITH V.A. and EASTY D.L.
Division of Ophthalmology, University of Bristol, UK.

Purpose In keratoconus the central cornea becomes thinned, conical and ultimately scarred. We have shown that MMP-2, the enzyme that hydrolyses Type IV collagen, is over-expressed by early-phase keratoconic keratocytes. The purpose of this enquiry was to determine how MMP-2 may be pathologically activated in keratoconic corneas.
Methods Keratocyte secreted MMP-2 was assayed using Type IV collagen as substrate and by zymography. The secreted proteins were radiolabelled and subsequently separated by SDS-PAGE, Western blotted, probed with antibody against MMP-2, Stromelysin, TIMP-1 or TIMP-2 and finally counted for radioactivity.
Results The results obtained showed :- (i) That TIMP-1 is the major TIMP secreted by corneal keratocytes. (ii) In normal keratocyte cultures the ratio of TIMP-1 / MMP-2 secreted is approx 1:1 but in early-phase keratoconic keratocyte cultures this ratio is approx 1:2. (iii) In keratoconic keratocyte cultures activation is induced by metabolic stress and correlates with zymographic visualisation of a gelatinase activity of M_r 43,000.
Conclusions. When subject to metabolic stress, the MMP-2 produced by early-phase keratoconic keratocyte cultures may autoactivate because of a deficit of TIMP-1.

1312

TOPICAL DEXAMETHASONE ON EXPRESSION OF STROMAL COLLAGEN I AND IV mRNA DURING CORNEAL ALKALI WOUND HEALING

CHUNG J-H[1], Lee J-S[2] and Kim W-K.[3]
1. Dept. Ophthalmology, Ewha Women's University, Seoul (Korea)
2. Dept. Medical Science, KNIH, Seoul (Korea)
3. Dept. Pharmacology, Ewha Women's University, Seoul (Korea)

Purpose The effect of topically instilled 0.1% dexamethsone on the expression of stromal collagen type I and IV mRNA was evaluated during the repair process of corneal alkali wounds.
Methods A central corneal alkali wound (6mm, 1N NaOH, 60s) was induced in one eye of each rabbit. Animals were treated with 0.1% dexamethasone q.i.d. for 8w and the control group was with BSS. The expressions of stromal collagen type I and IV mRNA together with β-actin gene were measured semi-quantitatively at 3-, 5-day, 1-, 2-, 4- and 8-week post injury by using RT-PCR.
Results The expression of β-actin gene revealed a two-phase pattern in both groups and was significantly lower in the dexamethasone treated eyes. The dexamethasone-treated group expressed a higher ratio of collagen type I mRNA than the control group throughout the examination period. The ratio of collagen IV mRNA to β-actin in the dexamethasone-treated stroma was significantly lower at 5-day, 4- and 8-week after initial damage compare to the control group.
Conclusions Topically administered dexamethasone seems to suppress the β-actin gene expression and enhance the expression of type I collagen mRNA throughout the observation period but suppress the type IV in the late healing period.

1313

IMMUNHISTOCHEMICAL DETECTION OF ESTROGEN AND PROGESTERONE RECEPTOR IN HUMAN CORNEA

VÉCSEI PV,[1] KIRCHER K,[1] KAMINSKI S,[1] NAGEL G,[1] and KOHLBERGER PD.[2]
1. Department of Ophthalmology, University Medical School, Vienna (Austria), 2. Department of Obstetrics and Gynecology, University Medical School, Freiburg (Germany)

Purpose Hormone therapy is favored by some clinicians for treatment of postmenopausal keratoconjuntivitis sicca. Up to now no assessment of the hormone receptor status has been performed in the human cornea. Immunhistochemical staining methods provide the opportunity to evaluate the staining reaction in the different histologic compartments of the cornea. The aim of our study was to provide the likely morphological basis of hormone receptor localisation in the human cornea. **Methods** Formalin-fixed and paraffin-embedded specimens of three pre- and three postmenopausal women were assessed for localisation of estrogen receptor (ER) and progesterone receptor (PR) expression with established immunohistochemical hormone receptor staining methods. **Results** We found only cytoplasmatic PR staining of the endothelial layer of the cornea in two cases. Nuclear staining reaction of hormone receptors was not present in the epi- and endothelial layers of the examined human corneas. The stroma of the cornea showed no hormone receptor staining in all cases. **Conclusions** Although the use of topical steroid hormone treatment has no morphological basis in the human cornea, hormone receptor expression in the conjunctiva may have an impact and in some patients show relief of symptoms in postmenopausal dry eye syndrom.

1314

HETEROGENIC DISTRIBUTION OF MEMBRANE BOUND GLYCOPROTEINS AND EXTRACELLULAR MATRIX PROTEINS (ECMP) IN PTERYGIUM

NAIB-MAJANI W[1], NIMMESGERN T[1], PLEYER U[2], WERNERT N[3], BORNFELD N[4], BREIPOHL W.[1]
1. Department of experimental Ophthalmology, RFW-University, Bonn; 2. University Eye Hospital, Charité, Berlin; 3. Department of Pathology, RWF-University, Bonn; University Eye Hospital, Essen.

Purpose: Preceeding studies of this group (Breipohl et al. 1998 a,b) on pterygial growth regulation have revealed new insights into the heterogeneous distribution of specific matrix components and localized expression of the c-ets1 protooncogene. This study was performed to characterize the presence and distribution of pterygial glycoproteins and further ECM proteins. **Methods:** Pterygia were investigated with 12 lectins, representing all five groups of Goldstein and Poretz (1986) and ECM antibodies against collagens I and IV, fibronectin and la-minin. Optimal lectin concentration was tested first and ranged between 5 and 66μg/ml. Control stainings were performed on murine colon and liver. **Results:** Positive though regional and tissue heterogeneous binding of lectin representatives and ECM P-antibodies was found. Surprisingly UEA-I binding, seen in other tissues with the blood vessels, was absent in pterygial and control tissue. Pterygial and intestinal goblet cells stained differently for some, but equally for other lectins. **Conclusion:** Pterygial growth is linked with heterogeneous distribution of ECM P, protooncogene transcription factors and glycoproteins.

1315

EXPRESSION OF APOPTOSIS PROTEINS IN HUMAN CORNEAL ENDOTHELIUM DURING CORNEAL STORAGE

THURET G[1,2], GAIN P[1,2], BURILLON C[1],MAUGERY J[1] and CAMPOS L[2]
1.Dept. of Ophthalmology, Bellevue Hospital, Saint-Etienne, (France)
2.Lab. of Haematology, University of medicine, Saint-Etienne (France)

Purpose To study the expression in human corneal endothelial cells of proteins involved in the regulation of apoptosis (Bcl-2, Bax, CPP32 and Hsp27) during corneal organ culture.
Methods Corneas were obtained from the corneal bank after different storage times (0 to 35 days) at 31°C in INOSOL ®. Endothelial cells were harvested from the Descemet by enzymatic method and cytocentrifugated. Immunocytochemical staining using monoclonal antibodies against Bcl-2, Bax, CPP32, Hsp27 was performed.
Results Whatever storage time, preliminary results showed that Bcl-2 and Hsp27 were expressed by corneal endothelial cells. Bax and CPP32 were not expressed in fresh or short time conserved corneas. A few cells expressed Bax or CPP32 after storage longer than 14 days.
Conclusions This is the first report of expression of Bcl-2 and Hsp27 in human corneal endothelium. We suggest that Bcl-2 and Hsp27 may play a role in the long life duration of endothelial cells by inhibiting programmed cell death. Expression of Hsp27 and Bcl-2 whatever storage time is not surprising because all studied cells are adherent and healthy. Nevertheless, apoptosis may be involved in endothelial cell loss observed during storage. Apoptotic cells probably rapidly desquam and thus can not be observed by our recovering method. In corneas stored for a long time, we observed some cells expressing pro-apoptotic proteins (Bax and CPP32) among a large majority of negative cells. These cells may be pre-apoptotic cells observed just before their desquamation.

1316

EPIDERMAL GROWTH FACTOR (EGF) IN CORNEAL EPITHELIAL CELLS: RESPONSIBLE FOR REGRESSION AFTER EXCIMER LASER PRK?

LOHMANN CP[1], REISCHL U[2] and MARSHALL J[3]
1. Universitäts-Augenklinik Regensburg, Germany
2. Institut für Medizinische Mikrobiologie und Hygiene
3. Dept of Ophthalmology, St Thomas' Hospital London, UK

Purpose: Corneal wound healing is of critical importance for the postoperative outcome of excimer laser myopic PRK. Among various cytokines EGF plays an important role in ocular surface wound healing. The synthesis of EGF in corneal epithelial cells varies individually and therefore individuals with high EGF levels might have a more aggressive wound healing reaction after PRK and subsequently show regression. Methods: EGF mRNA was measured in corneal epithelial cells of 60 patients prior to myopic PRK by PCR and measurements were correlated to postoperative refraction at 6 months. Based on preop refraction patients were allocated to 1 of 3 groups; i.e. -3.0 D, -6.0 D and -9.0 D group. Results: In our cohort 8 patients showed postoperative regression more than -1.0 D. These patients showed significant higher levels of mRNA EGF in corneal epithelial cells. We could not find any correlation between the preop degree of myopia and EGF mRNA concentration. Conclusions: Patients with higher levels of EGF mRNA in corneal epithelial cells show more likely postoperative regression. By the development of a quantitative PCR test a screening of such unsuitable patients prior to PRK might be possible.

1317

CORNEAL DNA CHARACTERIZATION FOLLOWING EXPOSURE TO LOW FREQUENCY ELECTRIC FIELD

El-REFAEI F.[1], HUSSEN E.[2], ALI F.[3] AND El-ABRAK E.[1]
1. Dept. Biophysics, Research Inst. Of Ophthal., Giza, (Egypt).
2. Agricultural and Genetic Engn Research Inst., Giza, (Egypt).
3. Dept. Biophysics, Faculty of Science , Cairo Univ., Giza, (Egypt).

Purpose. Studying the corneal deoxyribonucleic acid characterization of male albino rats as a result of in vivo exposure to low frequency electric field (30 – 50 Hz) of different strengths (1.5 – 5 KV/m).
Methods. Six groups of male albino rats (25 each) were used for control , direct and delay studies in this work . After separation and purification of corneal DNA the pooled samples for all studied groups were subjected to the following measurements : (a) UV absorption spectra , (b) concentration , (c) chromatographic analysis , (d) Electrophoretic mobility and (e) PCR and primers for location and amplification of any variation in different regions of the genome .
Results. There is a reduction of the amplitude of the eluted main peak without any changes in the molecular weight . As well ; there is a significant decrease in DNA concentration in addition there is a nucleotide variation or polymorphism at the DNA sequence levels after exposure to electric field .
Conclusion. The main effect of low frequency electric field is on the DNA highly active sites which are the ends of the macromolecule carrying on transcription processes .

1322

FLUORESCEIN ANGIOGRAPHY IN UVEITIS

LEHOANG P., LUMBROSO L.
Dept. Ophthalmology. La Pitié-Salpêtrière, Paris France.

Purpose : To describe the major fluorescein angiography characteristics of uveitis.
Methods : Several examples of elementary lesions and more frequently seen alterations (vasculitis, cystoid macular edema, papillitis) are studied as well as typical presentations of the major ocular inflammatory diseases.
Discussion : Fluorescein angiography is a very useful tool to evaluate patients presenting with posterior uveitis especially with a visual acuity decrease .
This exam allows the visualisation of the main complications of uveitis : cystoid macular edema, papillitis, retinal ischemic areas. Its repetition during follow-up also allows to evaluate the response to treatment.

1323

DIGITAL IMAGE COMPRESSION OF RETINAL IMAGES FOR TELEMEDICINE APPLICATIONS

EIKELBOOM RH, YOGESAN K, CONSTABLE IJ, MCALLISTER IL, TAY-KEARNEY ML, BARRY CJ
Centre for Ophthalmology and Visual Science, UWA, and Lions Eye Institute, Perth, Australia.

Purpose: The large size of digitised retinal images makes them impractical for transmission using telephone systems. This study was to determine the amount of digital image compression that can be permitted, while still allowing an experienced observer to screen for various retinal disorders such as drusen, macular degeneration and haemorrhages.
Methods: Colour retinal photographs of 15 subjects from a remote community were digitised at a high resolution. Ten of the subjects had various retinal disorders (most requiring careful observation), and five normal. An image compression algorithm that allowed different rates of compression was used to compress the images to five different levels. They were presented to three assessors.
Results: Image compression could go down to about 3% of original size before abnormal features in the retina could not be identified. This is independent of assessor.
Conclusions: Compression down to this level means that transmission of images can be reduced from over 30 minutes to less than 30 seconds. This has implications for telemedicine. These reduced transmission times makes it practical to transmit a large number of images from remote communities.

1324

USE OF ULTRASOUND B-MODE AND COLOUR FLOW MAPPING TECHNIQUES IN INFLAMMATORY EYE DISEASE

Marie Restori, Moorfields Eye Hospital, London

Purpose: Ultrasound is used routinely in the diagonistic assessment and monitoring of eyes with inflammatory disease when a direct view is restricted or precluded by opaque media.
Methods: A Sequoia (Acuson) scanner representing the latest technology is used to provide high resolution real-time B-Mode images and colour flow maps of blood vessels.
Results: Images and video sequences will be used to illustrate the importance of the real-time aspects of B-Mode and Colour flow mapping in vitreo-retinal disease. Examples of uveitis, trauma, toxocara and toxoplasmosis will be shown. In addition, the ultrasonic diagnosis and classification of posterior scleritis will be discussed in detail.

1325

THE USE OF X-RAY, CT-SCAN AND MAGNETIC RESONANCE IMAGING IN OCULAR INFLAMMATORY DISORDERS

F.-X. Borruat[1,2], CP Herbort[1,2], C Auer[2]
[1] Hôpital Ophtalmique Jules Gonin, Department of Ophthalmology, University of Lausanne, Switzerland
[2] La Source Eye Center, Lausanne, Switzerland

Purpose. Radiological tests may be necessary in the work-up of uveitis. In most situations these tests are ordered directly by the ophthalmologist on the base of his ocular examination or they are performed by the treating doctor following the indications given by the ophthalmologist. Our aim here was to make an inventory of the clinical situations in which radiological work-up is indicated and to illustrate the practical use of radiological investigations.
Methods. The charts of patients seen in the uveitis clinic at Hôpital Jules Gonin and La Source Eye Center were analysed, correlating specific radiological investigations with specific disease entities.
Results. Following associations were found : sacroiliac and lumbosacral X-rays with acute anterior HLA-B27 related uveitis; chest X-ray and/or chest CT-scan with anterior and posterior granulomatous uveitis; cerebral MRI with intermediate uveitis and/or vitritis and/or retinal periphlebitis, posterior scleritis, as well as unexplained inflammatory optic nerve head involvement. The indications to perform the different radiological investigations, their interpretation and their practical usefulness will be illustrated.

Minisymposium: Novel imaging techniques in ocular inflammatory diseases

1326

GENERAL PRINCIPLES FOR THE INTERPRETATION OF INDOCYANINE GREEN ANGIOGRAPHY IN POSTERIOR UVEITIS USING A STANDARD ANGIOGRAPHIC PROTOCOL.

HERBORT CP [1,2], LEHOANG P [3]
[1] Department of Ophthalmology, Hôpital Jules Gonin, University of Lausanne, Lausanne, Switzerland
[2] La Source Eye Center, 2 Avenue des Bergières, Lausanne,Switzerland
[3] Department of Ophthalmology, Hôpital Pitié-Salpétrière, Paris, France

Purpose. Indocyanine green angiography (ICGA) detects fluorescence produced by the ICG molecule in the near infrared wave lengths showing choroidal vascular structures. ICGA may prove useful in the work-up of uveitis with choroidal involvement. Our purpose was to test a standardized ICGA protocol for posterior uveitis in order to gather systematic and comparable data and to design a schematic approach for the interpretation of angiographic signs.
Methods. The proposed ICGA procedure included the search for pre-injection fluorescence. In the early phase of ICGA (until ± 2-3 minutes post-injection) posterior pole frames were taken in order to detect abnormalities in the retinal and choroidal arterio-venous circulation patterns. During the intermediate phase (12 ± 3 minutes) posterior pole frames and eight 360 degree panorama frames were taken in order to detect fluorescence abnormalities in the background impregnation of the choroid, the same sequence being repeated in the late phase (40 ± 5 minutes). A cohort of more than 300 patients was analyzed in this standard fashion in 2 centers..
Results. For uveitis the intermediate and late phases of ICGA were found to yield the most valuable information showing either ICG hyperfluorescence or hypofluorescence or both. ICG hyperfluorescence, always reflecting increased leakage or staining but not window defects as there is no pigment epithelium screen in ICGA, could originate either from increased leakage of the choriocapillaris, the large choroidal or the retinal vessels. The characteristic ICG hypofluorescent dark dots indicating impairement of physiological impregnation of the choroid could take at least five different patterns.
Conclusion. The proposed standardized ICGA protocol and schematized interpretation for posterior uveitis will help determine ICGA semiology for these disorders and might give new insights into their pathophysiology.

1327

THE CONTRIBUTION OF INDOCYANINE GREEN ANGIOGRAPHY (ICGA) TO THE UNDERSTANDING OF CHORIOCAPILLAROPATHIES.

HERBORT CP [1,2], BORRUAT F-X [1,2].
[1] Department of Ophthalmology, Hôpital Jules Gonin, University of Lausanne, Lausanne, Switzerland
[2] La Source Eye Center, Lausanne,Switzerland

Purpose & Background : Several inflammatory chorioretinopathies, including multiple evanescent white dot syndrom (MEWDS), acute posterior multifocal placoid pigment epitheliopathy (APMPPE), multifocal choroiditis (MC), serpiginous choroiditis and acute pigment epithelitis are thought to be due to ischemic involvement of the choriocapillaris, their clinical expression depending on the severity of the process. The study goal was to evaluate indocyanine green angiographic features in MEWDS and APMPPE.
Methods : Four cases of APMPPE and 5 cases of MEWDS were analyzed following a standard angiographic protocol used for inflammatory diseases.
Results : ICGA was similar in all 4 cases of APMPPE, showing random ly arranged hypofluorescent areas present in the early and intermediate (10') phases of angiography, being more well-delineated in the late phase of angiography (40') and corresponding to the areas that were hypofluorescent at the very early times of fluorescein angiography (FA) and hyperfluorescent in the late phase. These lesions nearly completed resolved in the convalescent phase of disease, indicating reversible choriocapillaris non-perfusion. MEWDS patients showed a similar pattern of hypofluorescent ICGA lesions corresponding to early hypo and late very faintly hyperfluorescent areas on FA. Four cases of non-acute multifocal choroiditis showed randomly scattered hypofluorescent areas in the intermediate and late phases of ICGA, indicating chorioretinal atrophy and giving no information on the possible mechanism during the acute phase of the disease.
Conclusions : The analysis of ICGA and FA patterns seen both in MEWDS and APMPPE suggest choriocapillaris non perfusion (ischemia) at the origin of the intermediate and late hypofluorescence on ICGA and very early hypofluorescence on FA, late hypefluorescence on FA being explained by reactional leakage from retinal vessels in the diseased areas. In cases with severe ischemia, irreversible atrophic areas develop that could be seen in APMPPE but never in MEWDS. In conditions like multifocal choroiditis and serpiginous chorioretinitis where choriocapillaris ischemia was reported in the acute phase, atrophic changes could be explained by more severe and/or progressive ischemia.

1328

INDOCYANINE GREEN ANGIOGRAPHIC FEATURES IN TOXOPLASMIC RETINOCHOROIDITIS

AUER C [1], BERNASCONI O [2], HERBORT CP [1,2]
[1] La Source Eye Center, Lausanne,Switzerland.
[2] Department of Ophthalmology, Hôpital Jules Gonin, University of Lausanne, Lausanne, Switzerland.

Background : Indocyanine green angiography (ICGA) detects the infrared fluorescence of indocyanine green (ICG) through the retinal pigment epithelium, thus providing visualization of the choroidal vascular network. The aim of this study was to analyze indocyanine green angiographic features in toxoplasmic retinochoroiditis
Methods : ICGA was performed according to a standard uveitis angiographic protocol in 28 consecutive patients with the diagnosis of acute toxoplasmic retinochoroiditis. ICGA data were compared to fundus colour photographs and fluorescein angiography (FA). Evolution of ICGA signs after therapy (pyrimethamine and sulfadiazine with or without a tapering course of oral corticosteroids) were further analysed.
Results : The main focus of retinochoroiditis was hypofluorescent at all phases of the ICG angiogram in 25/28 cases (89%), but late phase (35-45 minutes) ICG hyperfluorescence was seen in three cases that had all very superficial retinal involvement. The most striking features, however, were multiple hypofluorescent satellite dark dots (SDD) present in 21/28 cases (75%), not seen on funduscopy or FA in 17/21 cases. After therapy SDD disappeared in most of the cases. Furthermore the hypofluorescence under the main lesion was markedly reduced or even disappeared in some cases.
Conclusions : ICGA shows that toxoplasmic retinochoroiditis is a far more widespread process than is clinically suspected, since it extends beyond the visible lesions. ICGA appears useful in assessing the extent of choroidal involvement and the evolution of lesions. It might become an important follow-up parameter and might also give new insights into the pathophysiology of the disease. On the basis of the findings gathered so far, ICGA appears indicated in the work-up and management of toxoplasmic retinochroiditis.

1331

READING AND CONGENITAL MOTOR NYSTAGMUS.

FAHEY D. SAIDLEAR C and EUSTACE P.

Institute of Ophthalmology, Mater Hospital, Dublin [Ireland].

Purpose To illustrate the reading strategies in congenital motor nystagmus and to use this information to better understand normal strategies.

Methods 6 patients with congenital motor nystagmus had infrared oculographic recordings of their eye movements while reading a number of sentences projected on a screen.

Results There is an adaptation of a disorganised pattern of eye movements to allow normal reading. Instead of fixating on specific words there is an oscillation of their eyes across different points on the sentence.

Conclusion Two conclusions are possible regarding how these patients determine the meaning of a word. Either they use their parafoveal vision or they only require a brief foveal fixation. Our work supports the theory that only the first 50 msecs of a reading saccade is needed to understand text.

1332

ROLE OF ATTENTIONAL FACTORS IN THE DEVELOPMENT OF CHILDREN VISUAL SENSITIVITY

TSCHOPP C [1,2], SAFRAN AB [1] and VIVIANI P [2].

1 Neuro-ophthalmology Unit, Geneva University Hospitals,
2 Faculty of Psychology and of Educational Sciences, Geneva, Switzerland

Purpose Age-related changes in visual sensitivity is generally cited as evidence that sensory processing improves substantially during childhood. We evaluated the extent to which attentional factors unduly emphasized the effect of age on the purely physiological mechanisms.
Methods Sensitivity was fully evaluated in 62 normal children aged 5-8 years and 12 adults at two locations using a bracketing technique (Octopus 2000R). False-positive and false-negative (FN) catch-trials were interspersed with the sequence of stimuli.
Results As expected, age affected sensitivity. However, the general level of attentiveness varied not only with age, but also among subjects in the same age group. Indeed, controlled variance analyses indicated that factors for evaluating attentiveness (rate of FN responses, slope of the psychometric function at the median, and goodness of fit) were much better predictors than age of the sensitivity measured. More significantly, the grouping of subjects into homogeneous subgroups, on the basis of their attentional performance, showed that children as young as 5 years may have a visual sensitivity that is only marginally lower than that of adults.
Conclusions It follows that improved visual sensitivity mainly reflects a concomitant evolution of vigilance.

1333

PASSIVE MUSCLE FORCE GRADIENT CORRELATES WITH CLINICAL DATA AND LONG TERM RESULTS

ROSSILLION B, ROTH A, SANSONETTI-FERRARIO A.
University Eye Department, Genève (Switzerland)

Purpose : To determine if the passive muscle force imbalance between the horizontal recti is correlated with the minimum angle of squint in children with early esotropia. This study is a continuation of the previous data presented at JERMOV 1997.
Method : We have controlled 40 children who have undergone surgery for early esotropia between the ages of 1 and 8 years (1 to 4 years after the operation). The minimum angle of squint has been assessed on conscious subjects. Eye position in anesthesia and extensiblity gradient between the horizontal recti have been recorded during surgery. A complete ophthalmologic and orthoptic status was obtained at the follow-up examination.
Results : We found a significant correlation between eye position in anesthesia and extensibility gradient of its horizontal recti ($p < 0,001$). The minimum angle of squint correlates with the eye position in anesthesia ($p < 0,001$) and with the sum of the extensibility gradient of both eyes ($p < 0,001$). Post-operatively, the clinical results were considered as good in 60% of cases, satisfaying in 27% and not sufficient in 13%.
Conclusion : The significant correlation between minimum angle of squint and passive force imbalance of the horizontal recti in anesthesia suggests that the minimum angle depends at least partially on the muscle changes induced by abnormal eye position, the so-called anatomisation of the deviation. Being aware of this fact in early concomitant esotropia should lead to a better planning of surgery with better long-term results.

1334

ISOLATION OF PUPIL LIGHT REFLEX RESPONSE COMPONENTS - CLINICAL APPLICATIONS

Barbur[1] J.L. & Kardon[2] R.

1. Applied Vision Research Centre, City University, London EC1.
2. Department of Ophthalmology, Iowa University, Iowa City, USA.

Purpose New techniques have been developed and applied to isolate different components in the **P**upil **L**ight **R**eflex (PLR) response. The aim of this project was to understand and account for some of the observed variations in the pattern of abnormal pupil response. We wanted to explain why lesions to the primary visual cortex (V1) either eliminate or reduce the PLR response and why patients with optic nerve lesions that show clear, steady state, relative afferent pupil defects fail to show any constriction abnormality in response to brief, foal flashes of light (i.e., the dynamic PLR response).
Methods Visual stimuli that varied systematically in size and contrast were generated on a calibrated visual display unit and pupil measurements were made using the P_SCAN system. The different spatial and temporal response properties of the two components of the PLR response made it possible to mask either one or the other of these components using background perturbation techniques based on luminance contrast noise (Proc. Roy. Soc. Lond. B, *258*, 327-334, 1994). Pupil perimetry was also performed on some subjects.
Results PLR responses were measured to a range of stimulus sizes and contrasts in normal subjects and in patients with unilateral damage to V1, with or without luminance contrast noise. Patients with optic nerve lesions have also been examined. The results show that PLR responses to small, low contrast stimuli are either absent or reduced significantly in patients with damaged primary visual cortex. Some patients with optic nerve damage can, on the other hand, show selective loss of the large field component that controls the steady state size of the pupil, but not the dynamic, focal PLR response.
Conclusions The results obtained suggest that the PLR response is mediated by at least two components with different spatial properties. The absence of a PLR response to small stimuli in patients with damaged V1 suggests that one of these components may involve the central visual pathways.

1335

MOTION INTEGRATION AT THE THALAMIC LEVEL: CONTRIBUTION OF THE VISUAL CORTEX.

CASANOVA C., MERABET L., DESAUTELS A., MINVILLE K. and FILALI M.
Laboratoire des Neurosciences de la Vision, École d'optométrie, Université de Montréal. Montréal (Canada).

Purpose We have recently reported that neurons in the LP-pulvinar complex are part of a pathway involved in the signaling of the "true" direction of motion of objects.We have now investigated the possibility that the higher-order properties of LP-pulvinar cells are derived from signals originating within the anterior ectosylvian visual (AEV) area.

Methods Experiments were performed on anesthetized cats. LP-pulvinar units were characterized using drifting sine-wave gratings and symmetrical plaids differing in 120° in orientation. In 3 cats, the responses to plaid stimulation was investigated in LP following bilateral ablation of the AEV cortex. In 2 other cats, the ablation of the lateral suprasylvian (LS) cortex was also performed. The AEV cortex was also inactivated by injection of GABA and responses of LP cells to plaids were characterized prior, during, and after the cortical deactivation.

Results Pattern selective responses in LP persist even after destruction of the AEV cortex (20% of the units). Only half of the pattern-selective responses in LP were affected following reversible deactivation of the AEV cortex (15 cells successfully tested). No pattern selective responses could be found after ablation of both the AEV and LS cortices.

Conclusions These results suggest that the LP-pulvinar complex receives its pattern-selective signals mainly from the AEV cortex. The responses persisting after the AEV ablation may come from the projections of pattern selective cells in LS areas and/or from intrinsic computations being carried out within the LP itself. These findings lend credence to the notion that certain thalamic nuclei actively participate in the analysis of complex visual scenes in conjunction with the cortex and are not solely acting as mere relay stations as traditionally believed. *MRC, FCAR, FRSQ.*

1336

TEAM COOPERATION BETWEEN PSYCHOLOGY AND OPHTHALMOLOGY IN BENEFIT OF PATIENT'S QUALITY OF LIFE

PEDRUCO A, OLIVEIROS B, GRANDBERG L, LEITE E.
Centre of Ophthalmology, Biomedical Institute for Light and Image Research, Coimbra, Portugal

Purpose: The increasing number of cataract surgery performed with local or topical anaesthesia revealed the importance of controlling patients anxiety and depression previous to surgery.
Methods: 30 outpatients were submitted to cataract surgery (with standard procedures of local anaesthesia and surgical techniques) and psychological evaluation (12 hours before, and 1 month after surgery) with State-Trait Anxiety Inventory (STAI), Beck Depression Inventory (BDI), Visual Functioning Questionnaire (NEI-VFQ), and Symptom Checklist 90 Revised (SCL90R), in a prospective study. Patients were divided in to: group A (15 patients) - no control of anxiety or depression; group B (15 patients) - specific techniques (coping strategies) applied by a psychologist before surgery. No systemic drugs were used.
Results: The results showed a similar score level of anxiety/depression between groups after surgery, a significant lower level of anxiety in group B before surgery, and also a significant recovery in group A, showing that the functional visual results have already overcome the surgical stress procedures.
Conclusions: Specific techniques to control anxiety are of main importance to reduce the need of pharmacological drugs, and complications due to patients anxiety during surgery. The proposal support techniques appeared to be very important in reducing social-economic costs and maintaining the occupational status of our patients.

1337

FLEETING AND MIGRATING SCOTOMATA. A PECULIAR FORM OF VISUAL FIELD DEFECTS

SAFRAN AB, SUNARIC G and DESMANGLES P.
Neuro-ophthalmology and Strabology Unit, Geneva University Hospitals.

Purpose. Using a noise field, similar to the flicker seen on a television screen, allows the visualisation of certain scotomata. This method, also known as snowfield campimetry (SFC), has the advantage of instantly revealing the extent of perceived defects. We tested the use of SFC in subjects complaining of subtle, fleeting visual changes, which had escaped detection by visual acuity testing (VA) and threshold computerized perimetry.
Methods. Ten patients affected by conditions associated with altered ocular hemodynamics were evaluated monocularly by SFC. All had normal VA, and insignificant changes in threshold computerized perimetry.
Results. Using SFC, nine subjects described defective areas of the visual field, which appeared for a few seconds, and were rapidly followed by other transient defects in different locations.
Conclusion : Subtle, fleeting, and migrating scotomata can be demonstrated rapidly and easily using SFC. This form of visual change should be identified. It represents a striking manifestation of transient visual changes, which is usually missed using other test procedures. Conceivable pathogenic mechanisms include alterations in choroidal flow, and intermittent conduction blocks in the optic nerve.

1338

REMOTE ELECTRIC STIMULATION OF OPTIC NERVE IN ITS PARTIAL ATROPHY

Linnik L.F., Vlasova T.M., Antropov G.M.
Moscow Institute of Eye Microsurgery (Russia)

Purpose: To develop a method of direct electic stimulation of the optic nerve,which allows to conduct further treatment courses by this method without additional surgical interventions.

Methods: An induction minicoil is being implanted on an optic nerve. Its diameter is 6 mm, number of windings is 1000,induction voltage up to 5 V, power intensity up to 300 mcA(United States Patent Number: 5,147,284: Sept.15,1992). The duration of one session is 20 minutes. The course of treatment consists of 10 sessions and is conducted 3-4 times a year.

Results: Up to the present there have been operated on over 80 patients with the initial visual acuity of 20/1000 to 20/400. Positive result - the increase of vision up to 20/100 to 20/30 and the widening of visual field has been obtained in 35-60% of cases, depending on the etiology and remoteness of illness.

Experimental and clinical observations have shown that the improvement of visual functions has been caused by the restoration of the conduction of the nerve fibers,which are in the stage of parabiosis,and also by regeneration of myelinic membranes.
Conclusions: The worked out by us method allows to conduct secondary courses of the direct electric stimulation of the optic nerve without further surgical stimulations.The combination of the coercion of the magnetic field and electric current intensifies treatment effect.Definite placement of electrodes allows simultaneously make electric stimulation of the retina.

1411

RELATION OF PILOCARPINE AND TIMOPTOL TO FREE AMINOACIDS IN THE EYE-STRUCTURES

Oláh Z[1], Veselovský J[2], Veselovská Z[2], Veselá A[2], Herichová I[2].
1. Dep.of Ophthalmology, Fac.Med., Comenius Univ.,Bratislava (SR)
2. Dep. of Animal Physiology and Ethol., Fac. Nat. Sci. of Comenius University, Bratislava (SR)

Purpose. The substances increasing the aqueous humor outflow or inhibitors of its production are used to control of the IOP. According to our assumption their therapeutic effect is based on free aminoacids binded in the eye-structures.
Methods. We used the interaction of 2 % pilocarpine solution and 0,25 % timoptol with aminoacids in vitro using the ninhydrine reagent Na[I^{125}]tyrosine and Na[I^{125}]proteinA.
Results.
a/ Mixture of aminoacids with **pilocarpine** was blue colored; pilocarpine alone showed no changes. In Na[I^{125}] tyrosine mixture with pilocarpine radioactivity showed the most decrease in 60 min followed by biphasic curve and in Na[I^{125}]proteinA with pilocarpine in 5 minutes. From 15 up to 120 minutes it was equivalent to the proteinA followed by decrease in 24 hours. Pilocarpine resolved the proteinA into 16 fractions.
b/ Mixture of **timoptol** with aminoacids was blue-colored and timoptol alone showed no changes. The level of Na[I^{125}]tyrosine with timoptol decreased mostly in 15 minutes, after 24 hours showed biphasic character. After 24 hours 6 new fractions were detected.
Conclusions. Our results confirm the direct interaction of pilocarpine and timoptol with aminoacids resulting in new bioactive metabolite playing probably primary role in control of the elevated IOP. The timoptol metabolite is acting 45 minute faster with 50 % higher effect compared with pilocarpine.

1412

OUTFLOW FACILITY COEFFICIENTS AFTER INTRA-VITREOUS INJECTION IN RABBITS

HERMOÇO, A., RODRIGUES, M.L.V., ROMÃO, E. and LAURETTI-FILHO, A.

Dept. Ophthalmology and Otolaringology, Faculty of Medicine of Ribeirão Preto – University of São Paulo, Ribeirão Preto, SP (Brasil)

Purpose: to study the effects of the increase of volume in the posterior segment of the eye on the aqueous humor dynamic.
Methods: It was injected different volumes of saline in 19 eyes of 14 rabbits. The methodology used was manometry; and the outflow facility coefficients were measured in the pressure decay curve.
Results: The mean values of the outflow facility coefficients after in were: 0.14 (after injection of 0,01 ml), 0.08 (after injection of 0.08ml) and 0.07 (after injection of 0.03 ml).
Conclusion: The outflow facility coefficients obtained were significantly lower than the mean value for rabbits; thus, the increase of volume in the posterior segment of the eye acts on the aqueous humor dynamics.

1413

α-ADRENOCEPTORS MODULATE OUTFLOW FACILITY AND $[Ca^{2+}]_i$ ON BOVINE TRABECULAR MESHWORK CELLS

LINK B, GASULL X, LLOBET A, CANALS Ll and GUAL A.
Laboratori de Neurofisiologia, Facultat de Medicina - Fundació Clinic, Barcelona, Spain

Purpose: Drugs acting on the sympathetic nervous system are used in glaucoma therapy. The aim of this study is to investigate how they act on trabecular meshwork cells and how they influence outflow facility (*C*). Methods: Cultured bovine trabecular meshwork cells (BTMs) from 1st to 3rd passage were used. Cells were loaded with fura-2 AM and observed in an inverted microscope. Changes on intracellular calcium ($[Ca^{2+}]_i$) were evaluated. To study *C*, bovine anterior segments were perfused at constant pressure. Results: Epinephrine (EPI) at 10^{-8} M increased *C* by 17%, whereas at 10^{-4}, 10^{-5} and 10^{-6} M lowered *C* for 33%, 36% and 31% ($p<0.001$), respectively. Norepinephrine (NE) did not modify *C* at 10^{-8} M, but decreased *C* at 10^{-4} and 10^{-6} M (20% and 22%, respectively; $p<0.001$). A selective α_2-agonist (Dexmedetomide, 10^{-4} and 10^{-6} M) reduced *C* for 18% and 17% ($p<0.001$). EPI increased $[Ca^{2+}]_i$ on cultured BTMs in 40% (10^{-4} M), 29% (10^{-5} M) and 18% (10^{-6} M) of the cells. At 10^{-8} and 10^{-10} M, less than a 10% of the cells increased $[Ca^{2+}]_i$. NE showed a similar response, increasing $[Ca^{2+}]_i$ on 67% (10^{-4} M) and 34% (10^{-6} M) of the cells. Conclusions: Results show that the observed decrease on *C* and the increase in $[Ca^{2+}]_i$ at μmolar range of EPI and NE are partially mediated by α-adrenoceptors. The effect of Dexmedetomide on *C* suggests an involvement of the α_2-adrenoceptor subtype.

1414

INHIBITION OF cGMP-DEPENDENT PROTEIN KINASE BLOCKS ATRIOPEPTIN SUPPRESSION OF AQUEOUS HUMOUR FLOW AND INTRACELLULAR CALCIUM RELEASE IN BOVINE EYE.

SHAHIDULLAH, M. and WILSON, W. S.
Ocular Pharmacology Lab, IBLS, Univ. Glasgow, Scotland.

Purpose. Intracellular calcium (Ca^{2+}_i) is an important functional mediator in many cells. Here we have tried to correlate ciliary epithelial (CE) Ca^{2+} with aqueous humour (AH) formation rate in the bovine eye by studying effects of atriopeptin (AP) on the ATP-induced increase in Ca^{2+}_i in cultured CE and on IOP and AH formation in perfused eye.
Methods. IOP was measured in bovine eyes perfused through a ciliary artery with Krebs' solution and AH formation by fluorescein dilution (Wilson et al, 1993). CE cells were grown to confluence on glass coverslips, loaded with fura-2 and Ca^{2+}_i measured by the Grynkewicz method.
Results. AH formation rate ($K_{out} \cdot min^{-1} \times 10^4$) before and after AP was 48.3 ± 2.1 and 29.4 ± 1.9 ($p< 0.001$); after sodium azide, 25.7 ± 1.4 ($p< 0.001$). KT-5823, a selective inhibitor of cGMP-dependent protein kinase, blocked both these effects. KT-5823 also blocked IOP reduction by AP or azide. ATP-induced Ca^{2+}_i release in CE was also blocked by AP, azide or 8-bromo cGMP. Low doses of AP and azide were potentiated by zaprinast and reversed by KT-5823.
Conclusion. AP is active via a cGMP-dependent pathway to inhibit Ca^{2+}_i release in CE and to reduce AH formation. This correlation indicates that Ca^{2+}_i in CE may play an important role in control of AH formation.
Wilson, W. S. et al, (1993) Curr. Eye Res. **12**, 609-620.

1415

ERYTHRONIC AND THREONIC ACIDS IN HUMAN AQUEOUS HUMOUR

HARDING JJ[1], HASSETT P[1], RIXON K C[1],. BRON AJ[1] and HARVEY DJ[2]
1. Nuffield Laboratory of Ophthalmology, University of Oxford, Oxford, UK
2. Department of Biochemistry, University of Oxford, Oxford, UK.

Purpose While measuring sugars in the aqueous humour we found an unknown component and sought to identify it.
Methods The levels of sugars in human blood and aqueous humour from cataract patients with and without diabetes were measured using hplc of the nitrobenzoyl derivatives. Gas chromatography/mass spectrometry (gc/ms) was used to identify unknown components.
Results Very little fructose and sorbitol were found. Glucose levels were higher in both blood and aqueous from diabetic patients. During these analyses we found a major component that did not correspond to any sugar reported previously in aqueous humour. This was identified to be a mixture of threonic and erythronic acids.
Conclusions Aqueous humour contains sugars not previously identified that may represent breakdown products of sugar-protein adducts from surrounding tissues.

1416

OCULAR TOLERANCE OF TWO FORMULATIONS OF TOPICAL Na DICLOFENAC COMMERCIALLY AVAILABLE IN MEXICO: A COMPARATIVE, DOUBLE-BLIND, RANDOMIZED TRIAL.

ROCHA G, LOPEZ E, SALINAS J, RODRIGUEZ DE.
Hospital San Jose de Monterrey-ITESM, Mexico and Laboratorios Sophia SA de CV, Guadalajara, Mexico.

PURPOSE. To compare the signs and symptoms elicited by the topical instillation of two different commercially available formulations of 0.1% sodium diclofenac.
METHODS. 3A-Ofteno (Laboratorios Sophia, Mexico; carrier: Sophisen),Voltaren (Ciba Vision) and placebo were instilled into the conjunctival fornices of 60 healthy volunteers. Signs (redness, discharge) and symptoms (burning, itching and tearing) were observed and assessed in a questionnaire to the volunteers by an independent investigator. The two test drugs were compared against each other and against placebo in three distinct applications.
RESULTS. Burning was the most important symptom reported. Essentially no volunteers manifested itching, tearing, redness or discharge. 3A-Ofteno consistently showed less burning than Voltaren ($p<0.05$), and a non-statistically significant difference from placebo ($p>0.05$). Voltaren induced more burning than placebo ($p<0.05$). No adverse reactions were encountered.
CONCLUSIONS. 0.1% Sodium diclofenac as present in this formulation with Sophisen appears to be better tolerated than the other commercially available preparation. The study of Sophisen in other drug formulations is warranted.

1417

A NEW INTRAOCULAR LENS WITH CONTROLLED RELEASE OF FLURBIPROFEN

MARIZ M[1],FERREIRA P[1],SHACHT E[2],GIL MH[1],LEITE E[1]
1. Institute of Biomedical Research on Light and Image, University of Coimbra (Portugal)
2. Institute of Biomedical Technology, University of Gent (Belgium)

Purpose:
The main goal of this work is the preparation of a new intraocular lens (IOL) containing an anti-inflammatory drug - flurbiprofen. This system will have a preponderant role in preventing eye inflammatory processes at least for 1 week after IOL implantation.

Methods:

Different copolymers based on acrylate monomers were prepared. The drug was physically entrapped in these materials. The release kinetics were evaluated.

Results:
The results obtained showed that the drug release was favoured with hydrophylic and flexible copolymers.
The lowest release was obtained when the flurbiprofen was entrapped in a 100% MMA matrix – a hidrophobic and compact matrix.

Conclusions:

From the results obtained we can suggest that the hydrophylicity of the matrix increases the capacity of release.

1421

INDOCYANINE GREEN ANGIOGRAPHY IN BIRDSHOT CHORIORETINOPATHY.

HERBORT CP [1,2], FARDEAU C[3], LEHOANG P[3].
[1] Department of Ophthalmology, Hôpital Jules Gonin, University of Lausanne, Lausanne, Switzerland
[2] La Source Eye Center, Lausanne,Switzerland
[3] Department of Ophthalmology, Hôpital Pitié-Salpétrière, Paris, France

Purpose & Background : Birdshot chorioretinopathy is an ocular inflammatory disease involving both the retina and the choroid. The study goal was to evaluate indocyanine green angiographic features in birdshot chorioretinopathy in order to assess choroidal involvement.
Methods : Fifty-two patients with birdshot choroiretinopathy that had at least one concommittant fluorescein and indocyanine green angiography performed were studied. Indocyanine green angiography (ICGA) was performed according to a standard angiographic protocol used for inflammatory disorders. ICGA signs were correlated with fundus photographs, fluorescein angiography, degree of inflammatory activity and stage of disease.
Results : Forty-eight patients presented choroidal involvement shown by ICGA. In acute or active disease 4 main features were determined. The principal finding, found in 100% of patients with active disease, was the presence of hypofluorescent dark dots present at the intermediate phase of angiography. Their evolutionary pattern was twofold, becoming either isofluorescent or remainig hypofluorescent at the late phase of angiography. Two other signs were fuzziness of choroidal vessels and late diffuse choroidal ICG hyperfluorescence. Comparison of early fluorescein and ICG frames showed that arteriovenous perfusion delay seen by fluorescein was not present on ICG A that allows to analyze more precisely retinal hemodynamics. In chronic longlasting disease the characteristic finding was the presence of hypofluorescent dak dots persistent in the late phase of disease corresponding either to chorioretinal atrophy or to persistent choroidal granulomas.
Conclusions : Consistent ICGA findings in 52 patients allowed to establish a fairly presise ICGA semiology for birdshot chorioretinopathy. ICGA allowed to assess choroidal involvement and in selected cases it was also found to be a valuable diagnostic help and useful to monitor therapeutical intervention.

1422

INDOCYANINE GREEN ANGIOGRAPHIC FEATURES OF GRANULOMATOUS POSTERIOR UVEITIS

TJ Wolfensberger[1], B Piguet[1], CP Herbort[1,2] [1]Hôpital Ophtalmique Jules Gonin, University of Lausanne,Switzerland, [2]La Source Eye Center, Lausanne, Switzerland.

Purpose: Over the last few decades determination of chorioretinal involvement in posterior uveitis has depended on clinical examination and on fluorescein angiography. These techniques are not very sensitive to pick up subtle choroidal change. Recently indocyanine green (ICG) angiography has become available which allows more specific imaging of the choroidal circulation. This presentation will demonstrate the usefulness of ICG angiography in the diagnosis of chroidal involvement in granulomatous posterior uveitis due to sarcoidosis, tuberculosis or syphilis. **Methods**: Patients with posterior uveitis due to sarcoidosis, tuberculosis and syphilis were prospectively studied using ICG angiographies which were performed according to a standard uveitis protocol. **Results**: The ICG angiographic characteristics of these granulomatous diseases could be classified into four main categories: (1) Hypofluorescent dark choroidal lesions in the early and intermediate phases, invisible or not on funduscopy or fluorescein angiography and localised in the midperiphery and in the macula with an average dot diameter of 1/3 disc diameter and showing a confluent pattern in Tbc. These lesions either became isofluorescent in the late phase of the angiogram (Type 1) or remained hypofluorescent (Type 2). (2) Focal hyperfluorescence in the form of multiple small spots appearing in the mid and late phases. (3) Fuzzy choroidal vessels with leakage at around 10 minutes of the angiogram and (4) late diffuse choroidal hyperfluorescence with staining at around 40 minutes of the angiogram. Type 1 lesions, fuzzy choroidal vessels and diffuse choroidal hyper-fluorescence tended to regress with steroid and anti-Tbc treatment. **Conclusions**: ICGA allowed to assess and quantify the hitherto unknown extent of choroidal involvement in granulomatous posterior uveitis, and its characteristic appearance might represent an additional valuable tool for diagnosis and monitoring. Type 1 lesions are likely to represent active granulomas which may disappear with treatment, whereas type 2 lesions are due to atrophy and do not change in the course of the disease.

1423

INDOCYANINE GREEN ANGIOGRAPHY (ICGA) SIGNS IN VOGT-KOYANAGI-HARADA SYNDROME AND SYMPATHETIC OPHTHALMIA.

BERNASCONI O[1], AUER C[2], HERBORT CP[1,2].
[1] Department of Ophthalmology, Hôpital Jules Gonin, University of Lausanne, Lausanne, Switzerland
[2] La Source Eye Center, Lausanne,Switzerland

Purpose : To determine ICGA features in Vogt-Koyanagi-Harada syndrome (VKH) and in Sympathetic Ophthalmia (SO).
Methods : We analysed ICGA features in 4 cases of VKH uveitis and 2 cases of SO. Diagnosis was based on clinical signs and paraclinical investigations in VKH and on positive histology in SO.
Results : In chronic or healed VKH and in SO multiple dark hypofluorescent dots in the early and intermediate phases of ICGA, partially fading in the late phase, were seen, corresponding either to active lesions or to chorioretinal scars. The lesions were less evenly distributed in SO than in VKH. In acute VKH ICGA demonstrated additional diffuse choroidal vasculitis with fuzziness of choroidal vessels in the intermediate phase, late phase difuse hyperfluorescence as well as hyperfluorescent ICG pinpoints in the areas of exudatif retinal detachment.
Conclusion: ICGA appears specially suited to determine the extent of choroidal lesions in disorders involving primarily the choroid such as VKH and SO.

1424

INDOCYANINE GREEN ANGIOGRAPHIC (ICGA) FEATURES IN POSTERIOR SCLERITIS

AUER C[1], HERBORT CP [1,2]
[1] La Source Eye Center, Lausanne, Switzerland
[2] Hôpital Jules Gonin, Dpt of Ophthalmology, University of Lausanne, Lausanne, Switzerland

Purpose. To determine choroidal involvement in posterior scleritis by examining indocyanine green angiography (ICGA) features.
Methods. ICGA was performed according to a standard uveitis angiographic protocol in 8 consecutive patients with the diagnosis of posterior scleritis. ICGA data were compared to fundus color photographs, red-free photographs and fluorescein angiography (FA).
Results. The principal ICGA feature was diffuse zonal choroidal ICG hyperfluorescence in the intermediate (±10 min.) and late (±40 min.) phases of angiography present in all 8 patients, that regressed in response to anti-inflammatory therapy. In 4 patients (2 with massive subretinal exudation) additional fluorescing pinpoints were present in the zonal hyperfluorescent areas. Additional features included irregular delayed choroidal perfusion (5/8 cases), irregularly distributed dark dots that were present up to the intermediate phase and becoming isofluorescent in the late phase giving a mottled aspect to the choroid, and enlargement of draining choroidal veins. In bilateral cases clinical features and ICGA signs were roughly symetrical.
Conclusions. In posterior scleritis, ICGA allowed to indentify areas of choroidal hyperfluorescence possibly indicating areas of maximal inflammatory activity, and demonstrated regression of hypofluorescence in response to therapy. ICGA was found to be useful in assessing the extent of choroidal involvement and will probably serve as one of the follow-up parameters for disease evolution and response to therapy.

1425

OPTICAL COHERENCE TOMOGRAPHIC IMAGING IN OCULAR INFLAMMATORY DISEASES

TJ Wolfensberger, Y Guex-Crosier, CP Herbort, E Bovey
Hôpital Ophtalmique Jules Gonin, University of Lausanne,Switzerland

Purpose: Recently, optical coherence tomography (OCT) has become availabe to assess chorioretinal lesions at the posterior pole. This technique relies on infrared light scanning of the fundus resulting in a vertical optical section of the chorioretinal tissues. Some fundus pathologies associated with ocular inflammatory diseases are clinically subtle but may be detected using OCT prior to the appearance of a fullblown lesion.The purpose of this summary is to alert clinicians to the possibility of diagnosing macular changes in ocular inflammatory disease using this new technology.
Methods: This presentation will explain the physical basis of optical coherence tomography and the technical equipment needed to perform OCT scans. In a second part we will demonstrate the OCT findings of macular lesions associated with ocular inflammatory disease, their evolution and their possible response to therapy.
Results: OCT was useful to image the presence and evolution of cystoid macular changes in ocular inflammatory disorders such as anterior and posterior uveitis, cystoid macular edema associated with highly active antiretroviral therapy (HAART) as well as toxic cystoid macular edema associated with the use of latanaprost drops.
Conclusions: OCT allowed to assess and quantify the extent of cystoid macular involvement in ocular inflammatory disorders, and it may represent an additional valuable tool for early diagnosis and monitoring.

1426

USE OF HIGH-FREQUENCY ULTRASOUND BIOMICROSCOPY (UBM) FOR THE APPRAISAL OF INTRAOCULAR INFLAMMATORY DISEASES.

TRAN VT[1], HERBORT CP[1]
[1] Hôpital Jules Gonin, Dpt of Ophthalmology, University of Lausanne, Lausanne, Switzerland.

Purpose: To determine the use of high-frequency ultrasound biomicroscopy (UBM) in the assessement of inflammatory involvement of the anterior segment, ciliary body, anterior vitreous and pars plana .
Methods :Charts of patients seen from november 1994 to november 1997 in the uveitis clinic of Hôpital Jules Gonin, for whom an UBM examination (840 System, Humphrey Instruments, Inc.) had been performed, were reviewed. The proportion of cases where UBM contributed significant information for the diagnosis or for the management was determined.
Results : A total of 43 patients with the following conditions were analyzed : pars planitis (N=10), pseudophakia (N=6), Iris pathology (N=4), ocular sarcoidosis (N=3), scleritis (N=3), Toxocara uveitis (N=5), herpetic anterior uveitis (N=2), juvenile rhumatoid arthritis (N=2) and other s(N=9). UBM findings in specific diseases will be presented in detail. UBM examination was deemed essential in 10/38 cases (26%). UBM was most useful in the 6 hypotonic eyes examined, differentiating between tractional ciliary body detachment for which surgery was indicated (3 cases) and probably irreversible ciliary body atrophy (3 cases). In 5 patients with toxocara intermediate uveitis, for which the diagnosis was later proven by vitrectomy, UBM showed what appears to be caracteristic pseudo-cystic images in the vitreous adjacent to the pars plana on 360°. In 2 cases of chronic uveitis with dense cataracts, later diagnosed as Behçet's uveitis, UBM allowed to rule out pars planitis by showing absence of snowbanks and a diffuse type of vitreal infiltration. Other useful information obtained by UBM was the assessement of snowbanks and vitreoretinal relations in pars planitis (8 cases) and the localization of haptics within the ciliary body in pseudophakic uveitis (5 cases). **Conclusion** : UBM yielded essential information in nearly a third of this selected group of patients and appears to be useful in cases where retroiridal and/or ciliary body and/or peripheral vitreous pathology is suspected.

2111

OPTICS FROM PATHOLOGICAL CORNEAS: A FRT APPROACH.

PONS A.M., ILLUECA C., MAYEUR V., POHARDY N., LORENTE A., ARTIGAS, JM.
Dept. D'Optica. Universitat d'Alacant. (SPAIN)

Purpose: The use of Fractional Fourier Transform (FRT) approach for the optical peformance modelling of the eye allows the use of Fresnel exact modelling of the light propagation in the eye.In this work we have used a new Fresnel algorithm of image formation in order to evaluate the optical quality of pathological corneas.

Methods: From videokeratography,we have obtained the corneal surface and then derived the image of a point theoretically by Fresnel propagation by using the FRT algorithms.

Results: We have applied our methodology to different pathological corneas. The results are of special interest in the cases of keratoconus and megalocorneas, due to the possibility of an optical aid before surgical correction.

Conclusions: The propossed methodology allows us to obtain a rigorous description of the optical performance of a pathological cornea and it can be used in order to design ad-hoc compensations

2112

NEW SOLID STATE LASER (213NM) TESTED FOR REFRACTIVE SURGERY IN RABBITS

EIKELBOOM RH, VAN SAARLOOS PP, PELOUCH W, LLOYD D, PAZ S.
Centre for Ophthalmology and Visual Science, UWA, and Lions Eye Institute, Perth, Australia.

Purpose: To test a new solid state laser at 213nm for suitability for refractive surgery.
Method: Two trials performed PRK in rabbits.
1. Corneal haze was assessed weekly by slit-lamp in 2 groups of 8 rabbits (16 eyes); one group was treated with 193nm excimer laser as a control;
2. DNA damage was measured by autoradiography in 3 groups of 6 eyes (one positive control group treated with 266nm and a negative control group treated with 193nm).
The 213nm laser source was a prototype refractive surgery system made by TELCO (Perth, Australia).
Results:
1. Corneal haze formation levels, progression and clearing time were the same in the 193nm control group and 213nm group ($p>0.01$).
2. 213nm had the same effect as the 193nm negative control with 2% of cells with DNA damage. The positive control of 266nm had 47% of the cells damaged.
Conclusion: The 213nm laser should produce a similar result to current 193nm excimer lasers and clinical trials are beginning.

2113

KERATOCONUS AND CATARACT: ASSOCIATED PREVELANCE IN A LARGE IRISH FAMILY

FRAZER DG, JACKSON AJ, LOTERY AJ, MCKAY P, HUGHES AE, SILVESTRI G
Department of Ophthalmology, Royal Victoria Hospital, Belfast, N.Ireland

Purpose: To investigate the association between keratoconus and autosomal dominant cataract in a large Irish pedigree.
Methods: All family members underwent a full refraction and had distance and near visual acuities recorded through an optimal spectacle correction. Corneal curvatures were recorded using a B&L keratometer and in those cases where irregularities were noted corneal topographical analysis was performed. Corneal and Anterior segment findings were recorded using a portable slit lamp biomicroscope and retinal integrity was assessed using a direct ophthalmoscope. A comprehensive ophthalmic history was recorded in every case. DNA was stored for analysis.
Results: Of the 47 family members from 3 generations examined, 18 were found to be affected. Keratoconus, necessitating grafting, was found in 6 cases including 4 of the 5 affected individuals over the age of 30 years. The clinical phenotype of the cataract in each of the younger patients, who had immature lens opacities, was noted to be anterior polar. Of the 18 affected individuals 11 have had cataract surgery. The inheritance pattern is autosomal dominant with high penetrance.
Conclusions: These unusual findings in an otherwise healthy normal family, suggest a co-inheritance between the two conditions. Genetic linkage is currently underway.

2114

THE ROLE OF H2O2 GENERATING OXIDASES IN THE RABBIT CORNEA INJURED WITH UVB RAYS

ČEJKOVÁ J, ARDAN,T AND ANDONOVA Z.
Department of Eye Histochemistry, Institute of Experimental Medicine, Academy of Sciences, Prague (Czech Republic)

Purpose: To examine histochemically the role of H2O2 generating oxidases in corneas injured with UVB rays.
Methods: Rabbit corneas were irradiated with UVB rays (312 nm, 1 x daily for one till 8 days from a distance of 0.2 m with UV lamp, 6W). During the irradiation, some eyes were topically treated with allopurinol or catalase (both drugs 0.5 mg/1ml saline, dropwise, 5 x daily). Corneas were examined histochemically for xanthine oxidase, D-amino acid oxidase, monoamine oxidase and α-hydroxiacid oxidase using cerium methods. Normal corneas served as controls.
Results: H_2O_2 generating oxidases are present in the normal corneal epithelium and endothelium. UVB rays cause the increase of oxidase activities in the corneal epithelium and endothelium. Inflammatory cells present in the corneal stroma are also enzymatically active. Allopurinol (an inhibitor of xanthine oxidase) decreases the xanthine oxidase activity only. In contrast, the treatment with catalase (an enzymatic scavenger of H2O2) decreases the activities of all oxidases studied; the number of inflammatory cells is diminished. The damage of corneas is significantly reduced.
Conclusions: Results show that H2O2 generating oxidases contribute to the damage of corneas injured with UVB rays.
Supported by the grant No. G/16-3 of Ministry of Health (CR), by the grants No. 304/96/0908 and 307/96/K226 from GA (CR).

2115

Effect of Leukocytes on Cellular Proliferation and Wound Healing of the Cornea

Lisha Gan, Per Fagerholm
St. Eriks Eye Hospital, Karolinska institute (Sweden)

Purpose. This study was performed to establish if fucoidin by blocking the adhesion of leukocytes on the limbal vascular endothelium prevents extravasation of the cells from the blood stream into the limbal stroma as well as the wounded area after corneal injury. A consequence of successful leukocyte blocking was to investigate the influence of leukocytes on the corneal cellular proliferation after corneal wounding.

Method. Thirty-two New Zealand white rabbits were used. Photorefractive keratectomy (PRK) and a standardised alkali corneal wound were used as models in two sets of experiments. In half of the injured rabbits fucoidin was used to prevent leukocytes from leaving the local vessels. The efficiency of the blocking technique was evaluated by counting the number of leukocytes in the limbal and wounded corneal areas. Proliferating cell nuclear antigen (PCNA) was employed as a marker for proliferative activity.

Results. The infiltration of leukocytes into the limbus and the cornea after PRK and alkali injuries can be blocked by fucoidin. The healing rate of corneal epithelium after alkali burn was retarded without the presence of leukocytes. The PCNA expression was enhanced in the presence of leukocytes. The fucoidin per se has no influence on the corneal cell proliferation and wound healing.

Conclusion. 1. Polymorphonuclear leukocytes (PMNs) can be prevented to enter the corneas in vivo by fucoidin after PRK and after alkali burn. 2. The corneal epithelial healing rate was delayed without the presence of PMNs in vivo. 3. PCNA expression was increased by the presence of leukocytes.

2116

THE INFLUENCE OF LEUKOCYTES ON PROLIFERATION OF CORNEAL VASCULAR ENDOTHELIAL CELLS

Per Fagerholm, Lisha Gan St. Eriks Eye Hospital, Karolinska Institutet (Sweden)

Purpose: In this study, we want to investigate the role of extravasated leukocytes on the proliferation of corneal vascular endothelial cells in the limbal area. We have previously (Invest Ophthal. 1997 vol. 38) demonstrated the efficiency of i.v. fucoidan to prevent leukocytes leaving the blood stream in the limbus.
Methods: Ten New Zealand White rabbits (2.5 kg) were divided to two groups. The central cornea of the right eyes were exposed to a 5.5 mm paper soaked in 1 N NaON solution for 60 seconds. Seven rabbits were given 2ml of 5 % fucoidan (Sigma) intravenously every 2h for up to 35 h to prevent PMNs from leaving the blood stream. The corneal epithelium healed within 35h. At 35 h all rabbits were sacrificed. The corneas fixed in 10% formaldehyde for 12 h and embedded in paraffin. 4μm sections were used for immunohistological PCNA staining. **Results**: Intense leukocytes infiltration were found in non-fucoidan treated corneas from the limbal region into the wound margin. The number of PCNA (PC10) positive vascular endothelial cells was significantly higher in the non-fucoidan treated corneas. Very few of these cells stained positive in the treated corneas and were negative in the normal corneas. **Conclusions**: The infiltration of leukocytes following alkali injury coincides with marked endothelial cells proliferative activity. This may be the first sign of corneal neovasculazation.

2117

EXPOSED AREAS OF CORNEA AND SCLERA IN ELEVATED AND DEPRESSED GAZE

TIFFANY, J.M., BAKER, M.R.
Nuffield Lab. of Ophthalmology, Oxford University (UK)

Purpose We have developed a computer program (Ocularea®) to calculate the exposed areas of cornea and sclera from on-screen images of the human eye, and tested it for level gaze. We wished to measure ocular area with elevated and depressed gaze, by tilting the head rather than re-positioning the camera.
Methods The original Zeiss head-frame permits adjustment of the brow-band by a screw mechanism, in addition to chin height. The screw was calibrated so that any head tilt from +15° to -15° (relative to level gaze) could be selected. Angles were checked by side-photographs showing wedge angles relative to the Frankfurt plane. Video images were captured for a series of up- and down-gaze head positions and the Ocularea program applied.
Results Linear relationships were confirmed between the screw setting, the angle of gaze and the facial tilt. Areas measured for gaze angles of 0°, ±5°, ±10° and ±12.5° gave total exposed areas between 1.87 (-12.5°) and 3.13 (+12.5°) cm^2, palpebral heights from 7.3 to 13.2 mm, and corneal/scleral area ratios from 0.772 (-12.5°) to 1.329 (+12.5°). The total area / palpebral height relationship was A = 0.289 h + 0.244, close to that determined from direct gaze.
Conclusions Head-tilt on a calibrated frame gives a quick and easy way of obtaining images for different directions of gaze, and their corresponding ocular areas. These results are useful in studying ocular usage and fatigue in the workplace, and the effects of environmental factors on ocular comfort.

2121

MODIFICATIONS IN THE CORTICAL SOLUBLE CRYSTALLINS FROM AGEING HUMAN LENSES.

COLICCHIO P.[2],STIUSO P.[2],LIBONDI T.[1,3] AURICCHIO G.[1] G.F.J.H.VRENSEN[4] and COLONNA G.[1,3]
1Eye Clinic, 2Dept. of Biochem. and Biophys, 3CRISCEB 2nd University of Naples, Italy, 4Dept.of Morphol., Netherlands Ophthalmic Res. Inst., Amsterdam.

Purpose. Recently we reported some observations regarding the protein composition of human nuclear soluble crystallins durig ageing. We want to study differences between cortex and nucleus of the same lenses. **Methods**. The cortex of normal human lenses of different ages were homogenized in Tris-buffer and centrifuged at 15000 rpm, to obtain the water soluble fraction. The concentration normalized crystallins were processed through HPLC, by using two sequential gel filtration Bio-Sil SEC columns(250-400), equipped with diode array photodetectors. SDS-PAGE was performed. **Results**. Native α-fraction concentration remains costant at all ages. There is an increase in the concentration of the **HMW** fraction during ageing, while the **LMW** fraction (less then 10 kDa) decreases . By SDS-PAGE the **LMW** and 43 kDa fractions are detected at around 40yo and tend to increase thereafter. Also the fluorescence (exc360-em420nm) of **HMW,** which is barely detectable before 40yo, increase thereafter. Native α-fraction and **LMW** fraction do not show significant change in the relative fluorescence intensity. **Conclusion.** The quantitative and qualitative characteristics found in cortical ageing crystallins are different from those found in the nuclei of the same human lenses. Supported by MURST 40% and 60% and CNR grants

2122

CHAPERONE ACTIVITY OF α-CRYSTALLIN PRESERVES IMMUNOLOGIC DETERMINANTS OF BOVINE β_S-CRYSTALLIN

BOURS J.
Dept. of Exptl Ophthalmolgy, University of Bonn, Bonn, Germany.

Purpose: Aim of the present study is to demonstrate the chaperone activity of α-crystallin which preserves the immunologic determinants of β_S-crystallin, isolated from the WI-crystallin fraction.
Methods: β_S-Crystallin was isolated from the water-insoluble (WI) fraction of 9-year-old bovine lens equator by preparative column isoelectric focusing (IEF). The WI-crystallins were isofocused in a special glass column in a sucrose density gradient. Before isofocusing the WI sample was dissolved in 7M urea and applied immediately on the column. The sample was characterized by thin-layer IEF, SDS- and microimmunoelectrophoresis (MIE) with polyvalent and monovalent antisera.
Results: Urea releases β_S-crystallin from the WI α-crystallin complex. Upon isofocusing, the β_S-crystallin moves towards its isoelectric point (IEP), while the WI α-crystallin moves downwards, to precipitate at its IEP of 4-4.9. The released β_S-crystallin is isofocused around pI= 7.00. After completion of the isofocusing process, a β_S-crystallin fraction is aspirated from the top of the column, for testing by IEF, SDS and MIE. IEF of purified β_S-crystallin resulted in 2 bands with pI 6.80 and 7.00. With SDS 2 bands with MW's of 23.2 and 24.8 kDa could be detected. Only one precipitin line with β_S-crystallin mobility was detected, when tested by MIE with 2 polyvalent antisera against bovine embryonic lens and calf lens cortex. Similarly, one precipitin line appeared when using a bivalent antiserum against β-crystallins. The β_S-crystallin isolated from WS-fraction of the same age and lens part was immunologically identical to WI β_S-crystallin, characterized also by identical pI's and MW's.
Conclusions: The immunologic determinants of β_S-crystallin were preserved in its WI form by the chaperone activity of α-crystallin, and were identical to those from WS β_S-crystallin. Obviously, the chaperone activity of WI α-crystallin protects β_S-crystallin from denaturation.

2123

HUMAN SENILE CATARACT CLASSIFICATION: AN APPROACH AT A MOLECULAR LEVEL IN THE NUCLEUS OF THE LENS.

LIBONDI T.[1,3], STIUSO P.[2], COLICCHIO P.[2], COLONNA G.[1,3] and AURICCHIO G.[1]
1Eye Clinic, 2Dept. of Biochem. and Biophys, 3CRISCEB 2nd University of Naples, Italy.

Purpose. Our goal is to study at a molecular level the morphological differences that can be seen clinically among the cortical, nuclear, posterior subcapsular and total human senile cataracts. **Methods**.The water soluble fraction of nuclear lens crystallins was processed through HPLC, by using two sequential gel filtration Bio-Sil SEC columns(250-400), equipped with diode array photodetectors. SDS-PAGE was performed. **Results**.The relative concentration of the **HMW** fraction is much higher in nuclear and total cataracts (opaque nucleus) than in cortical and subcapsular ones, which present a trasparent nucleus. A parallel behaviour is shown by the **LMW** fraction. By SDS-PAGE the nuclei from cortical cataracts present the highest concentration of **LMW.** The fluorescence of **HMW** (exc360-em420nm) disappears in the total cataract, while is very high in the nuclear one. In nuclear and total cataracts we observe a very high level of fluorescence intensity of **LMW** fraction (less then 10Kda). **Conclusion.**Quantitative and qualitative composition of nuclear soluble proteins from different types of cataract are different. Human senile cataracts is not a single entity; the differences in the protein content may address to the different etiopathogeneses. Supported by "Regione Campania"grant

2124

Morphologic Criteria in cultured bovine Lens Epithelia

Ursula M.Mayer
Dpt.Ophthalmology and Eye Clinic, Univ.Erlangen-Nbg.

Background: Cultured lens epithelia represent a model for evaluation of noxious agents. As cells have a different morphology in the original tissue or in culture , there was interest in criteria for evaluation of the morphology of cultivated cells.
Material and methods: The presented cultures are prepared from bovine lens epithelium as described by MAYER in 1969. The medium: TCM 199 plus the usual antibiotics, 20% FCS, 2% glutamine and 5% HEPES buffer. The nocive agents: amphotericin B, fluconazol, x rays (5 Gy) and 5 to 1 200 mg% glucose. Culture flascs containing 200 000 cells from the first subculture of bovine lens epithelia were exposed to the noxious agent , were reincubated for another two days and were photographed. Cell morpgology was observed in generally 100 projected slides of one experimental set. By two persons scores were ruled out for the following criteria: inclusions, vacuoles, nuclear alterations, alterated cell walls („pseudopodium-like", „microaneurysm-like"), very thin cell fibres.
Results: In antimycotic drugs alterations of the cellular wall were impressing; after x-rays the main criteria were vacuoles and nuclear alterations; in hypoglycemia no cell proliferations occurred, and in hyperglycemia both, vacuoles and cell wall alterations, were to be seen.

2125

SURAMIN INHIBITS MIGRATION OF HUMAN LENS EPITHELIAL CELLS IN VITRO

RIECK P., KRIEGSCH J. and HARTMANN CHR.
Dpt. Ophthalmology, Charité, Berlin (Germany)

Purpose: New approaches to prevent posterior capsule opacification focus on a pharmacological therapy. In this study, we investigated the effect of the naphthylurea suramin in vitro in a cell culture model.
Material and Methods: Human lens epithelial cells (HLEC) isolated from lens capsules of cornea donors were cultured in DMEM+10% FCS until they reached confluency. A central circular "wound" was made on these monolayers by means of a modified hand trephine. Cultures were then incubated with different concentrations of suramin (0,1; 0,5; 1 and 5 mM) over varying incubaton times (1-72 hours). Unsupplemented cultures served as controls. After 5 days, the number of cells that had migrated into the denuded area was determined by counting. Analysis of suramin toxicity was carried out using trypan blue staining.
Results: A dose-dependent significant effect of suramin on the inhibition of HLEC migration was found even after short (1h) incubation times. Higher doses (>3 mM) revealed toxic effects.
Conclusions: These results demonstrate the efficiency of suramin in vitro to inhibit migration of HLEC which can be explained by blocking growth factor-mediated effects on the cells. The use of suramin represents an interesting perspective in pharmacological prevention of secondary cataract. In vivo studies will follow to investigate possible side effects of suramin on other intraocular tissues.

2126

TEMPERATURE THRESHOLD FOR CELL DEATH OF LENS EPITHELIAL CELLS IN A CAPSULAR BAG MODEL

Y van Tenten 1, B Willekens 2, A De Wolf 2, GFJM Vrensen 2, MJ Tassignon 1
1 Dep Ophthalmology University Institute Antwerp
2 Dep Morphology The Netherlands Eye Research Institute

Purpose: Posterior capsule opacification (PCO) is a main complication of cataract surgery (20-40% of cases) and its treatment is costly and not without complications. Despite improvement of surgical procedures and pharmacological interventions, no obvious reduction in PCO prevalence occurred over the last 10 years.
The aim of this study was to determine an optimal temperature and duration for cell death of lens epithelial cells (LEC's), in order to find a means of prevention of proliferation and migration of LEC's in the capsular bag after cataract surgery (ECCE).
Materials and methods: Over 100 capsular bags were prepared from donor eyes using an ECCE procedure and heated at temperatures of 37°, 55°, 60° or 65° for 2 minutes. Directly after heating or after culture in MEM with 2% FCS for 2 or 7 days, the specimens were fixed in glutaraldehyde/paraformaldehyde and examined with LM, SEM and TEM and MTT (viability assay).
Results: Immediately after ECCE, a destructive effect of temperature on LEC's was observed. However, structural and viability assays show that after 2 or 7 days in culture, LEC's heated at temperatures up to 55° start to reproliferate and to form a multilayer in the bag whereas LEC's heated at temperatures ≥ 60° are totally destroyed and loose their ability to proliferate.
Conclusion: It was found that there is a direct effect of heating on LEC's, and that for temperatures up to 55° recovery occurs after culturing. Temperatures ≥ 60° during 2 minutes are needed to fully destroy the LEC's in the capsular bag.

2127

An in vitro model for prevention of secondary cataract by irradiation

AM Joussen, G Kolling, FE Kruse
University Eye Hospital Heidelberg, INF 400, 69120 Heidelberg, Germany

Introduction: Secondary cataract is one of factors which limit visual function after cataract surgery. Various experimental methods using pharmacological inhibition of lens epithelial cells have been proposed. However diffusion of toxic substances into the antrerior chamber may lead to damage of corneal endothelial cells. We therefore investigated an alternative for inhibition of lens epithelial cell proliferation by low dose irradiation.
Methods: Rabbit lens epithelial cells were removed from the lens capsule and cultivated in modified SHEM / Ham´s F12 with 10% serum. Passages 3 to 5 were used. 10^5 cells per 60 mm dish were seeded and irradiated with external photon beam in different dosages. Cell counts and morphological observations were performed every 3 days. Proliferation was examined by incorporation of BrdU.
Results: Controls showed an increase of cell number from 46±9 / field on day 2 to 274±32 / field on day 12. In contrast irradiated cultures showed slow proliferation up to day 6 and no increase or decreasing cell numbers thereafter (depending on the irradiation dosage). E.g. irradiation with 15 Gy resulted in a decrease of the cell number to less than 70 % of the seeded cells on d 12. In addidion BrdU labeling index droped from 4,2 in contrast to 0,7 on day 6 afteeeerrr irradiation with 15 Gy .
Conclusion: Irradiation has been known to cause damage to lens epithelial cells. We investigated the dose-dependent effect of photon irradiation on proliferation in vitro in order to use the observed growth inhibition for prevention of secondary cataracts. Based on this study in vivo experiments are currently under investigation.

2128

PHACOEMULSIFICATION CATARACT SURGERY: IS ROUTINE REVIEW NECESSARY ON THE 1ST POST-OPERATIVE DAY?

TAN J(1), NEWMAN D(2), KLUNKER C(3), WATTS S (3), BURTON RL(3).
1. St. James's University Hospital, Leeds (UK)
2. Addenbrooke's Hospital, Cambridge (UK)
3. West Norwich Hospital, Norwich (UK)

Purpose: To determine the value of routine post-operative review at 1 day following uneventful phacoemulsification cataract surgery.
Methods: Prospective study of 234 consecutive patients undergoing phacoemulsification cataract surgery. Per-operative complications occurred in 8 patients who were excluded. Local anaesthesia was used for 97% of patients. The findings of the 1st day post-operative review were analysed.
Results: 98.3% of patients had no complications at the 1st day post-operative review. Complications detected comprised raised intraocular pressure >35 mmHg (1.33%), corneal abrasion (0.44%), iritis (0.44%), corneal oedema (4.42%) and hyphaema (0.88%).
Conclusions: Routine review at 1 day following uneventful phacoemulsification cataract surgery may not be necessary given the low incidence of complications.

2131

Light-induced retinal apoptosis : preventing effects of free radicals scavengers.

Ranchon I.[1], Droy-Lefaix M.Th.[2], Doly M.[1].
1. University of Auvergne, Laboratory of Biophysic, Clermont-Ferrand, France ; 2. IPSEN Laboratory, Paris, France.

Purpose : Apoptosis has been implicated in retinal degenerative diseases. Firstly we determine if apoptosis is induced in our validated model of photoreceptor degeneration by light. Secondly we seek to evaluate the involvement of free radicals in apoptosis triggering.
Methods : Retinal light damage is induced by exposing Wistar rats to 24 hours of light at 1700 lux. Animals were treated with DMTU (500mg/kg; i.p) or Ginkgo Biloba Extract (EGb 761, IPSEN, 100 mg/kg/day, per os). One day, 15 and 29 days after light exposure, apoptotic cells were detected using ApopTag®Plus in situ detection kit peroxidase (Appligene-Oncor, Illkirch, France).
Results : No apoptotic cells were detected in control retinas. Numerous apoptotic cell staining were observed in light-exposed rat retinas. These cells were localized essentially in the superior and central part of the retina. At 15 days after exposure the apoptotic cells disappear. When animals were treated with DMTU or EGb 761, the staining of apoptotic photoreceptor cells is significantly decreased one days after exposure. No detectable apoptotic cell is observed at 15 and 29 days later.
Conclusions : Our model of photoreceptor degeneration by light induced an apoptotic mechanism. The inhibition of cell death by DMTU or EGb 761, two antioxidants, suggests that oxygenated free radicals play a major role in light-induced apoptosis of photoreceptor cells.

2132

SODIUM SALICYLATE REDUCES APOPTOSIS IN THE RDS AND RD MOUSE RETINA

REICHEL MB[1], SCHLICHTENBREDE FC[1], TANNAPFEL A[2], ALI RR[3] and WIEDEMANN P[1]
1. Dept. Ophthalmology, Leipzig University, Leipzig (Germany)
2. Dept. Pathology, Leipzig University, Leipzig (Germany)
3. Dept. Mol. Genetics, University College London, London (UK)

Purpose Apoptosis has been identified as the final common pathway of photoreceptor cell death in multiple mouse models as well as in humans. One treatment strategy for retinal degeneration is the modulation of apoptosis. Sodium salicylate has been shown to be neuroprotective *in vitro* by the inhibition of neuronal factor κB which is an important mediator in the apoptotic cascade. The aim of this experiment was to investigate the role of sodium salicylate in the modulation of apoptosis in the retinal degeneration of the *rds* and the *rd* mouse.
Methods DL-Lysinmono(sodium salicylate) was injected daily i.p into rds and rd pups from day 0. Three different dosages ranging from anticoagulative to antiinflammatory effect were administered according to body weight. Controls were injected with physiological sodium chloride solution. Mice were sacrificed at day 16. A total of 50 animals were procedured. Post-mortem the eyes were enucleated, fixed in formalin and paraffin embedded. Coated slides with 5μm thick sections were immunostained for apoptosis with a modified dUTP nick end labelling protocol (TUNEL). Positive photoreceptors were counted by two independent observers.
Results Light microscopy revealed no abnormalities of retinal morphology and other ocular structures. Apoptotic cells occurred only within the degenerating photoreceptor cell layer of both strains. Compared to the retinas in the control group which showed an average of 160 TUNEL positive photoreceptors per section the number of labelled cells in the treated mice was significantly reduced. The reduction observed was dosage dependant with best effect at 0,2 mg per g body weight.
Conclusions The peak of apoptotic nuclei which is known to occur in both mouse strains at day 16 has been reduced significantly by systemic administration of sodium salycilate. This shows *in vivo* the neuroprotective potential of this drug in two models of retinal degeneration. The investigation of long term photoreceptor cell rescue is the subject of ongoing experiments.

2133

F2-ISOPROSTANES AS MARKERS FOR OXIDATIVE STRESS IN HUMAN RETINA

NOUROOZ-ZADEH J[1] AND PEREIRA P[2]
1. Dept. of Medicine, Division of Clinical Pharmacology and Toxicology, University College London (England)
2. Dept. Ophthalmology, Biomedical Institute for Research in Light and Image, Coimbra (Portugal)

Purpose: To establish if F2-isoprostanes are formed in human retina *in vivo* consisting of a marker for retinal oxidative damage. Material and Methods: Human retinas were obtained from Coimbra University Hospital Eye Bank (n= 16). Retinas were sealed under nitrogen and frozen at -80 C. Fatty acids were isolated and analysed by gas-chromatography as methyl esters. F2-isoprostanes were isolated from total lipid extract by a solid phase extraction, followed by derivatization and final analysis by GC-MS. Results: Human retinas present detectable amounts of esterified F2-isoprostanes, although there were no detectable amount of free (non-esterified) isoprostanes. The amount of F2-isoprostanes did not correlate with the age of donors. Conclusions: It is suggested that oxidative damage occurs *in vivo* in human retina, while arachidonic acid being esterified to phospholipids. Moreover, levels of F2-isoprostanes may be accurate and reliable markers of such ongoing oxidation. Oxidation of retinal tissue may be involved in various forms of retinal degeneration, including age-related macular degeneration and diabetic retinopathy.

2134

RPE CELLS ISOLATED FROM DYSTROPHIC RCS-RPE CELLS HAVE A DIFFERENT Ca^{2+}-METABOLISM COMPARED WITH NORMAL LE-RPE CELLS

STALMANS P., HIMPENS B.
Laboratorium voor Fysiologie, KULeuven, Belgium

Purpose. To determine the rate of a mechanically induced intra- and intercellular Ca^{2+}-wave propagation in RPE cells and to investigate the subcellular properties of the Ca^{2+}-wave.
Methods. Confocal microscopy and Ca^{2+}-measurements using the fluorescent dye fluo-3 were used to measure the spatiotemporal characteristics of the Ca^{2+}-wave propagation during a mechanical stimulation in the stimulated and in the neighboring cells in Long Evans (LE) RPE cells or dystrophic Royal College of Surgeons (RCS) RPE cells.
Results. A regenerative Ca^{2+}-wave with a decreasing rate of propagation was found in the stimulated cells. The rate of propagation was significantly slower in RCS-RPE cells compared to LE-RPE cells. Incubation with thapsigargin significantly lowered the propagation rate in both LE and RCS-RPE cells. The amplitude of the intracellular Ca^{2+}-rise in the nucleus and cytoplasm was differentially modulated by protein kinase C in RCS-RPE cells, but not in LE-RPE cells.
Conclusion. A nucleocytoplasmic Ca^{2+}-gradient is found in cultured rat RPE cells. It is suggested that RCS-RPE cells have intracellular Ca^{2+}-regulating properties which are different from those of LE-RPE cells.

2135

THE LOCALISATION OF ZINC IN RAT PHOTORECEPTORS VARIES DURING LIGHT AND DARK ADAPTATION

UGARTE M and OSBORNE N.N.
Nuffield Laboratory of Ophthalmology, Walton Street, University of Oxford (UK)

Purpose: The aim of our studies was to localise chelatable zinc in dark- and light-adapted rat retinas.
Methods: Female rats were dark-adapted for 3 hours or exposed to laboratory light for 5 hours, deeply anaesthetised and perfused/fixed with Na_2S, paraformaldehyde and glutaraldehyde in the dark or light, respectively. Retinas were then stained for localisation of chelatable zinc (Ugarte M., Osborne N.N., General Pharmacology 30 (1998): 297-303)
Results: Chelatable zinc in the light-adapted retina is associated with the RPE cells, the photoreceptors, both plexiform layers, perikarya in the vitreal part of the inner nuclear layer and cells in the ganglion cell layer. The localisation of zinc within the photoreceptors changed during dark-adaptation. In the light-adapted retinas, zinc was mainly localised at the level of the inner segments; whereas in dark-adapted retinas zinc was associated with the photoreceptor perikarya and absent from the inner segments.
Conclusions: Endogenous zinc is localised mainly in the photoreceptors and RPE cells in the mammalian retina. The localisation of zinc within the photoreceptors changes during dark- and light-adaptation. The results suggest that zinc plays a part in the visual transduction process of photoreceptors

2136

RETINAL CAPILLARY BLOOD FLOW IN DIFFERENT LIGHT CONDITIONS

LANZL I[1], NICHOLL J[2].
1. Dept. of Ophthalmology, Technical University, Munich (Germany)
2. Glaucoma Service, Wills Eye Hospital, Philadelphia (USA)

Purpose: Retinal capillary flow is autoregulated within certain boundaries. Different light conditions influence retinal metabolism and possibly blood flow. Changes in retinal capillary blood flow after dark adaptation (part I) and after exposure to bright light flashes (part II) are investigated.
Methods: Heidelberg Retina Flowmeter (HRF) measurements were obtained in 20 healthy volunteers in ambient room light conditions. These values were compared to the values in the same volunteers obtained after 30 minutes of dark adaptation (I), and after exposure to repeated 100 W/sec light flashes (II). Paired 2-tailed t-testing was used for analysis.
Results: After dark adaptation as well as after exposure to bright light flashes an increase in retinal capillary flow of about 12% was measured for the group ($p<0.001$).
Conclusions: Measurement error for HRF flow values has been established in different studies to range between 5% and 8%. The observed increase seems to be a real effect. We postulate that the increase in retinal capillary flow after dark adaptation as well as after exposure to bright light is a physiologic response to increased metabolic demand. Illumination levels should be taken into account, when conducting retinal capillary blood flow studies.

2137

Ontogenical study of Mineralocorticoid Receptor in the rat retina

Golestaneh N., Nicolas C., Ferrari P., Agarwal M.K., Mirshahi M.
INSERM U 86,15 rue de l'Ecole de Médecine 75006 Paris

Purpose. Mineralotropic hormones regulate the hydrosodic balance in many cell types of mesodermal and ectodermal origins via appropriate ion channels in the cell membrane. Recently we reported the immunochemical demonstration of the Mineralocorticoid receptor (MCR) in human and rat ocular tissues (Mirshahi et al, Biochem. Biophys. Reas. Comm. 1996; 219,150-156 and Neuroendocrinology, 1997; 65, 70-78). In this study we investigate the presence of MCR in retina from differents 2, 4, 9, 13 days old rats.
Methods: immunohistochemical analysis of rat retina was performed by specific rabbit anti MCR purified from rat kidney. RT-PCR analysis of retina mRNA followed by sequence analysis was assessed using the specific MCR primers.
Results: In 2 days old rats, MCR staining predominated in pigmented epithelium layer and in inner neuroblastic layer. At day 4 outer neuroblastic layer was also stained. and at day 13 immunoreactivity was observed in pigmented epithelium, outer and inner nuclear layers, ganglion cell layer and epithelial cells from ciliary body. The expression of the MCR in the rat retina in sequential events was confirmed with a predicted 843 bp having 100% homology with rat kidney MCR.
Conclusion: The presence of MCR in early age of rat retina suggests that MCR play a fundamental role in eye development. Both the neuronal and the epithelial compartments of the ocular tissues form interesting new targets of action of mineralotropic hormones. Aided in part by financial assistance of AFRP.

2138

CRYOPRESERVATION OF RETINAL PIGMENT EPITHELIUM: CELL SURVIVAL WITH VARIOUS CRYOPROTECTANTS

SISTANI F, HARTMANN U, KUSTER S, HAGENAH M, STEINHORST UH.
Dept. Ophthalmology, Medizinische Hochschule Hannover, Hannover (Germany)

Purpose Preservation of living cells and tissues can be achieved by cryopreservation. We evaluated the survival and recovery of retinal pigment epithelial cells (RPE) after preservation at -196°C using various cryoprotectants.
Methods Cultured RPE-Cells were incubated with various concentrations of glycerol, dextran, and chondroitin sulfate. The cells were frozen at different cooling rates. After thawing, the cell viability was determined by vital staining (trypan blue) and cell counts were done. The cells were incubated under normal culture conditions for 10 days. Finally, the cells were cultured again and stained for viability.
Results The best survival rates were found with freezing rates of 1°C/min. All cells exhibited a marked decline in numbers immediately after thawing, which failed to recover during subsequent culturing. With regard to survival rates, chondroitin sulfate and glycerol yielded the best results (approx. 20%). However, all cell numbers declined during re-culturing. The highest recovery rate was found with chondroitin sulfate at a rate of approx. 15%.
Conclusions Cell survival rates of 20% may be too low to provide functional cells for grafting. The parameters used in this study do not appear to be suitable for long-term preservation of RPE.

2141

CLINICAL PATHOLOGY OF MALIGNANT UVEAL MELANOMA

DAMATO B
St. Paul's Eye Unit, Royal Liverpool University Hospital, Liverpool (UK)

Uveal melanoma is the most common primary ocular malignancy and it has a high rate of metastatic spread despite successful treatment of the primary tumour. This review summarises the clinicopathological features of more than 1500 uveal melanomas, describing the tumour size, extension, location and cell type according to sex, age at presentation, and laterality, and their interrelationship. Specifically, ocular changes after conservative therapy will be demonstrated, highlighting the benefits of special histopathological procedures. Furthermore, limitations of predicting survival according to current pathological criteria will be demonstrated, highlighting the need for additional prognostic indicators. Such prognostication is required both for eventual targeting of screening for metastatic disease and for selecting patients who might benefit from future adjuvant systemic immunotherapy or chemotherapy.

2142

MICROCIRCULATION ARCHITECTURE OF CHOROIDAL AND CILIARY BODY MELANOMAS: DIAGNOSTIC AND THERAPEUTIC IMPLICATIONS

PE'ER J,[1] MANIOTIS AJ,[2] HENDRIX MJC[2] and FOLBERG, R[3]
1. Dept. of Ophthalmology, Hadassah University Hospital, Jerusalem (Israel)
2. Dept. of Anatomy and Cell Biology, University of Iowa, Iowa City (USA)
3. Dept. of Ophthalmology, University of Iowa, Iowa City (USA)

The presence of microvascular networks of loops and parallel vessels with cross-linking is strongly associated with death from metastatic choroidal and ciliary body melanoma. The classification of tumors into high and low risk categories tends to be consistent throughout various section planes. Two non-invasive imaging techniques show promise in detecting these patterns: confocal ICG scanning laser angiography, and ultrasound parameter imaging.

The consistent appearance of microvascular loops and networks in the metastatic lesions is independent of the target organ. Disruption of the molecular events that generate and maintain these microcirculatory patterns may therefore provide novel and effective treatment strategies for both primary and metastatic lesions.

2143

HLA AND UVEAL MELANOMA

Jager MJ, Hurks HMH, Blom DJR, De Waard-Siebinga I
Dept. of Ophthalmology, Leiden University Medical Center, Leiden, The Netherlands

HLA molecules play an essential role in the recognition of tumor cells by the immune system. HLA expression blocks Natural Killer cells, while absence of HLA-Class I expression blocks cytotoxic T cells. We examined the expression of HLA-Class I antigens on sections of primary uveal melanomas, and observed that a lack of HLA-A and -B expression was associated with a better patient survival rate. Since uveal melanoma metastases spread hematogeneously, we hypothesized that NK cells play a role in the development of metastatic disease by killing HLA Class I-negative tumor cells. Only HLA-Class I positive cells are thus able to escape to peripheral sites. which agrees with our finding that uveal melanoma metastases express high levels of HLA Class I antigens. However, we observed downregulation of specific HLA-Class I alleles on uveal melanoma cell lines, which may result in an inefficient immune attack by both NK cells and cytotoxic T cells. We were able to influence HLA expression by a variety of treatments, including hyperthermia, photodynamic therapy and the addition of cytokines. The knowledge about modulation of HLA expression may not only help to scientifically elucidate the underlying immune regulation, but also help with the development of effective immunotherapy in the future.

2211

LASER IN SITU KERATOMILEUSIS FOR CORRECTION OF HYPEROPIC ASTIGMATISM

NGUYEN-KHOA JL, LOPEZ Ph and LEBUISSON DA.
Dept. Ophthalmology, Foch Hospital, Suresnes (France)

Purpose : To assess the efficacy and safety of laser-in-situ keratomileusis (LASIK) used to treat positive cylinder at the flattest meridian in hyperopic astigmatism.

Methods : We retrospectively reviewed results of 19 eyes that underwent LASIK for correction of simple or compound hyperopic astigmatism and mixed astigmatism with at least 3 months of follow-up. Corneal flaps were created with Chiron Automed Corneal Shaper® or Hansatome® microkeratomes. Using Chiron Technolas 117 Planoscan™ excimer laser with a personalized nomogram, photoablation of positive cylinder was performed in all eyes to steep the flattest meridian.

Results : Mean preoperative cylinder of +2.1 ± 1.3 D (range 0.5 to 5 D) was reduced postoperatively to +0.7 ± 0.6 D (range 0 to 2 D). Vectorial analysis showed a mean surgically induced astigmatism of +1.8 ± 1.6 D (range 0.25 to 4 D). Uncorrected visual acuity of 20/40 or better was achieved by 78% of patients at 3 months postoperatively. No eye lost more than two lines of best spectacle corrected vision.

Conclusions : Correction of hyperopic astigmatism at the flattest meridian seems to be safe and effective. Lack of refractive change at the opposite meridian related to cylinder treatment appears to be a major feature of this approach. Using this pattern of photoablation reduces amount of stromal tissular removal.

2212

Combined surgery to correct high myopia: Worst iris claw phakic intraocular lens (IOL) and laser in situ queratomileusis (LASIK)

Vázquez Barrero Mercedes, Güell Villanueva José Luis, Gris Oscar, Cardonel Antonio, Manero Felicidad, Muller Ana

Purpose: To evaluate the results of a combined surgery, implant of Worst phakic iris claw IOL followed by LASIK to correct high myopic patients. Methods: A prospective study of 6 high myopic patients (8 eyes) having Worst phakic iris claw IOL implantation followed by LASIK, was undertaken. The IOL dioptric power was standard: -15.0 D. as well as the optical zone, 6 mm. The residual refractive error was corrected by LASIK. Results: After the second procedure, the LASIK, uncorrected visual acuity ranged from 0.6 to 0.7 (0.62 ± 0.04) at 12 months postoperatively. Spectacle corrected visual acuity improved 2 or more lines in 62.5 % of the patients when compared to preoperative values. All of the eyes were within ± 1.0 D. of emmetropia at 12 month postoperatively. We did not have any major complication. No significant endothelial damage ocurred. There was no change in contrast sensitivity. Conclusions: The accurate refractive outcome, the absence of major complications, the stability of the results, and the most important, the improvement in quality vision experienced by these high myopic patients even though under dim illumination conditions, are enough reasons to considere this combined technique instead of using each procedure separately. In our cases, thanks to the greater optical zone of the Worst iris claw IOL and LASIK (6 mm) the glare and nocturnal halos were drastically reduced or dessapeared completely, and the final visual acuity was not altered under dim illumination conditions.

2213

EARLY STROMAL CHANGES AFTER LASIK

VESALUOMA M,[1] LINNA T,[1] PETROLL WM,[2] TERVO T,[1] ALIO J,[3] and PEREZ-SANTONJA J.[3]
1. University of Helsinki (Finland)
2. U.T. Southwestern Medical Center, Dallas, Texas (USA)
3. University of Miguel Hernandez, Alicante (Spain)

Purpose: To study the early stromal changes after LASIK.
Methods: 33 patients were examined using in vivo confocal microscopy at 2 hours to 2 weeks after myopic LASIK.
Results: At 2 - 5 hours after LASIK the opaque flap interface (IF) presented with bright particles and few low-reflective keratocyte nuclei. At 3 days post-IF keratocyte nuclei were irregular and highly reflective, and keratocyte processes, sometimes with granular material, were clearly visible. At 1 wk keratocyte nuclei were more easily distinguished at IF. At 2 wk post-IF keratocytes were still brighter than normal midstromal keratocytes, but the processes were difficult to perceive.
Conclusion: LASIK-induced changes in corneal stroma and keratocytes can be observed with confocal microscopy as early as 2 hours postoperatively. The highly reflective irregular keratocyte nuclei with clearly visible processes may represent dying keratocytes. By 2 wk excessive production of extracellular matrix could not be observed.

2214

CORNEAL INTERFACE PARTICLES AND MICROFOLDS AFTER LASIK

TERVO T,[1] LINNA T,[1] PETROLL WM,[2] PEREZ-SANTONJA J,[3] ALIO J,[3] and VESALUOMA M.[1]
1. University of Helsinki (Finland) 2. U.T. Southwestern Medical Center, Dallas, Texas (USA) 3. University of Miguel Hernandez, Alicante (Spain)

Purpose: To study the occurrence of corneal interface particles and microfolds after LASIK. Methods: 67 patients were examined at 3 days to 2 years after LASIK using slit lamp and in vivo confocal microscope (CM). Results: Microfolds were observed in all patients using CM, although slit lamp examination showed fine striae in only 30 patients. In slit lamp examination 15 patients presented with metallic interface particles, 9 patients with nonmetallic deposits, and 11 patients with diffuse interface infiltration or dust. Epithelial ingrowth was observed in 7 cases, and initial stromal melt in one patient. CM, however, revealed interface particles in every case. The number of these particles appeared higher in the flap margin than in the central area. In general, the number of these particles was lower in the patients with a longer postoperative recovery. Conclusion: Confocal microscopy reveals interface problems in every case following LASIK. The nature of these particles cannot be judged by their appearance in CM. Some of these particles may, however, be of cellular origin, such as damaged keratocytes or inflammatory cells.

2215

CORNEAL SENSITIVITY AND REGENERATION OF SUBEPITHELIAL NERVES AFTER LASIK

LINNA T,[1] VESALUOMA M,[1] PETROLL WM,[2] PEREZ-SANTONJA J,[3] ALIO J,[3] and TERVO T.[1]

1. University of Helsinki (Finland) 2. UT Southwestern Medical Center, Dallas, Texas (USA) 3. University of Miguel Hernandez, Alicante (Spain)

Purpose: To study corneal sensitivity, and morphology of the basal epithelial/subepithelial (bep) nerves after LASIK. Methods: 57 patients were examined using Cochet-Bonnet aesthesiometer, slit-lamp and in vivo confocal microscope after LASIK. The corneal sensitivity was recorded centrally, 2 mm nasally and 2 mm temporally. Bep nerves were calculated from digitized confocal microscopy images. Results: The mean corneal sensitivities (mm) were as follows (central - nasal - temporal): at 3 d 16.2 - 33.5 - 23.5, at 1 wk 12.9 - 25.7 - 14.3, at 2 wk 14.4 - 25.6 - 12.5, at 1 Mo 20.8 - 37.5 - 17.5, at 2 Mo 34.2 - 53.3 - 39.2, at 3 Mo 36.0 - 47.0 - 37.0, at 6 Mo 55.0 - 51.7 - 41.7, and at 1-2 yrs 59.0 - 60.0 - 59.0. Confocal images of bep-nerves will be presented. Conclusion: At the earlier time points the hinge area of the LASIK flap preserved its sensitivity better than central or temporal areas. After 6 Mo the sensitivities of all areas had recovered quite well. In general, at earlier time points mostly short bep leashes were observed in the central corneas. Later the morphology of the bep leashes resembled that observed preoperatively.

2216

CORNEAL HAZE DEVELOPMENT FOLLOWING PRK IS REGULATED BY VOLUME OF STROMAL TISSUE REMOVAL

MØLLER-PEDERSEN T,[1] CAVANAGH HD,[2] PETROLL WM,[2] and JESTER JV.[2]
Departments of Ophthalmology at [1]Århus University Hospital (Denmark) and [2]University of Texas, Southwestern Medical Center, Dallas (USA).

Purpose. To establish the relationship between initial depth of keratocyte and stromal loss and the subsequent development of corneal haze.
Methods. Five rabbits received a 5-mm diameter, monocular epithelial debridement by manual scraping. An additional five rabbits received a 5-mm diameter, excimer laser transepithelial photoablation to a preset (intended) depth of 60 µm to ensure complete epithelial removal and to generate a superficial stromal keratectomy in all corneas. At various times during a 3-month-period, animals were evaluated by *in vivo* Confocal Microscopy Through Focusing (CMTF), which generates a quantitative image intensity depth profile of the cornea providing measurements of: 1) depth of keratocyte loss, 2) epithelial and stromal thickness, and 3) backscattered light from the anterior cornea as an objective estimate of corneal haze.
Results. Photoablation induced 36 % less initial keratocyte loss (69 ± 19 µm) in the anterior stroma than manual debridement ($p < 0.01$), but was associated with intense concomitant inflammation. Photoablated corneas showed significantly more light backscattering ($p < 0.01$) compared to manually-debrided corneas with a three-fold increase at three-weeks (4397 ± 1367 U) and a six-fold increase at three-months (1483 ± 1172 U compared to 234 ± 91 U). Backscattering of light or haze increased proportionally with increasing stromal keratectomy depth ($r = 0.95$, $p<0.001$) but was unrelated to depth of induced keratocyte death. The increased backscatter in photoablated corneas appeared related to: 1) a more pronounced keratocyte repopulation response with a higher density and reflectivity of migratory fibroblasts; and 2) myofibroblast transformation following repopulation.
Conclusions. The magnitude of corneal wound repair and the development and duration of corneal haze increased proportionally with increasing stromal photoablation depth but were unrelated to depth of initial keratocyte loss.

2217

POST KERATOPLASTY ASTIGMATISM AND IT REDUCTION WITH LOW-DOSE EGF APPLICATION

FRYCZKOWSKI A[1], SZAFLIK J[2], TESLA P[2], FRYCZKOWSKI P[2]

1. P.A.F., Institute of Aviation Med. Warsaw
2. Dept. of Ophthalmol. Univ. of Warsaw, Warsaw, Poland

Purpose: To study an effect of the hnEGF low dose application on the corneal wound healing after penetrating keratoplasty (PK).

Methods: Fifty patients undergo the PK. From these: 25 received hnEGF factor with doses vary from 500 to 1000 ng/per drop, three times a day, starting on the operating table, and continued for three weeks. Remaining 25 patients did not received hnEGF and was a control group treated in standard way.

Results: From 25 patients treated with hnEGF -18 showed increased healing pattern, and developed minimal (+/-) 0.5-0.75 D cyl (with rule) astigmatism. Six patients had (+/-) 0.75 - 1.0 D astigmatism and one -1.25 D astigmatism. This was much better comparing with a controls

Conclusions: This preliminary results suggest a positive hnEGF influence on the post PK healing.

2218

PRECRYSTALLINE LENSES FOR THE CORRECTION OF HIGH MYOPIA

Profesor Joaquín Barraquer
Instituto Barraquer (Barcelona)

The Author has designed a precrystalline posterior chamber lens for correction of high myopia in phakic eyes leaving the crystalline lens "in situ". The IOL to correct high myopia, between - 13 and - 26 D, is a concave-convex lens made of methyl-metacrylate with flexible haptics supported in the sulcus.
The lens is located in the posterior chamber behind the iris, centered with the pupil, in front of the crystalline lens. The anterior surface of the IOL, slightly convex, does not interfere with the normal iris movements and does not produce pigment loss. Optic correction of the high myopia is essentially obtained by the concave posterior surface. Contact with the anterior crystalloid is minimal. Two lateral grooves ensure adequate circulation of the aqueous between the IOL and the crystalline lens to avoid the "vacuum effect" which might produce contact between the posterior surface of the IOL and the lens, as has been observed with the first generation of these lenses. To prevent capture of the lens by the iris when the pupil dilates, a third generation of lenses has been created and is used at present. These lenses have a "body" of 9 mm. (6 mm.optic and two 1.5 mm. rigid haptic plates) which prevents lens capture even if the pupil dilates and two flexible haptics, making up a total diameter of 14 mm.
Very encouraging results have been obtained, with adequate, stable correction of the myopia.

2221

MICRONUCLEI IN LENS EPITHELIA AFTER *IN VIVO* CORTICOSTEROID AND X-RAY TREATMENT

JUNK A. K. and WORGUL B. V.
Eye Rad. & Environ. Res. Lab., Columbia Univ., (USA)

Purpose To establish a model for secondary cataracts that allows differentiation of multiple risk factors, as observed in bone marrow transplanted patients. Although development of posterior subcapsular cataracts are well known side effects, their combined effects of the modalities and their interactions in cataractogenesis have yet to be evaluated.
Methods The right eyes of 4 week old Brown-Norway rats were irradiated (10 Gy X-rays). Subgroups were treated with Dexamethasone s.c. (10 mg/kg body weight) and/or received vitamine E deficient food. Cataract development was followed by weekly slit lamp examinations. Micronucleus (MN) formation was studied in lens epithelial whole mounts.
Results Cataractous changes were first observed 36 days after irradiation in the exposed lenses of all animal groups. MN analyses revealed quantitative differences compared to controls. Dexamethasone treatment in combination with irradiation causes an increase in MN number with an apparent increase in large MN's.
Conclusions Whereas small MN's are more likely to appear after clastogenic damage to chromosomes, as following irradiation, large MN's indicate the exclusion of whole chromosomes. This difference may be useful in distinguishing damage due to radiation and corticosteroids.

2222

AN UPDATE ON THE UKRAINIAN AMERICAN CHERNOBYL OCULAR STUDY (UACOS)

WORGUL BV[1], LIKHTAREV I[2], KUNDIEV Y[3], MEDVEDOVSKY C[1], SERGIENKO N[4], PARKHOMENKO G[4], CHUMAK V[2], RUBAN A[4], VITTE P[3], WEGENER A[5] and JUNK, AK[1]
1 Eye Rad. & Environ. Res. Lab., Columbia Univ. (USA)
2 Ukrainian Scientific Center for Rad. Med. (UKRAINE)
3 Institute of Occupational Health (UKRAINE)
4 Center for Eye Microsurgery (UKRAINE)
5 Institute of Exp. Ophthal., Univ of Bonn (GERMANY)

Purpose: The UACOS was established as a comprehensive program to monitor the ocular health of the clean-up workers (Liquidators) at Chernobyl.
Methods: The planned 30 year study has three main thrusts; (1) an extensive cohort study of cataract incidence in relation to dose and other factors, (2) a quantitative, longitudinal, non-subjective assessment utilizing Scheimpflug image acquisition and, finally (3) calibration of the micronucleus (MN) test in lens epithelia against known doses of radiation. The study population involves subsets of the approximately 285,000 Liquidators exposed to a range of doses up to 6 Gy.
Results: The Scheimpflug study is in its 5th year and the subjects are currently in the second round of follow-ups. The cohort analysis, a classic epidemiological study, has been initiated and involves a subset of 12,000 Liquidators examined biennially. The lens MN calibration is also underway and the initial tags have been analyzed.
Conclusions: These studies and details of the results thus far will be discussed.

2223

LENS FIBER ARCHITECTURE AFTER ULTRAVIOLET IRRADIATION

MICHAEL R, LÖFGREN S, AYALA M, SÖDERBERG P G
Karolinska Institutet, St. Erik's Eye Hospital, Stockholm, Sweden

Purpose. To investigate the lens fiber order after in vivo close-to-threshold exposure to ultraviolet radiation (UVR). **Method.** Fifteen Sprague-Dawley rats received 5 kJ/m^2 UVR (λ_{MAX} = 300 nm, $\lambda_{0.5}$ = 10 nm) unilaterally for 15 min in vivo. Animals were sacrificed 24 h, 1 and 8 weeks after exposure. Both lenses were removed and microphotographs taken. Coronary paraffin lens sections were stained with fluorescein-conjugated wheat germ agglutinin to visualize the fiber membranes. **Results.** No changes in the lens fiber architecture was seen at 24 h post-exposure. At one week post-exposure, the lens had anterior and equatorial subcapsular opacification, which corresponded to swollen superficial fibers and equatorial vacuolation. At 8 weeks post-exposure, a thin shell-shaped opacity was visible between 280 and 370 μm below the capsule. The membrane staining showed irregular fiber order and swollen fibers between 250 and 350 μm below the capsule. **Conclusion.** After a threshold UVR damage, newly grown fibers resume a normal regular order. However, damaged fibers remain in the lens cortex at longer survival times.

Supported by: Anders Otto Swärds Stiftelse, Carmen och Bertil Regnérs Stiftelse.

2224

DETERMINATION OF THE MINIMAL LEVEL OF UV-A RADIATION THAT CAUSES DAMAGE TO THE EYE LENS

DOVRAT A and AZZAM N.
B. Rappaport Faculty of Medicine, Technion - Israel Institute of Technology, Haifa (Israel).

Purpose To determine the minimal level of UV-A radiation which effects the eye lens. Epidemiological studies have suggested damage to the eye lens by sunlight. Ultraviolet light UV-A (320-400nm) penetrates the cornea and therefore high levels of this radiation reach the lens, which absorbs it more efficiently than any other ocular tissue.
Methods. We have investigated the nature of the damage caused by UV-A irradiation at 365nm on the bovine eye lens using a unique system for culturing eye lenses in vitro. In our system it is possible to give controlled amounts of radiation and monitor changes in lens optical quality. The optical properties are monitored in association with enzyme activities.
Results. Using our system, we have shown that lens optical quality and enzyme activities are affected by UV-A irradiation of $29J/cm^2$ but the lenses can recover from that damage.
Conclusions. Bovine lenses in organ culture can recover from the UV-A damage of $29J/cm^2$

Supported by a grant from the Committee for Research & Prevention in Occupational Safety, Ministry of Labor, Israel.

2225

IN VIVO MEASUREMENT OF ATTENUATION OF ULTRAVIOLET RADIATION IN THE CRYSTALLINE LENS

SÖDERBERG P[1,2], LÖFGREN S[1], MICHAEL R[1], AYALA M[1]

1. St. Erik's Eye Hospital, Karolinska Institutet, Stockholm, Sweden
2. Dept. of Biomedical Engineering, University of Miami, USA

Purpose To measure the attenuation of ultraviolet radiation (UVR) in the crystalline lens in vivo.

Methods Sprague Dawley rats were unilaterally exposed in vivo to UVR 300 nm to 90 kJ/m^2. The distribution of LDH activity in the lens exposed and its contralateral was stained histochemically and measured with densitometry at 0, 2 and 6 h. after exposure. The inhibition of LDH induced by the UVR was measured as the ratio of the absorbance between exposed and contralateral lens for equivalent positions. The inhibition of the UVR in each position along the optical axis is directly proportional to the intensity at each point during the exposure. The inactivation profile along the optical axis was therefore used to estimate the attenuation of the UVR.

Results The LDH activity dropped towards the center of the lens independent of time after exposure. The penetration depth ($1/\tau$) for UVR 300 nm was estimated to 0.45 mm.

Conclusions Histochemistry for UVR chromophores may be used for in vivo assay of UVR penetration in the eye.

2226

DIFFERENTIAL GENE EXPRESSION IN BOVINE LENSES EXPOSED TO TOXIC LEVELS OF HYDROGEN PEROXIDE

MARAINI G,[1] FORONI C,[1] PETRUCCO S[2] AND OTTONELLO S[2].

1. Institute of Ophthalmology, University of Parma, Parma (Italy)
2. Institute of Biochemical Sciences, University of Parma, Parma (Italy)

Purpose mRNA differential display, a non-targeted gene searching procedure that does not require any prior knowledge of either gene function or identity, was used to identify lens mRNAs that are modulated in response to a severe hydrogen peroxide stress.
Methods Bovine lenses were incubated in AAHS medium in the presence or absence of 10 mM H_2H_2. Total RNA, extracted from epithelium/capsules was subjected to mRNA differential display (DD) analysis using 7 different combinations of primers. Differentially expressed cDNAs were eluted, re-amplified, cloned, sequenced, and further analyzed by RNase protection assay using amplicon-derived antisense riboprobes.
Results Twenty three genes were up- and seven genes were down-regulated in stressed with respect to control lenses. Fourteen of them were cloned, sequenced, and further analyzed by RNase protection assays. Eight of them correspond to known mammalian genes. The most up-regulated (3 to 5-fold) amplicon is 99% identical to the β-subunit of the bovine mitochondrial F1-ATPase. Under identical experimental conditions no up-regulation of the cognate F1-ATPase α-subunit could be detected.
Conclusions We have used RT-PCR-DD to visualize variations of the pattern of gene expression in H_2O_2 stressed lenses and have identified several differentially expressed genes. Further studies of these genes may provide insight into the mechanisms of the lens response to oxidative stress, an established model for cataractogenesis.

Supported by BioMed grant BMH4-CT96-1593

2227

ULTRAVIOLET RADIATION - INDUCED CATARACT; EFFECT OF AGE AND POST-EXPOSURE TIME

LÖFGREN S, MICHAEL R, SÖDERBERG PG and AYALA M.
St. Erik's Eye Hospital, Karolinska Institutet (Sweden)

Purpose. Previously, we have shown that young rats develop more severe cataract than old rats (EVER/JERMOV -97). Now we wanted to investigate if the degree of UVR cataract at different ages changes with a longer follow-up time.
Methods. Totally 66 SD rats at the age of 6 and 17 weeks and 1 year were exposed unilaterally to UV radiation (λ_{max} 300 nm, FWHM 9 nm, corneal dose 8 kJ/m^2, 15 min exp). Eight weeks after exposure the rats were killed and the lenses put in buffered saline. The lenses were photographed and the degree of cataract was quantified by measurement of intensity of forward light scattering.
Results. All three age groups developed pathologic light scattering, i.e. cataract. The light scattering was at least twice as high in the exposed lenses as in the non-exposed. The youngest group had the most severe cataract.
Conclusions. With the current experimental set-up, UVR-induced light scattering increases between one and eight weeks after exposure.

Supported by: Carmen och Bertil Regnérs fond, S:t Eriks Ögonforskningsstiftelse, Sigvard & Marianne Bernadottes Forskningsstiftelse för Barnögonvård, Karolinska Institutets Resestiftelser.

2228

IN VIVO CATARACT AFTER REPEATED EXPOSURE TO ULTRAVIOLET RADIATION

AYALA M, MICHAEL R, LÖFGREN S, SÖDERBERG PG.
Research Department, St Erik's Eye Hospital, Stockholm (Sweden)

Purpose. To determine the in vivo additivity effects of two close-to-threshold exposures to ultraviolet radiation (UVR). To find out the time interval for the maximum forward light scattering in the lens, after UVR exposure.
Methods. One hundred Sprague-Dawley rats received two exposures of 4 kJ/m^2 UVR-B unilaterally for 15 min. The animals were divided in five groups according to the time lapse between the two exposures, ranging from 6 hours to one month. The animals were sacrificed one week after the last exposure. Both lenses were removed, intensity of forward light scattering was measured for each lens in BSS and microphotographs were taken.
Results. Evaluating the difference between exposed and non-exposed eyes, the highest forward light scattering was found in the group of 3 days interval between doses. The lowest light scattering was found in the group of one month interval between exposures. Conclusions. Maximum lens opacities occur when the UVR exposure is repeated after 3 days. For longer time intervals between UVR exposures, additivity effects seem to decrease.

2231

MATRIX METALLOPROTEINASES AND METALLOPROTEIANSE INHIBITORS IN CHOROIDAL NEOVASCULAR MEMBRANES

KVANTA A, SEJERSEN S, BERGLIN L, SEREGARD S, STEEN B
St. Erik´s Eye Hospital, Karolinska Inst., Stockholm, Sweden

Purpose Matrix metalloproteinases (MMP) are a family of extracellular matrix degrading enzymes associated with the development of neovascularization. We have analyzed the mRNA expression of MMPs and tissue inhibitors of metalloproteinases (TIMPs) in subfoveal fibrovascular membranes from patients with age-related macular degeneration (AMD).
Methods Surgically removed subfoveal fibrovascular membranes from 5 eyes were analyzed for the expression of different MMP and TIMP mRNAs using *in situ* hybridization.
Results MMP-2 (72-kD gelatinase) and MMP-9 (92-kD gelatinase) mRNA were detected in all specimens. Most of the membranes also expressed TIMP-1, TIMP-2 and TIMP-3. MMP-2 expression appeared to be localized mainly to the vascular endothelial cells whereas MMP-9 expression was distinctly expressed by cells at the margins of the membranes and often in close proximity to a thickened Bruch's membrane-like layer under the retinal pigment epithelial cells.
Conclusions The results support a role for MMPs in the development of choroidal neovascularization in AMD. The localization of MMP-2 and MMP-9 suggest that they may cooperatively be involved in the progressive growth of choroidal neovascular membranes in AMD.

2232

EFFECT OF GROWTH FACTORS ON THE MIGRATION AND PROLIFERATION OF RPE CELLS

AMANN J, KAVEN C, SPRAUL CW, LANG GK, and LANG GE
Department of Ophthalmology, Universitiy of Ulm (Germany)

Purpose Retinal pigment epithelial (RPE) cells play an important role in proliferative vitreoretinopathy (PVR). The aim of this study was to investigate the effect of EGF, aFGF, bFGF and TGFβ on the migration and proliferation of bovine RPE cells in vitro.
Methods Bovine RPE cells ($2x10^4$) were cultured until they reached confluence. Proliferation was inhibited with mitomycin C [10μg/ml]. Half of each well was denuded with a cell scraper. The cultures were then observed in the presence of EGF, aFGF, bFGF and TGFβ [10ng/ml] or DMEM +5% FCS (control medium) alone after 20 hours. Migration was assessed by counting the number of cells in the denuded zone (number/microscopic field). RPE-cells were also assayed for proliferation with above growth factors as measured by ^{3}[H]-thymidine uptake (ccpm).
Results Exposure of RPE cells to EGF, aFGF and bFGF resulted in a significantly higher RPE cell migration and proliferation compared to control medium ($p \leq 0.005$). bFGF (48.9 cells/microscopic field; 3302 ccpm) was most potent among the growth factors tested, followed by aFGF (43.7 cells/microscopic field; 1728 ccpm), and EGF (39.2 cells/microscopic field; 1524 ccpm). TGFβ has no significant influence on RPE migration and proliferation.
Conclusions The data suggest that there is a positiv effect of bFGF, aFGF, and EGF on RPE cell migration and proliferation. These growth factors may play an important role in mediating RPE cell migration and proliferation in PVR.

2233

PDGF ENHANCES IGF-1-INDUCED RPE MIGRATION AND PROLIFERATION

KAVEN C, AMANN J, SPRAUL CW, LANG GK, and LANG GE
Department of Ophthalmology, Universitiy of Ulm (Germany)

Purpose To investigate interactions of insulin-like growth factor 1 (IGF-1) and platelet-derived growth factor (PDGF) on the migration and proliferation of bovine RPE cells, in assumption of a synergistic effect, which has been reported for DNA synthesis and for wound healing models.
Methods Migration was performed in 34 mm 6-well-plates, confluently covered with RPE cells. After inhibition of proliferation and denudation of half of each well, cells were incubated for 20 hr with DMEM containig 5% FCS and either 10 ng ml^{-1} IGF-1, PDGF, and IGF-1 plus PDGF. DMEM with 5% FCS served as a negative control, DMEM with 20% FCS as a positive control. Migration was measured as the number of cells that had entered the denuded area after 20 hr. Proliferation was assessed by ^{3}[H]-incorporation after growth factor stimulation for 20 hr.
Results RPE migration and proliferation was significantly stimulated by PDGF ($p < 0.002$) and IGF-1+PDGF ($p < 0.002$) compared to the negative control. IGF-1 stimulated only RPE migration ($p = 0.003$). The response on IGF-1-induced RPE proliferation and migration was significantly enhanced when combined with PDGF ($p < 0.002$).
Conclusions The combination of IGF-1 and PDGF enhances their single stimulatory effects, for RPE cell migration even in a synergistic manner. PDGF reportedly acts as a competence factor, which prepares cells for progression factors such as IGF-1 and probably works as an amplifyer of intracellular signaltransduction.

2234

DIFFERENTIAL EXPRESSION mRNA ANALYSIS REVEAL AN UPREGULATED EXPRESSION OF THE SERINE PROTEASE FAPα IN PROLIFERATING RPE CELLS

KOCIOK N, ESSER P, SCHRAERMEYER U, GRISANTI S AND HEIMANN K.
Dept. of Vitreoretinal Surgery, Univ. of Cologne (Germany)

Purpose To find new genes that change their expression in proliferating RPE cells we conducted a differential mRNA expression analysis (DEmRNA-PCR) of human RPE cells.
Methods RNA was prepared from cultured human RPE cells of passage 0 and 3 followed by DEmRNA-PCR. A band with enhanced expression in P3 was excised, reamplified and sequenced. RT-PCR with gene specific primers was used to estimate the expression in RPE cells from P0 to P8.
Results DEmRNA-PCR revealed an enhanced expression of a specific RNA from P0 to P3. A sequence alignment search manifested its 99% identity with the 3'-end of the coding sequence of the human fibroblast activation protein α (FAPα) or seprase. Upregulation of FAPα/seprase expression was estimated by semiquantitative RT-PCR in RPE cells from the eye, P0, P3 and P8.
Conclusion Differential mRNA expression analysis of cultured RPE cells is a useful tool for the identification of previously unknown proteins that may play an important role in diseases involving proliferating cells like PVR.
Supported by DFG (Es 82/5-1, He 840/6-1), Köln Fortune program and Retinovit Foundation

2235

FGF SOLUBLE RECEPTOR 1 ACTS AS A NATURAL INHIBITOR OF FGF2 NEUROTROPHIC ACTIVITY DURING RETINAL DEGENERATION

MASCARELLI F., GUILLONNEAU X., REGNIER-RICARD F., JEANNY J.C. and COURTOIS Y.
Développement, vieillissement et pathologie de la rétine, INSERM U. 450, affiliée CNRS, Association Claude-Bernard (France)

Purpose Fibroblast growth factor (FGF) 2 and its tyrosine kinase receptors (FGFR) are present throughout the adult retina. FGF2 is a potential mitogen, but adult retinal cells are maintained in a non proliferative state unless the retina is damaged. Our work aims to find a modulator of FGF signaling in normal and pathological retina.
Methods We used a PCR-based approach to amplify a rat retina cDNA encompassing the first half of the IgII loops to the second half of the Ig III loop of FGFR1. Clones were selected and sequenced. We generated a recombinant protein and a polyclonal antibody directed against this new FGFR.
Results We identified a truncated, soluble FGFR (SR1) which corresponds to the extracellular domain of FGFR1. SR1 is mainly distributed in the inner nuclear layer of the retina and the pigmented epithelium. During light-induced retinal degeneration SR1 and FGFR1 mRNA levels are upregulated independently. Injection of SR1 before retinal degeneration inhibits the neurotrophic activity of exogenous FGF2 and increased damaging effects of light.
Conclusions This study highlights the significance of the control of FGF function by its soluble receptor.

2236

DETECTION OF CYTOKINE mRNA PRODUCTION IN INFILTRATING CELLS IN PROLIFERATIVE VITREORETINOPATHY(PVR) USING RT-PCR

EI-GHRABLY IA[1], ORR G[1], DUA HS[1], TIGHE PJ[2]
[1]Department of Ophthalmology, [2]Departments of Immunology & Ophthalmology, Nottingham University (England)

Purpose: detection of interleukin-6(IL-6), interleukin-1β (IL-1β) and tumour necrosis factor α (TNF α) mRNA in the vitreous and subretinal fluid (SRF) samples from patients with proliferative vitreoretinopathy (PVR).
Methods: The presence of mRNA coding for HPRT, IL-6, IL-1β and TNFα was investigated in cellular infiltrates of 12 vitreous samples and 8 SRF samples from patients with PVR. 10 vitreous samples from patients with macular hole were examined as control. RNA was extracted from the samples 2-3 hours after surgery, then cDNA reverse transcribed and stored at -70°C until used for PCR reaction.
Results : HPRT mRNA was detected in all samples of PVR and 5 from 10 samples (50%) of control cases. For the 20 samples of PVR, IL-6 mRNA was detected in 16 (80%), in 10 from 12 of vitreous and in 6 from 8 SRF samples. IL-1β mRNA was detected in 12 samples (60%), 6 from 12 vitreous and 6 from 8 SRF samples. For TNFα, mRNA was detected in 10 samples (50%), 6 from 12 vitreous and 4 from 8 SRF samples. 6 cases were +ve for all the cytokines tested, 10 were +ve for IL-6 and IL-1β, 9 were +ve for IL-6 and TNFα and 7 for TNFα and IL-1β. No mRNA for IL-1β and TNFα was detected in any of control cases and only 1 sample was +ve for mRNA of IL-6.
Conclusion: mRNA encoding for IL-6, IL-1β and TNFα is significantly detected by RT-PCR in vitreous and SRF samples of patients with PVR, indicating local production of these cytokines by vitreous and SRF cells and their possible role in pathogenesis of the disease.

2237

VEGF RECEPTOR EXPRESSION IN PROLIFERATIVE DIABETIC RETINOPATHY

Toke Bek, Department of Ophthalmology, Århus University Hospital

Purpose: Proliferative diabetic retinopathy is assumed to develop because of vascular growth stimulation from cytokines, notably VEGF, which is released from areas with ischaemia secondary to retinal vascular occlusion. Histopathologically two different pathological cellular growth patterns have be recognised, i.e. invasion of Müller cells to occlude retinal vessels, and proliferation of vascular endothelial cells to form the new vessels. It can be hypothesized that the identification of VEGF receptors on the surface of these cells may contribute to a further understanding of the pathological growth mechanisms involved.
Methods: Immunohistochemistry was performed in six autopsy eyes of six patients with proliferative diabetic retinopathy using antibodies directed against as well intracellular as extracellular parts of the two VEGF receptors KDR and flt-1.
Results: Intracellular and extracellular parts of the two receptors were equally expressed. There was no difference in VEGF receptor immunoreactivity between proliferating and not proliferating retinal endothelial cells and Müller cells. In these cells KDR immunoreactivity was more extensive than was flt-1 immunoreactivity.
Conclusions: There is differential expression of different VEGF receptors in pathologically growing cells of the retina from diabetic patients indicating a complex mechanism of action of this cytokine in the pathogenesis of proliferative diabetic retinopathy.

2238

INTRAOCULAR FLUID (IOF) IS A RETINA & OPTIC NERVUS (RON) METHABOLISM ADDITIONAL FACTOR

G.A.SHILKIN-1, N.S.YARTSEVA-1, E.M.MIRONOVA-2, A.G.SHILKIN-2, A.N.ANDREITSEV-1

1.Moscow Medical Stomatological Institute
2.Eye Microsurgery Complex. Moscow, Russia

Purpose. To study the role of IOF as an additional factor of RON methabolism.
Methods. 320 patient eyes of glaucoma, retina distrophies & ablatio, myopia were studied by tonography, oculography, plethismography, slit -lamp biometry, echography.
Results. A transparent retina with extensive avascular zones and optic nervus have similarity to both structures: optical media and cerebral cells. Biological fluid is a variety of their methabolism by neuroglia or pigmental epithelium functionally closed to it. There are several systems of IOF production & transport including chorioidea. Biomechanical system complex: pupil, irido-lens dyaphragma, pulse waves drive IOF to RON as well as to optical media. IOF is a factor supporting RON methabolism in the pathology. IOF discirculation can leads to its stagnation or leakage, and in result to IOP increase, as well as myopia, RON distrophy, cataract.
Conclusion. IOF can be additional factor of RON methabolism.

2241

FUNCTIONAL MAGNETIC RESONANCE IMAGING IN THE VISUAL CORTEX

McFADZEAN R.
Glasgow

Functional magnetic resonance imaging (fMRI), through the postulated measurement of changes in cerebral blood flow, allows objective determination of the behaviour of the visual cortex during resting and activated conditions in a non-invasive manner. As the measured change in cerebral blood flow is small, it is important to optimise the conditions under which fMR images are obtained. Activation studies in both humans and non-human primates demonstrate mapping images which can be compared with traditional perimetric and electrophysiological concepts. In particular comparisons can be made with the perimetric revised representation of the visual field hypothesis in humans and direct occipital cortical electrode recordings in non-human primates. In pathological conditions, fMRI may be used to objectively confirm subjective visual field defects e.g. in occipital infarction. The potential for greater understanding of visual cortical function is considerable using different experimental paradigms. The technique and its applications will be discussed.

2242

READING DISABILITIES IN CHILDREN

Eustace P
Institute of Ophthalmology,
University College Dublin,
60 Eccles Street, Dublin 7, Ireland.

Specific reading strategies in childhood disorders are evident when eye movements are studied using infra-red oculography.

This paper presents an analysis of 50 children with developmental dyslexia. Their strategies are compared with age-matched normal controls and with the strategies adopted in amblyopia, strabismus and motor neuro-ophthalmological disorders.

2243

MITOCHONDRIAL DISORDERS AFFECTING VISION AND EYE MOVEMENTS

De Laey J.J.[1], Meire F.[1], Leys A.[2]
[1] Dept. Ophthalmology, University Hospital Ghent, Belgium
[2] Dept. Ophthalmology, University Hospital Leuven, Belgium

There is increasing evidence that a number of human diseases, often involving skeletal and cardiac muscle impairment, are characterized by functionally abnormal mitochondria. Although most mitochondria are encoded by nuclear genes, some mitochondrial proteins have been identified that are encoded solely by mitochondrial DNA. These include parts of the respiratory-enzyme complexes of the inner mitochondrial membrane. Both males and females may be affected, but transmission occurs only by affected women.
Deletions or point mutations in the mitochondrial DNA have already been identified in a number of ophthalmological diseases. Best known are Leber's hereditary optic atrophy and chronic progressive external ophthalmoplegia or Kearns-Sayre syndrome. However, there is also a mitochondrial form of Wolfram syndrome and recently mitochondrial point mutation at position 3243 has been found in patients with diabetes and deafness associated with a macular pattern dystrophy.

2244

REGENERATION AND GRAFT OF THE OPTIC NERVE

RUNGGER-BRÄNDLE, E.

Laboratoire de Biologie cellulaire, Clinique d'Ophtalmologie, Genève (Switzerland)

Conditions permitting functional rescue in the central nervous system can be ideally tested in the optic nerve, thanks to the spatial separation of ganglion cell bodies in the retina from the synapses in the optic tectum. The intrinsic capacity of ganglion cells to regrow damaged axons varies among species and is modulated by local environmental influences (glial cells, soluble factors).
Optic nerve axotomy leads to apoptosis of ganglion cells, a longlasting process that can in part be overcome by adding exogenous survival factors or by inhibiting the proteolytic activity of microglia. A fraction of such protected neurons are able to regrow axons, provided that the inhibitory activity of oligodendrocytes and astrocytes is eliminated by grafting a piece of peripheral nerve or embryonic central nervous tissue onto the optic nerve stump. Such grafts promote axonal outgrowth, produce survival factors, and sustain the specific formation of synapses between axon and the target. Visual function (luminance perception and pattern recognition) can thus be restored.

2245

THE DIMENSIONS OF PAIN IN OPHTHALMOLOGY

SAFRAN A.B.

Department of Ophthalmology, Geneva University Hospitals, Geneva, Switzerland.

Few medical conditions, if any, are of greater concern to patients than pain. Yet, surprisingly little attention has been paid to it in ophthalmological literature and training. With the recent development of medicine that is more patient-oriented, the physician-patient relationship is changing with regard to pain management. This process is favored by advances in the understanding of pain mechanisms, including recognition that pain occurs in infants, that nervous plasticity takes place following pain in young individuals, and recognition of the importance of pain in the chronically ill elderly. Several aspects of pain interpretation and management are specific to ophthalmology. They take into account the variety of pain mechanisms involved in different eye conditions, and the projection of pain to the ocular area from distant disorders. The pathophysiology of different forms of photophobia is also becoming better understood, both in ocular and central conditions. Clinicians should be aware of these changes.

2311

ASSOCIATION OF UNEQUAL INTRAOCULAR PRESSURE AND GLAUCOMATOUS OPTIC NERVE HEAD DAMAGE ASYMMETRY IN NORMAL TENSION GLAUCOMA

GUGLETA K, ORGÜL S, De MEL T, and FLAMMER J
University Eye Clinic Basel, Switzerland

Purpose Studies comparing visual-field asymmetry with interocular difference in intraocular pressure (IOP) suggested that IOP might contribute to optic nerve head damage in normal-tension glaucoma (NTG). Because part of glaucomatous visual-field defect might be functional, and, thus, reversible, it is warranted that, for the assessement of the role of IOP in NTG, asymmetry in optic nerve head damage is compared with interocular difference in IOP in NTG.
Methods Two diurnal-tension curves of 15 NTG patients done within three months were used to calculate the interocular IOP difference for each patient. None of the patients received either topical antihypertensive therapy or systemic medication known to lower IOP, and none had abnormal ophthalmological findings other than glaucomatous optic nerve head cupping and visual field defects consistent with glaucoma. IOP assymetry was present in at least three readings, always in the same direction. Three images of each eye were obtained using Heidelberg Retinal Tomograph (HRT), and the mean topography image was computed. Interocular differences in HRT parameters (disc area, cup/disc ratio, cup and neuroretinal rim volume, nerve fiber layer thickness (NFLTh) and retinal nerve fiber cross sectional area (RNFLCA)) were correlated with IOP asymmetry using Spearman's rank correlation factor.
Results Average age of 9 female and 6 male NTG patients was 62.4±16.9 years. IOP difference varried from 0.25 to 4 mmHg. The strong negative correlation was found between interocular IOP difference and interocular difference in NFLTh (R= -0.652, p=0.0083) and RNFLCA (R= -0,702, p=0,0034).
Conclusion Although factors other then IOP have been suggested to be risk factors in NTG, IOP must still be considered as an important contributor to the observed damage in these patients.

2312

FLUDROCORTISONE IN THE TREATMENT OF SYSTEMIC HYPOTENSION IN PRIMARY OPEN-ANGLE GLAUCOMA PATIENTS

ORGÜL S, GUGLETA K, STÜMPFIG D, DUBLER B and FLAMMER J
University Eye Clinic Basel, Switzerland

Purpose Low systemic blood pressure has been suggested to be a risk factor in glaucoma. The present study evaluated whether glaucoma patients with low systemic blood pressure could benefit from treatment with fludrocortisone. Fludrocortisone is a potent mineralocorticoid, has no direct vasoactive properties, and is the first-line drug for treatment of orthostatic hypotension.
Methods A retrospective analysis of the charts of glaucoma patients of the University Eye-Clinic Basel was performed. Twenty-two patients with open-angle glaucoma under treatment with fludrocortisone-acetate were selected. The selected patients had one 24-hour blood pressure recording immediately prior to treatment with fludrocortisone and one recording at least 2 months after starting treatment. Twelve patients had also microscopic examination of nailfold capillaries, parallel to the assessment of the 24-hour systemic blood-pressure evaluation. Paired t-test was used to assess changes in systemic blood pressure and capillary microscopy.
Results The mean systolic blood pressure (baseline: 108.68±8.89mmHg, follow-up: 111.73±8.08mmHg, p=0.032), median systolic blood pressure (baseline: 108.23±9.52mmHg, follow-up: 111.77±9.29mmHg, p=0.025), and the lowest systolic blood pressure over 24-hour recording (baseline: 79.64±10.15mmHg, follow-up: 86.05±11.69mmHg, p=0.019) showed a statistically significant increase during follow-up. Capillary blood-flow velocity increased (baseline: 0.49±0.35mm/s, follow-up: 0.79±0.36mm/s, p=0.023) and capillary blood-flow standstill time after cold provocation decreased under fludrocortisone therapy (baseline: 51.54±48.58 sec., follow-up: 13.38±20.46 sec., p=0.0078).
Conclusion Fludrocortisone might well be suitable for the treatment of systemic hypotension in glaucoma patients. Hemodynamic parameters show a tendency towards improvement in a magnitude which might be of clinical relevance. Whether Fludrocortisone might help preserve visual field in glaucoma needs to be assessed in a further study.

2313

FOCAL VERSUS DIFFUSE OPTIC NERVE DAMAGE IN THE GLAUCOMAS

JONAS JB, BUDDE WM

Dept. Ophthalmology, Friedrich-Alexander Universität Erlangen-Nürnberg, Erlangen (Germany)

Purpose To evaluate how often glaucomatous optic nerve atrophy is purely localized, purely diffuse, or shows a mixture of the pattern of damage.
Methods Retinal nerve fiber layer photographs of 232 eyes with open-angle glaucoma were evaluated for localized defects and diffuse loss. Purely localized damage was defined as the occurrence of one or more than one localized retinal nerve fiber layer defects with all the rest of the nerve fiber layer being normal. Purely diffuse nerve fiber layer loss was defined as a generalized loss in all fundus regions with the physiologic relative differences between the fundus sectors being preserved.
Results Localized defects of the retinal nerve fiber layer with an otherwise normal appearing retinal nerve fiber layer were found in 22 (9.6%) of the glaucomatous eyes. Purely diffuse loss of retinal nerve fiber layer was detected in 24 (10.3%) of the eyes.
Conclusions Both, a purely localized pattern and a purely diffuse type of optic nerve damage in glaucoma are rare. Most glaucoma eyes exhibit a mixture of localized and diffuse optic nerve damage with predominance of the diffuse pattern. Thus the question arises, whether the concept of different patterns of damage in different types of glaucoma still holds true.

2314

HIGH PREVALENCE OF GLAUCOMA IN SLEEP APNEA SYNDROME PATIENTS

GOLDBLUM D,[1] MATHIS J,[2] HESS CW,[2] FLEISCHHAUER J,[1] KOERNER F,[1] MOJON DS.[1]
1. Dept. of Ophthalmology, 2. Dept. of Neurology, University of Bern (Switzerland)

Purpose: To determine the prevalence of glaucoma in sleep apnea syndrome (SAS), an entity characterized by repetitive upper airway obstructions during sleep, inducing hypoxia and sleep disruption with the risk of cardiovascular and neurological sequelae.
Methods: 114 caucasian patients referred for evaluation of suspected SAS had complete masked ophthalmological examination, including computerized perimetry and simultaneous optic disk photographs
Results: According to the sleep studies, 69 of the 114 patients had SAS (61%). Three of the 114 patients had primary open-angle glaucoma (POAG) and two normal-tension glaucoma (NTG). All glaucoma patients had SAS. Our observed prevalence of glaucoma in SAS patients (7.2%) was significantly higher than what expected in a normal caucasian population (2%) ($p < 0.01$, Chi-square with Yates correction).
Conclusions: SAS patients constitute a high-risk population for glaucoma and should, therefore, be screened for glaucoma. At the moment we might only hypothesize, that SAS treatment might also stabilize the glaucomatous optic neuropathy.

2315

SLEEP APNEA SYNDROME IS ASSOCIATED WITH GLAUCOMA

MOJON DS,[1] HESS CW,[2] GOLDBLUM D,[1] FLEISCHHAUER J,[1] BOEHNKE M,[1] KOERNER F,[1] GUGGER M,[3] BASSETTI C,[3] MATHIS J.[2]
1. Dept. of Ophthalmology, 2. Dept. of Neurology,
3. Dept. of Pneumology, University of Bern, Switzerland

Purpose: To determine the prevalence of sleep apnea syndrome (SAS) in patients harboring primary open-angle glaucoma (POAG) and normal-tension glaucoma (NTG). SAS is a disease characterized by repetitive upper airway obstructions during sleep, inducing hypoxia and sleep disruption with the risk of cardiovascular and neurological sequelae.
Methods: 30 POAG and 14 NTG patients had a sleep evaluation (allnight polysomnography and/or allnight oxymetry).
Results: 20% (6/30) of POAG and 43% (6/14) of NTG patients had SAS. Both prevalences of SAS were significantly higher than in controls of same age and sex ($p < 0.005$, Chi-square test).
Conclusions: POAG and NTG patients should be screened for SAS to prevent late cardiovascular and neurovascular sequelae. At the moment, we might only hypothesize, that SAS treatment might also stabilize the glaucomatous optic neuropathy.

2316

MYOPIA AND GLAUCOMA. RESULTS FROM A VERY LARGE POPULATION SCREENING.

GRØDUM K, BENGTSSON B, HEIJL A
Malmö University Hospital, Sweden

Purpose: Myopia has often been implicated as a possible risk factor for glaucoma. We wanted to examine this association in a very large population.
Methods: We used data from a glaucoma screening conducted between 1992 and 1997 with 32,918 participants from Malmö. Refraction was measured by autorefractor. No cycloplegics were used. Patients were 57-79 years of age. Glaucoma eyes had specific and repeatable field defects on automated static perimetry (Humphrey 24-2 Full Threshold Program).
Results: Mean refraction was significantly lower in the 452 glaucoma subjects than in the controls, and more than 1 D lower than controls in the youngest group. Mean refraction increased by 0.6 D between 55 and 70 years of age in the controls and 1.3 D in the glaucoma cases.
Discussion: In this large, cross-sectional study, we found that myopia was more common in the glaucoma group than in the controls. An apparent hyperopic shift between 55 and 70 years was observed in both the glaucoma group and in the controls, but seemed to be twice as large in subjects with glaucoma. Possible explanations will be discussed.

2317

VASOREGULATION AND OCULAR BLOOD FLOW IN NORMAL PRESSURE GLAUCOMA

F.GALASSI°,A.SODI°,F.UCCI°,M.G.ROSSI°,E.MASINI*
°Eye Clinic, University of Florence (Italy)
*Department of Pharmacology, University of Florence (Italy)

Purpose:We comparatively considered ocular hemodynamics, possible vasospastic disorders and endothelium-dependent vasoregulatory dysfunction in NPG.
Methods:Our series consisted of 10 NPG patients and 10 age-matching normal subjects. Ocular hemodynamics was studied by means of CDI and vasospasm by measuring peripheral capillary blood cell velocity; then plasma levels of endothelin-1 (by RIA test) and nitric oxide (by cyclic GMP) were considered.
Results:NPGs showed a significant reduction of Ophthalmic Artery systolic ($p=0.01$) and diastolic velocity ($p=0.04$) in comparison with the controls.The endothelin-1 plasma levels were significantly higher ($p=0.03$) and the nitric oxide plasma levels significantly lower ($p=0.02$) in the NPG patients than in normal subjects.The correlation coefficient between endothelin and nitric oxide plasma levels was -0.65 ($p=0.03$). The diastolic velocity of the Short Posterior Ciliary Arteries showed a significant inverse correlation with endothelin plasma levels ($r=-0.85;p=0.003$) and a significant positive correlation with nitric oxide plasma levels ($r=0.91;p=0.000$). NPGs with vasospatic response showed higher endothelin-1 and lower nitric oxide plasma levels.
Conclusions: Our data support the role of vascular factors in the pathogenesis of NPG.

2321

The Pattern ERG in Clinical Practice

G E Holder, Moorfields Eye Hospital, London, UK.

In recent years the pattern ERG (PERG), the retinal response to a structured isoluminant stimulus such as a reversing checkerboard, has become an invaluable part of the diagnostic armamentarium. The normal PERG contains two main components, P50 (at 50msec) and N95 (95msec). There is strong evidence that the PERG has inner retinal origins, and it seems that N95 arises in relation to ganglion cell activity. However, although some of P50 is similarly derived, there also appears to be a contribution from more distal retinal structures.

The PERG is a sensitive indicator of central retinal function; a normal P50 component depending upon a normally functioning macula. Patients with macular dysfunction usually show reduction in PERG P50, and data will be presented from a large series of patients with outer retinal dystrophies (which may or may not have central retinal involvement) to show that early PERG abnormalities are often present at a stage when visual acuity is still unaffected. In addition to the value of the PERG in the objective assessment of disease progression, this may also assist prognosis and counselling. The PERG is often extinguished when visual acuity is significantly reduced.

Diseases which primarily affect the ganglion cells, such as Leber Hereditary Optic Atrophy and Dominant Optic Atrophy, give PERG abnormalities confined to N95 in early stage, but there may be P50 amplitude loss, with concomitant latency *reduction*, as disease progresses. N95 loss can also occur from retrograde degeneration to the ganglion cells in optic nerve disease such as demyelination and compression. PERG extinction is not a feature of optic nerve disease.

As a delayed pattern VEP is a common finding both in optic nerve and macular disease, the different PERG findings in macular and optic nerve disease allow improved interpretation of delayed pattern VEPs, and assist in the distinction between maculopathy and optic neuropathy.

2322

PERSPECTIVES FOR NOVEL STIMULI IN CLINICAL VEP PRACTICE

SPILEERS W.
Dept. of Ophthalmology, University Clinic, Leuven (Belgium)

Since 30 years clinical visual evoked potentials (VEPs) use a pattern stimulus as a standard. The pattern reversal mode has gained wide application. There is now firm evidence that the human visual system uses parallel processing along two major pathways extending from the retina in the extrastriate cortex: a dorsal and a ventral stream were described. Several attributers of visual perception such as motion and color are processed differentially along those streams.
Clinical research now focuses on the investigation of stimulus conditions specifically addressing one of the two pathways. The aim is to develop more sensitive diagnostic techniques by selectively stimulating one or the other pathway. The current state of knowledge on motion and color VEPs and their possible relevance for clinical applications will be discussed.

2323

VISUAL EVOKED RESPONSES TO STATIONARY PATTERNS

MACALUSO C[1], PAVESI G[2] and CAMPARINI M[1]
[1]Department of Ophthalmology, University of Parma (Italy)
[2]Department of Neurology, University of Parma (Italy)

Purpose The lack of visual perception during saccades (so called "saccadic suppression") prompted us to explore the possibility that the onset of fixation naturally occurring after a saccade is a visual stimulus able to evoke cortical responses (VECP) from stationary patterns. Moreover, correspondence of such saccade-related VECP with pattern onset-offset VECP was examined.
Methods The subjects alternatively fixated a checkerboard and an equiluminant background, while eye movements (EOG) and cortical activity were recorded. The end of every saccade directed to the checkerboard (i.e. fixation-onset) or away from the checkerboard (i.e. fixation-offset) triggered acquisition and averaging of cortical activity.
Results Cortical responses to fixation-onset were highly reproducible, and single traces were generally well defined without averaging. The waveform was almost identical to pattern-onset VECP and different from pattern-reversal. Similarly, cortical responses to fixation-offset were comparable to fixation-offset VECP. A stationary pattern printed on paper was equally effective in evoking saccade-related VECP.
Conclusions A visual cortical response naturally occurs at the end of every saccade (EEG lambda waves) without need to temporally modulate the stimulus. We demonstrate that the cortical response evoked by the fixation-onset occurring at saccade-offset actually is a pattern-onset VECP. Similarly, the cortical response evoked by the fixation-offset occurring at saccade-onset actually is a pattern-offset VECP. Saccade-related VECPs are an effective way to study VECPs in a quasi-spontaneous condition from readily available stationary patterns (VECP from paper, VECP from anything?).

2324

PATTERN AND FLASH VISUAL EVOKED POTENTIALS (VEPs) ELICITED BY THE MULTIFOCAL TECHNIQUE

C Barber[1], W Gao[1,3], R Inoue[2], Y Oguchi[2], H Ohde[2], H Walkey[1]

[1]Queen's Medical Centre, Nottingham, UK;
[2]Keio University School of Medicine, Tokyo, Japan;
[3]Institution for Prevention and Treatment of Eye Diseases, Harbin, China.

The multifocal stimulation technique offers the possibility to record multiple responses to localised stimulation within a practicable time-frame. Thus the confounding of responses from different areas of the visual field may be avoided. The presentation of the waveforms as kernels of different orders offers further possibilities for dissection of the responses.

This presentation reviews the responses to the commonly-used stimuli: hexagon flash elements, checkerboard onset and checker-board reversal. It discusses the similarities and differences between them; the spatial and temporal interactions within each class; and the interactions between them.

It also relates responses obtained through the use of the new technique with those obtained by the standard method of synchronous averaging.

2325

THE MULTIFOCAL EVOKED RESPONSE TO FLASH, PATTERN AND MOTION STIMULI

Keating D[1,2] and Parks S[1,2]
1. Department of Clinical Physics and Bio-Engineering, University of Glasgow, (Scotland)
2. Tennent Institute of Ophthalmology, Western Infirmary, Glasgow, (Scotland).

Purpose. To investigate features of the multifocal evoked response to flash, pattern and motion stimuli.
Methods. A custom designed multifocal electrophysiology system has been developed to enable a wide variety of stimulus parameters and signal processing algorithms to be evaluated. Key features of the system include improved stimulus generation using digital stimuli, new padded sparse stimulation sequences to reduce anomalies in non-linear components and wide (120^0) field of view.
Results. A combination of multifocal flash, pattern and motion stimuli enables detailed objective functional information to be obtained from the visual pathway. Example waveforms are presented for a wide variety of stimuli to illustrate the potential for the technique.
Conclusions The application of random signal generation techniques for multifocal studies adds a new dimension to electrophysiology which promises real clinical benefit in terms of earlier diagnosis and in monitoring of disease processes

2331

LOCAL AND SYSTEMIC AUTOIMMUNE REACTIONS IN PATIENTS WITH DIABETIC RETINOPATHY AND GLAUCOMA.

L.E.Teplinskaya, N.S.Zaitseva, L.M.Balashova, E.V.Mazanova, L.V.Korzencova.
Helmholtz Inst.of Eye Diseases, Moscow, Russia

Purpose. Study of local and systemic autoimmune status of patients with diabetic retinopathy(DR) and primary open-angle glaucoma(POAG).
Methods. Elisa Method to mark antibodies(AB) to antigens(AG): collagen 2,4 types, DNA, tissues of liver, kidney and heart.
Results. AB to collagen(C) in the lacrimal fluid of 182 patients(232eye) with DR were detected in 34,1% of eyes, mostly in early stages of process (45,1%) as compared with proliferative stage (16,7%, p 0,01), especially in patients with diabetes 2 type(35,5%). Serum AB to C in all stages of DR were revealed rarely(3,6%-16,7%). AB to DNA in lacrimal fluid (23,3% of eyes) were detected with the same incidence rate as in serum(21,8%) and didn't correlate with type of diabetes. AB to liver established in 15,2% of eyes, and in serum of 18,2% of patients with diabetes 1 type mainly At the same time systemic autoAB to tissues of heart, kidney, lungs, myelin basic protein(MBP), elastin were revealed(14,5-3,6%). AB to C were detected in lacrimal fluid of patients with POAG in 33,7% of eyes(149p-298eyes), and were correlated with increased IOP in decompensation of POAG (55,5% of eyes). AB to C in tears of 27 children with congenital glaucoma were revealed rarely (6,3%). AB to DNA and MBP were detected in 18,7% and 12,5% accordingly. AB to C in serum of adults and children were revealed in single cases.
Conclusions. In immunopathogenesis of these eye pathology local autoimmune response prevailed over systemic. Peculiarity of pathogenesis of these diseases is development of autoimmune reactions in early stages of DR and in decompensation of glaucoma.

2332

ASSAY OF CYTOKINES IN VITREOUS HUMOR IN PROLIFERATIVE DIABETIC RETINOPATHY AND VITREORETINOEATHY.

LEKAA, A.MOEMEN, Dept. OF BIOCHEMISTRY, AHMED, T. SHOEIR, Ophthalmology DEPT.ANDTAREK, M.ELSERGANY Clinical pathology dept. Research Institute of Ophthalmology, EGYPT

Purpose : The levels of interlukin (IL1B) and IL6 were assayed in vitreous and plasma of patients with proliferative diabetic retinopathy (PDR), proliferative vitreoretinopathy (PVR), vitreous hemorrhage, macular hole and giant tear .trying to evaluate their roles in pathogenesis of these ocular diseases.
Methods : 32vitreous samples were collected, undiluted from 14patients with PVR, 6patients with PDR, 2patients with vitreous hemorrhage and 9patients with macular hole or giant tear. Quantitative determination of Il1B and IL6 by enzyme linked immunoadsorbent assays were done.
Results : In11vitreous samples of 14PVR patients(78.5%) Il1B were below detection limit. IL6 ranged from 41 to 518 pg/ml. In PDR patients ,3vitreous samples were below detection limit (50%). IL6ranged from 19 – 335 pg/ml and only one sample below detection limit. In the macular hole and giant tear group IL1B in all vitreous samples were below detection limit except one samples . Vitreous IL6 values ranged from 6-535 pg/ml. The cytokines values were compared in different groups. IL6 values in vitreous of PVR were significantly elevated.
Conclusion : our study suggests that cytokines particularly IL6 having an implifiying role in the pathology of PVR. It acts as a common inflammatory mediator. The inflammatory reaction could further exacerbate disease severity in eye of patients with proliferative retinopathy.

2333

Retinal Pigment Epithelium (RPE) Hypersensitivity.

Thirkill CE.
University of California, Davis, Ophthalmology Research. 1603 Alhambra Blvd, Sacramento CA. 95816.

Purpose: Evaluate indications of ocular hypersensitivity in patients with cancer-associated (CAR), and idiopathic retinopathies.

Methods: Western blot analyses, indirect immunohistochemistry, and metabolic inhibition assays on the antigens, and viability of *in vitro* propagated retinal pigment epithelium.

Results: Indications of complement-fixing autoantibody reactions with cytoplasmic components of RPE cells were identified in association with the retinal degenerations of the CAR syndrome, and in patients in whom no causal effect of vision loss could be identified.

Conclusions: Retinal degenerations can occur in association with abnormal immunologic reactions involving the RPE. Immune-mediated loss. or inhibition of the essential functions of this cell population could cause, or contribute to a variety of retinal degenerations.

2334

ENDOTOXIN-INDUCED-UVEITIS PROMOTES THE PROLIFERATION OF SYNGENEIC RETINAL CELLS INJECTED IN THE RAT VITREOUS.

D. CHAUVAUD[1], F. BEHAR-COHEN[1], Y. de KOZAK[2]
[1] Hôtel-Dieu of Paris hospital, [2] INSERM U450 (France)

Purpose: To analyse the proliferative potentiality of syngeneic retinal pigmented epithelial (RPE) and Müller glial (RMG) cells injected in the vitreous of rats developing an Endotoxin-Induced-Uveitis (EIU). **Material and methods:** RPE and RMG cells of post-natal Lewis male rats were purified and intravitreally injected (10^5 cells / $2\mu l$ of saline 0.9%): either RPE (n=8) or RMG (n=8) or both cell types (n=8). One group of rats received also the induction of EIU by injection of 150 μg LPS. Retinophotographies were performed at 8, 15 days and 4 weeks. At this time, eyes were fixed and embeded for histology and immunohistochemistry. **Results:** When EIU was induced, RPE cells injection resulted in a limited intravitreal proliferation of cells, while RMG cells injections induced an extended proliferation of GFAP positive cells at the surface of the retina. Both type of resulted in a tractionnal proliferation with retinal detachment at 3 weeks together with an aggravation of EIU. When no LPS was injected, a moderate proliferation was observed. **Conclusions:** Inflammation promotes a tissular proliferation originating from syngeneic retinal cells into the vitreous, which aggravate the inflammation. The co-injection of RPE and RMG cells induced a tractionnal proliferation suggesting that proinflammatory mediators could enhance proliferative interactions between RPE and RMG cells.

2335

HISTOLOGY OF EXPERIMENTAL AUTOIMMUNE UVEITIS (EAU) AFTER TOPICAL TREATMENT WITH ALLOPURINOL (AL)

LOEFFLER KU,[1] SEKUNDO W,[2] GRUS FH,[1] SPITZNAS M,[1] and AUGUSTIN AJ.[1]
1. Dept. Ophthalmology, Univ. of Bonn (Germany)
2. Dept. Ophthalmology, Univ. of Marburg (Germany)

Purpose: Recently, systemic AL has been investigated as a new potential drug in the treatment of EAU. In this study we have examined the morphologic changes associated with a topical treatment regimen. Methods: EAU was induced in male Lewis rats (n=21) with crude retina extract. Therapy groups received AL as a gel (1%, ALG) or prednisolone eye drops (1%, Pred) 8x/day for 2 weeks. Then one eye was enucleated for light microscopic evaluation while the other eye was submitted for biochemical analysis of lipid peroxides (LPO) and myeloperoxidase activity (MPO). Histologic changes were evaluated at three different tissue levels, and the inflammatory cell infiltrate was graded according to a score from 0 to 4+ and correlated with the biochemical results. Results: Histologic changes as well as LPO and MPO were significantly reduced by ALG as compared to untreated controls ($p<0.01$). Pred led to a significant reduction of MPO only ($p<0.01$) but did not exert a tissue protective effect. Conclusion: AL – even when applied topically – proved to be very effective not only in lowering biochemical parameters of inflammation but also in reducing the morphologic damage due to EAU.

2336

SEROLOGICAL AND PCR ANALYSIS OF OCULAR FLUIDS IS AN IMPORTANT TOOL IN THE DIAGNOSTIC WORKUP OF A UVEITIS PATIENT PRESENTING AS A DIAGNOSTIC DILEMMA

Kijlstra A, Ongkosuwito J, Wienesen-van Doorn M and van Doornik C
Diagnostic Uveitis Centre, The Netherlands Ophthalmic Research Institute, Amsterdam (The Netherlands)

Purpose To evaluate the outcome of diagnostic ocular fluid analysis in the diagnosis of uveitis patients presenting as a diagnostic dilemma.
Methods During 1997 the diagnostic uveitis centre in Amsterdam received 171 ocular fluid samples taken from uveitis patients. Depending upon the amount of material received we determined the presence of DNA or local antibody production for Toxoplasma gondii, Herpes simplex virus, Varicella Zoster virus or Cytomegalovirus.
Results An overall positive test result was obtained in 36 % of cases. Of the 61 positive tests (DNA and/or local antibody positive), an isolated positive PCR test was only observed in 8 cases (13 %). Although these laboratory tests often confirmed the suspected clinical diagnosis, there were several cases in which a suspected Toxoplasma uveitis was positive for a Herpes virus and vice versa.
Conclusions Ocular fluid analysis is an important tool in the diagnostic workup of an atypical uveitis patient. Serological analysis is the test of choice in case of limited ocular fluid volume in immunocompetent patients.

2341

TEAR BASAL SECRETION IN SJÖGREN'S SYNDROME

ARAGONA P, TRIPODI G, SPINELLA R, LAGANA' E and FERRERI G

Institute of Ophthalmology, University of Messina (Italy)

Purpose Sjögren's syndrome (SS) is a systemic disease characterized by dry eye and dry mouth. Schirmer's I test is used as test of election to detect a dicreased tear secretion. Since Schirmer's I test has proved to have a low sensibility we have compared this test with a modified Jones's test which studies the basal secretion.
Methods Three groups of patients were studied: group 1, 93 SS patients (mean age ± SD: 47.2±15.7); group 2, 21 non SS connective tissue diseases patients (49.4±14.5); group 3, 53 conjunctival diseases patients (37.2±17.5). To assess the presence of SS the European criteria were followed. Schirmer's I (positive values ≤5 mm/5') and Jones' test (positive values ≤5 mm/5' and ≤3 mm/5'). The Jones' test was modified to determine a more ponounced anesthesia of ocular surface and eyelids. 2x2 tables were used to assess the specificity and sensitivity of the tests.
Results For SS, Schirmer's I test showed a specificity of 96.6% and a sensitivity of 32.8%; the modified Jones' test showed a specificity of 85.1% and a sensitivity of 74.1% with a positivity value of ≤5 mm/5', while a specificity of 97.3% and a sensitivity of 55.4% with a positivity value of ≤3 mm/5'.
Conclusions In SS patients the Jones' test showed a similar specificity to Schirmer I test but a higher sensitivity when considered positive for values ≤5 mm/5' which gave the best results. We suggest to use both these tests for a reliable diagnosis of dicreased tear production in SS patients.

2342

TOPICAL CYCLOSPORINE-A IN THE TREATMENT OF KERATOCONJUNCTIVITIS SICCA IN PATIENTS WITH SJOGREN'S SYNDROME

VAIKOUSSIS E[1], MARAGOU M[2], RONTOGIANNI D[3]

[1]Dept. Opthalmology, General Hosp. of Piraeus-Greece
[2]Dept. Rheymatology, "Evangelismos" Hosp. Athens-Greece
[3]Dept. Pathology, "Evangelismos" Hosp. Athens-Greece

Purpose The study was conducted in order to evaluate the use of topical Cyclosporine-A (CsA) as a therapeutic alternative on Keratoconjuctivitis Sicca (KCS) in patients with Sjogren's syndrome (Ss).
Methods We performed conjuctival biopsies from 15 patients with Ss and 8 normal controls. Two weeks later patients were started on 1% CsA in artificial tears 4 times daily for 6 weeks. Patients were evaluated every week during the treatment period. The evaluation was based on patient assessment and objective measurements, including Schirmer's test, BUT, Rose Bengal staining. At the end of treatment period the conjuctival biopsy was repeated.
Results a) There was a significantly greater number of $CD4^+$ cells in the epithelium and substantia propria in the Ss group before treatment when compared with the normals. b) After treatment the number of $CD4^+$ cells was reduced significantly. c) The clinical improvement was very poor as was noted by patients subjective assessment or by objective parameters.
Conculsions The topical installation of 1% CsA in patients with Ss produces an improvement of conjuctival immunopathological profile but the clinical benefit concerning the signs and symptoms of KCS was very poor

2343

REVERSAL OF SQUAMOUS METAPLASIA IN DRY EYE PATIENTS AFTER PUNCTAL OCCLUSION

OSAMA SHALABY, LUIS RIVAS, A.I.SANZ, M.A. OROZA, JUAN MURUBE

HOSPITAL RAMON Y CAJAL, MADRID- SPAIN

PURPOSE: This study was designed to study the time of reversal of squamous metaplasia which is a constant feature of dry eye patients, after restoration of the ocular surface by the occlusion of the lacrimal puncti. **METHODS:** 20 patients with aqueous deficiency dry eye undergoing punctal occlusion by punctal patch which is a technique in which a 2 x 2 mm square of the epithelium surrounding the punctum is excised, then a square of lower bulbar conjunctiva of similar or slightly larger size is placed in the bed and fixed with 4 sutures. Impression cytology specimens were taken from all patients before the interference, one week, 2 weeks, one month, 3 months, 6 months and one year after the occlusion. **RESULTS:** We have noticed that the improvement in the shape of the epithelial cells has noticed starting from the second week after the occlusion increasing gradually during the first month, becoming more significant from the second month noting the cells more closer to each other with N/C ratio 1/3 or 1/ 2 . This improvement is much more increased reaching six months after the occlusion, nearly normalising the ocular surface similar to healthy persons by the first year after canalicular occlusion. **CONCLUSION:** Squamous metaplasia in dry eye patients is early reversed after restoration of ocular surface by adequate punctal occlusion.

2344

AN EVALUATION OF DRY EYE SYMPTOMS AND THEIR ECONOMIC AND DAILY LIFE IMPACT.

GUHL A.K.[(1)]; KOZMA C.M.[(2)]; EBERLE M[(3)]; ERB C.[(3)]
(1) Allergan UK , (2) Uni.South Carolina, USA, (3) Uni. Eye Clinic, Basel, Switzerland

Purpose: To capture data on Dry Eye, explore its impact on daily activities and associated costs, and to further investigate causal and psychosomatic aspects of the disease.
Methods: A specially developed questionnaire of over 100 items was completed by 109 subjects in a naturalistic environment. Data were analysed using descriptive statistics.
Results: Respondents experienced an average of 6.7 dry eye symptoms per person over the past year. Average severity was1.8 on a four point scale from mild to very severe. Frequency of doctor visit data and drug utilisation data indicated a significantly higher medical cost burden due to dry eye symptoms in the 12% of patients self-rating symptoms as severe. Overall 23% of medication was obtained on prescription. 43% of working subjects indicated that they had worked in the past 3 months more than 5 days with dry eye symptoms with an effect on their productivity. 7% indicated there had been days they were prevented from working due to their dry eye symptoms. The most frequently reported impacts on daily life were forced changes or restrictions to leisure activities, and the presence of frequent mood swings. Overall the survey highlighted significant areas for future research.
Conclusions: Dry eye symptoms create a medical cost burden for both the patient and healthcare payers, interference with leisure activities, and can have an appreciable impact on productivity in the working population.

2345

READING STRATEGIES IN ALZHEIMER'S DISEASE

MURPHY CC, SAIDLEAR C, BERGIN D, WRIGLEY M, and EUSTACE P.
Institute of Ophthalmology, Mater Misericordiae Hospital, Dublin (Ireland)

Purpose: To determine if a specific reading strategy exists in Alzheimer's disease (AD). A specific strategy could be a marker for early disease.

Methods: Reading strategies were recorded in 9 patients with AD and compared with 9 age-matched controls using infrared oculography and were analysed for accuracy (the number of hypo- and hypermetric saccades), velocity, duration, and fixation instability (the number of square-wave jerks).

Results: During reading, the saccades were slower and longer than normal but were accurate. Fixation instability was a feature of both the AD patients and the controls, but did not differ between the two groups.

Conclusions: Widespread loss of cortical neurons in AD disrupts the neural circuits that control saccades. While velocity and duration of saccades are abnormal during reading, no specific abnormalities in the reading strategies were identified that would make their recording a useful confirmatory diagnostic test in AD.

2346

THE EYE IN COHEN SYNDROME: A LONG-TERM FOLLOW-UP

SUMMANEN P,[1] KIVITIE-KALLIO S,[2] NORIO R,[3] RAITTA C[1]
Department of [1]Ophthalmology, [2]Department of Pediatrics, University of Helsinki, and Department of Medical Genetics, The Finnish Family Federation, Helsinki (Finland)

Purpose: To assess the frequency and progression of ophthalmological changes in the Cohen syndrome.
Methods: 22 Finnish Cohen syndrome (MIM No. 216550) patients (M:F 10:12) aged 2.7 to 57 y (median, 33) underwent an ophthalmological examination. Fourteen had data of previous examinations, including fundus photographs over a period ranging from 8.5 to more than 30 y.
Results: The eyes had a typical flame-shaped outline and eyebrows and lashes were thick. All but the second youngest patient were myopic, the myopia being progressive and often high grade. Strabismus was common and lens opacities occurred early. Pigmentary fundus changes were seen in all after teens. Hemeralopia was complained at the age of 5 to 6, and constriction of visual fields thereafter. The macula had bull's eye appearance. Central vision persisted until fourth decade, after which they were legally blind.
Conclusions: The phenotype of Cohen syndrome is uniform in Finland including nonprogessive mental and motor retardation, typical dysmorphic features, granulocytopenia and marked ophthalmic changes.

2347

CREUTZFELDT-JAKOB DISEASE THIRTY YEARS AFTER CORNEAL TRANSPLANTATION

THIEL HJ
University Eye Hospital, Tübingen (Germany)

We report a 45-year-old woman, who had undergone corneal transplantation for keratoconus thirty years before she presented neurological symptoms like cerebellar syndrome, severe ataxia and dysarthria. She rapidly deteriorated and died of respiratory complications eight months after onset of the disease. EEG demonstrated generalized slow activity, the level of NSE (neuron specific enolase) was markedly elevated. Consequently the diagnosis of Creutzfeldt-Jakob disease was established. We must assume that the donor cornea was the source of transmission in the patient.

2348

PARTIAL OCULAR ALBINISM INDICATING ADULT CHEDIAK-HIGASHI SYNDROME (CHS)

FOETZSCH R [1], JACOBASCH E[1], JACOBASCH L[2], PAAZ U[2], KUNATH B[1], EHNINGER G[2].
1. Dept. of Neurology,
2. Dept. of Internal Medicine I,
Faculty of Medicine Carl-Gustav Carus
Techn. University Dresden (Germany)

Purpose
CHS is a rare autosomal recessive disorder. It is characterised by partial oculocutaneous albinism, increased susceptibility to infections, bleeding tendency and the presence of abnormal organelles in most granule-containing cells. Whilst the vast majority of patients die in infancy, we present two adult cases. The two sibs born to healthy parents in 1961 and 1963 presented with a ten year history of an unsteady and slowly deteriorating gait.
Methods
Extensive additional investigations were performed: ENG, VEP, nerve conduction studies, cranial MR, abdominal ultrasound, hematological and molecular studies, microscopical studies of skin biopsies and hair
Results
In peripheral blood and bone marrow films typical giant granules were detected.
Conclusions
CHS should be considered even in adult patients with ocular albinism. The diagnosis can be confirmed by examination of peripheral blood or bone marrow films.

2411

EARLY RESULTS OF INTRASCLERAL APPLICATION OF MITOMYCIN C AND RELEASABLE SUTURES IN FILTERING PROCEDURES IN PRIMARY OPEN ANGLE GLAUCOMA

PETKOVA N
University Eye Clinic, Alexandrov's Hospital, Sofia, Bulgaria

A comparisson of early postoperative results of Trabeculectomy (TE) with intrascleral application (under the scleral flap) of Mitomycin C (MMC) 0,5 mg/ml for 3 minutes and Releasable sutures (RS) and TE without MMC and RS was performed.
41 persons (49 eyes) with Primary Open Angle Glaucoma (POAG) of which 10 persons (19 eyes) with average age 25 years -group A and 31 persons (31 eyes) with average age 61,9 years, group B, underwent TE with MMC and RS. The results of group A were compared to those of 14 persons (14 eyes) and group B to 89 persons (89 eyes) with POAG with similar average age, who underwent TE without MMC and RS. Intraocular pressure(IOP) control below 21 mm Hg was achieved in 94,8% of the eyes in group A and 96,7% of the eyes in group B. Similar I0P control was achieved in the groups without MMC and RS. Most common complications were flat anterior chamber in 5% of group A,6,6% of group B and 14,6% in the groups without MMC and RS. Chorioidal Detachment was present in 8% of the eyes with TE without MMC. Hyphaema was observed in 5,5% of group A,3% of group B and 10% of the eyes without MMC and RS. The lower incidence of complications in the early postoperative period after TE with MMC and RS we explain with the use of RS. Intrascleral use of MMC and RS in TE lead to good IOP control and less complications in the early postoperative period.

2412

EVALUATION OF EFFICACY OF LATANOPROST IN SECONDARY GLAUCOMAS PROVOKED BY ANGULAR DYSGENESIS

Mortemousque B., Barac'h D., Bertel F., Vérin Ph.

Purpose : Latanoprost is considered to be effective in many cases of badly controllable glaucoma. We treated patients with secondary glaucoma due to angular dysgenesis with Latanoprost eyedrops which did not respond satisfactorily to conventional medical glaucoma therapy.
Methods : 12 patients between 8-41 years old(mean 26.08 ($\pm$ 10.91), 5 males 7 females) were affected by bilateral angular dysgenesis, with forms of trabeculodysgenesis (6 cases), Axenfeld syndrome (4 cases) and Rieger anomaly (2 cases). They were treated with Latanoprost eyedrops one time a day. Each patient had undergone previous surgery and had received at least two different types of treatment (Betablocker, Dorzolamide, Iopidine, Pilocarpine). Mean intraocular pressure was 20.25 $\pm$ 2.5mmHg and visual field of every patient was endangered.
Results : One month later, mean IOP was 28.83 $\pm$ 5.99mmHg.
Conclusion : Latanoprost seems to be inadequate for treating secondary glaucoma due to angular dysgenesis probably because uveo-scleral drainage of aqueous humor is limited or absent.

2413

LIGANDS WHICH ACT AS BOTH 5-HT$_{1A}$ AGONISTS AND α_1-ADRENERGIC ANTAGONISTS LOWER INTRAOCULAR PRESSURE IN RABBITS

CHIDLOW G, CUPIDO A and OSBORNE NN.
Nuffield Lab. of Ophthalmology, University of Oxford, U.K.

Purpose:

α_1-adrenoceptor antagonists (e.g. prazosin) and 5-HT$_{1A}$ receptor agonists (e.g. 8-OH-DPAT) have previously been shown to reduce intraocular pressure (IOP) in rabbits. The purpose of this study was to explore whether a range of ligands which function as both agonists at 5-HT$_{1A}$ receptors and antagonists at α_1-adrenoceptors reduce IOP more effectively than drugs with affinity for only one receptor type.

Method:

IOP was measured using an applanation tonometer previously calibrated for use in rabbits.

Results:

Topical administration of all of the compounds tested caused dose-dependent decreases of IOP in treated eyes of rabbits with a rank order of potency of WB-4101>flesinoxan>5-methyl-urapidil>urapidil=BMY-7378.

Conclusion:

5-HT$_{1A}$ receptor agonists / α_1-adrenoceptor antagonists are effective hypotensive agents in the rabbit and offer a potential new class of drugs for reducing IOP.

2414

CLINICAL EXPERIENCE WITH BRIMONIDINE 0.2% AS FIRST-LINE AND ADJUNCT THERAPY.

MELAMED, S.[1], for The Brimonidine Study Groups
1The Sam Rothberg Glaucoma Center, The Goldshlager Eye Institute (Israel)

PURPOSE: To present accumulated data on the efficacy, safety, quality of life effects, and clinical success rate of brimonidine 0.2% BID compared to timolol 0.5% BID or betaxolol 0.25% S BID as monotherapy, and to pilocarpine 2.0% TID as adjunct therapy with beta-blockers in ocular hypertensive or glaucoma patients. **METHODS**: Over 2000 patients were enrolled in six multicenter, randomized, double-masked, parallel group trials. The primary efficacy variable was IOP lowering, with ocular and systemic safety parameters monitored in each study. Other variables included physician evaluation of clinical success and quality of life questionnaires. **RESULTS**: Brimonidine monotherapy demonstrated significant and sustained efficacy comparable to timolol and superior to betaxolol as measured by mean reduction in IOP and investigators evaluation of clinical success. As adjunct therapy, brimonidine demonstrated significant IOP-lowering additivity to beta-blockers equivalent to that of pilocarpine, with superior patient preference. Overall, brimonidine was well tolerated by patients and produced no clinically significant changes in heart rate or blood pressure. The incidence of ocular allergy was 12.7% in 1 long-term or less in short-term studies. **CONCLUSION**: Brimonidine 0.2% provides ocular hypotensive efficacy for up to three years and is well tolerated as both first-line and additive therapy for ocular hypertension and glaucoma.

2415

SILICONE OIL SUBSTITUTION AND PHOTOCOAGULATION OF THE RETINA AND THE CILIARY PROCESSES FOR MANAGEMENT OF HEMORRHAGIC GLAUCOMA DURING VITRECTOMY

K.U. BARTZ-SCHMIDT, A. PSICHIAS and K. HEIMANN
Department of Ophthalmology, University of Cologne, Germany

Purpose. Prospective, consecutive case control study to demonstrate the impact of silicone oil as an insulator for vascular growth factors and for prevention of secondary complications due to vitreoretinal surgery.
Methods. Thirty-two patients underwent silicone oil vitreous substitution following vitrectomy and photocoagulation of the retina and the ciliary processes for neovascular glaucoma and vitreous hemorrhage associated with diabetic retinopathy (14 patients) or central retinal vein occlusion (18 patients). Follow-up intervals: 3 (n=32), 6 (n=27), 12 (n=25), 24 (n=19) and 36 (n=9) months after surgery. Control for intraocular pressure, visual acuity and complications respectively revision procedures.
Results. Four patients died (2 during the first 6 months and 2 patients after the first year after surgery), not more than 4 patients were non-compliant at each control examination. In 14 eyes visual acuity kept stabile or increased. At the 12 month interval, intraocular pressure was normal (below 21 mmHg and above 7 mmHg) in 17 of 25 patients (68%), Hypotony was present in 2 eyes (8%). Silicone oil was removed in 7 eyes, not earlier then 2 months. One eye went to phthisis bulbi and was enucleated. Four eyes (16%) had revision surgery for refractive glaucoma. One revision became necessary for vitreoretinal complications.
Conclusions. Silicone oil can successfully be used as an vitreous substitute in the treatment of neovascular glaucoma and vitreous hemorrhage. Effects of silicone oil vitreous substitution are rapid regression of rubeosis iridis and prevention of severe complications, reported following vitreoretinal surgery for neovascular glaucoma, like recurrent vitreous hemorrhage, extensive fibrin formation and retinal detachment.

2416

COMBINED PHACOEMULSIFICATION, IOL IMPLANTATION AND TRABECULAR ASPIRATION IN PATIENTS WITH PSEUDOEXFOLIATION GLAUCOMA..

JACOBI PH. Köln

In a prospective study 71 eyes of 64 cataract patients suffering from medically uncontrolled PEX-G were randomly assigned to either of three treatment groups: [1] PE/IOL, [2] PE/IOL/TA and [3] PE/IOL/TE. The main outcome measures included pre- and postoperative intraocular pressure (IOP), number of medications to achieve IOP control, and vísual acuity. The incidence of intra- and postoperative complications was also recorded.
In group 1 (n=19), IOP decreased on average(±SD) by 2.8±0.9 mmHg at 2 years follow-up. At the same time interval, IOP reduction was 16.3±2.8 mmHg and 17.5±3.9 mmHg in group 2 (n=28) and group 3 (n=24), respectively. Medication was discontinued in 21%, 71%, and 92%, respectively. Visual recovery was excellent the day after surgery in 92% (66 out of 71) of all cases. In group 1, there were no operative or post-operative complications except transient IOP elevation. In group 2, blood reflux from Schlemm´s canal occurred in 68%, however with no further sequelae. Transient phases of hypotony (n=4), flattening of the anterior chamber (n=3), and reversible choroidal effusion (n=2) were observed in group 3 exclusively.
The performance of PE/IOL/TA in cataract patients complicated by uncontrolled PEX-G resulted in effective lowering of IOP which permitted the reduction or elimination of glaucoma medication, postoperatively.

2417

RELEASABLE STITCHES AND THE EARLY COMPLICATIONS OF TRABECULECTOMY

SIAROV N, APOSTOLOV V.
GLAUCOMA CLINIC,SOFIA,MEDICAL UNIVERSITY (BULGARIA)

Purpose: To determine whether the use of releasable sutures alters the complications and the success rate of trabeculectomy.
Methods: A retrospective series of 216 eyes of 204 consecutive patients who underwent trabeculectomy with releasable sutures (RSTE) was compared with a demographically similar control group of 245 eyes of 232 patients who had a standard trabeculectomy (StTE) performed. The early postoperative intraocular pressure (IOP) and the rates of the complications were investigated.
Results:

	RSTE Group	StTE Group
postoperative IOP	17.02 mm Hg	13.28 mm Hg
hypotony	16 eyes (7.4%)	70 eyes (28.5%)
shallow AC	14 eyes (6.5%)	56 eyes (22.9%)
flat AC	1 eye (0.5%)	14 eyes (5.7%)
hyphaema	13 eyes (6.0%)	30 eyes (12.2%)
chor. detachment	7 eyes (3.2%)	39 eyes (15.9%)

Conclusion: The use of releasable sutures with trabeculectomy resulted in a significant reduction of both incidence and severity of the early postoperative complications.

2421

LATER ONSET OR 'ACQUIRED' ESOTROPIAS

SPIRITUS M.(UCL Cliniques St Luc, Brussels)

Acquired esotropia (ET) occurs after 6 months of age. Since normal binocular vision (NBV) is present from fourth month of age on, complete restoration of binocular functions may be achieved provided adequate treatment is started without delay.

According to the motor fusional divergence amplitude, the esodeviation will be latent (esophoria), intermittent (intermittent esotropia) or manifest (esotropia).

Symptomatic esophoria (asthenopia, headache) requires the same treatment as esotropia does. Orthoptics treatment must be rejected; it may result in permanent diplopia.

1- Accommodative Esotropia

- onset at any age : average between 2 and 4 vears;
- initially intermittent, becomes constant with time;
- variable angle; increases when accommodation is sollicitated.

<u>1.1 Fully refractive accommodative ET</u>
(normal AC/A ratio)

Cause : hypermetropia (Donders);

Mechanisms:
(a) excessive convergence evoked by accommodation;
(b) insufficient fusional divergence amplitude

Full cycloplegic hyperopic correction eliminates the deviation at all distances. No surgery.

<u>1.2. Nonrefractive accommodative ET (hi-h AC/A ratio)</u>

Mechanism : abnormally high accommodative convergence response to each unit of accommodation.

After full optical correction of the refractive error-range from myopia to moderate hyperopia-, no deviation at far but a large deviation is present at near.

Treatment : bifocals (Franklin)
surgery (bimedial retro-equatorial myopexy).

<u>1.3 Partially accommodative ET with normal or high AC/A ratio.</u>

Mixed type of esodeviation. A residual anale (basic angle) persists in spite of full refractive error correction and/or bifocals. Surgery is advocated to correct the basic deviation. Unilateral amblyopia is frequent.

2- Essential Esotropia of Late Normosensorial Esotropia (Hugonnier, Lang, Costenbader)

Mechanism: anomaly of "position of rest" which is no more controlled by fusional divergence. No accommodative factor is present.

Surgery.

3- Secondary Esotropia

- Sensory
- Consecutive

2422

INFANTILE OR EARLY ONSET STRABISMUS

SPIELMANN A. (Nancy)

Infantile strabismus or early onset strabismus occurs before the age of 6 months, that is before the maturity of binocular vision. It is opposed to late onset strabismus that appears after this period.

Infantile Strabismus In the absence of development of binocular vision, the fixation system remains immature. It conserves for instance its temporal-nasal asymmetry: symptoms appear which are fixation-linked defects. They are attenuated by bilateral retinal stimuli which seem to compensate for the absence of binocular vision.

Infantile strabismus symptoms are

- absence of normal binocular vision
- fixation-linked defects improve during fixation with both eyes open
- on the fixing eye : fixation in adduction with head-turn and pseudo abducens palsy, manifest/latent nystagmus
- on the excluded eye : dissociated deviations.

Absent in the absence of fixation, these deviations are triggered during fixation on the excluded eye (occlusion, nasal screen spontaneous exclusion).

They may be :
Dissociated Vertical Deviations (DVD = elevation) frequently misdiagnosed as inferior oblique overaction;
Dissociated Horizontal Deviations (DHD = esodeviation).
Dissociated Torsional Deviations (DTD = extorsion).

Their main feature is their variability.

These symtoms are present in the "Congenital functional monophthalme syndrome" where binocular vision development is rendered impossible because of unilateral organic congenital amblyopia.

Infantile Strabismus may be esotropia. exotropia, orthotropia. It all depends on the Position without fixation upon which the symptoms are superimposed.

Treatment aims to make retinal stimuli as symmetical as possible, as early as possible. This is obtained by

- conservative treatment (optical correction, treatment of amblyopia, optic filters)
- surgery through orthotropisation. Horizontal surgery results are usually good (Fadenoperation $\pm$ bilateral recti recession). Vertical Recti and inferior Oblique recessions improve DVDs and DTDS.

2431

AN IMMUNOHISTOCHEMICAL STUDY OF COLLAGENS IN TRACHOMA AND VERNAL KERATOCONJUNCTIVITIS

ABU EL-ASRAR AM[1] ; GEBOES K[2] ; AL-KHARASHI S[1] ; AL-MOSALLAM A[1]; TABBARA K[1]; AL-RAJHI A[3]; MISSOTTEN L[4];
1. Dept. of Ophthalmology, King Saud University; 3.King Khaled Eye Specialist Hosp., Riyadh (Saudi Arabia); 2. Lab. Of Histochemistry & Cytochemistry; 4.Dept. of Ophthalmology, Univ. Hospital, St. Rafael, Leuven (Belgium);

Purpose: To analyze the distribution and types of collagen in the conjunctiva of patients with trachoma, and vernal keratoconjunctivitis (VKC).
Methods: Conjunctival biopsy specimens were collected from 9 patients with active trachoma, 9 patients with scarred trachoma, 6 patients with active VKC, and 4 control subjects. The presence and distribution of collagen was assessed microscopically with immunohistochemical techniques.
Results: In normal conjunctiva, the staining for types I, and III collagen was localized to the substantia propria. Collagen type IV was located in the epithelial, vascular endothelial, and accessory lacrimal gland basement membranes. Staining for type V collagen was absent. New collagen type V deposition close to basement membranes was noted in active trachoma, scarred trachoma, and VKC. The extent of deposition of collagen type V was markedly increased in scarred trachoma when compared with active trachoma. Staining for type IV collagen showed irregularly thickened epithelial basement membrane in active trachoma, and a marked increase in basement membrane-collagen type IV was noted in scarred trachoma. Immunoreactivity of collagen types I, and III increased in active trachoma and decreased in scarred trachoma. VKC conjunctiva contained increased amounts of collagen types I, III, and IV due to marked increase in the thickness of vascular endothelial basement membrane and very prominent deposition of collagen types I, and III around stromal vessels.
Conclusions: Our data indicate new collagen type V formation in the conjunctiva from patients with active trachoma, scarred trachoma, and VKC. Increased deposition of collagen types I, III, and IV is noted in VKC, and active trachoma. Our findings suggest that increased deposition of collagen IV and new collagen type V formation contributes to the development of conjunctival fibrosis in scarred trachoma.

2432

CONJUNCTIVAL PROVOCATION TEST WITH DERMATOPHAGOIDES PTERONYSSINUS IN THE DIAGNOSIS OF ALLERGIC CONJUNCTIVITIS DUE TO HOUSE DUST MITES

Bertel F. (1), Mortemousque B. (1), Barac'h D. (1), Vérin Ph. (1), Sicard H. (2), André C. (2).

Purpose : Perennial conjunctivitis due to house dust mites is the most frequent form of allergic conjunctivitis in urban environments. However, its diagnosis remains difficult for ophthalmologists. In this study, we evaluated a conjunctival provocation test (CPT) using standardized extracts of Dermatophagoides pteronyssinus (Dpt) and compared it to the diagnosis methods commonly performed in allergology : prick tests with dust and house dust mites, specific IgE assay.
Methods : We performed a CPT on 60 volunteer patients, between the ages of 8 and 64 years, corresponding to 30 patients sensitized to house dust mites with the presence of specific IgE and chronic conjunctivitis,
21 patients not sensitized to house dust mites, but presenting features of chronic conjunctivitis, and 9 asymptomatic patients. A house dust mite desensitizing treatment did not represent an exclusion criterion for a number of allergic patients. CPT were performed in only one eye and asymmetry of the ocular response was evaluated by the cumulative clinical score of Abelson Chambers and Smith.
Results : The statistical correlation between specific IgE and the other allergological tests in favour of allergic conjunctivitis to house dust mites was 0.93 for CPT, 0.46 for prick test to Dpt, 0.33 for prick test to dust respectively. The diagnosis sensitivities and specificities for each test were 90 % and 100 % for CPT, 60 % and 70 % for prick test to dust, 70 % and 76 % for prick test to Dpt respectively. Beyond an antigenic cut-off value of 11 RI, we also observed greater hypersensitivity reactions for patients with lacrimal IgE or elevated specific IgE levels.
Conclusion : The results obtained with CPT confirm its high antigenic quality. It represents a particularly useful, rapid and perfectly safe clinical test. It is the only test able to establish a relationship between ocular manifestations and specific IgE. We emphasize the value of CPT for the follow-up of conjunctivitis during immunotherapy, and its possible applications in pharmacology, or for nasal or bronchial allergies.

2433

DEMONSTRATION OF CYTOMEGALOVIRUS IN GRAFTED CORNEA AND AQUEOUS HUMOR IN EYES WITH IDIOPATHIC CORNEAL ENDOTHELIITIS

NAO-I N[1], NAGAYOSHI Y[1], MINEMATSU T[2], and MINAMISHIMA T[2]
Departments of Ophthalmology [1] and Microbiology[2], Miyazaki Medical College, Miyazaki (Japan)

Purpose Investigation of possible association of cytomegalovirus (CMV) infection with idiopathic corneal endotheliitis.
Methods Grafted cornea and aqueous humor were obtained during second keratoplasty from a 74-year-old male patient and examined for CMV by isolation with human embryonic lung fibroblasts and for CMV DNA by polymerase chain reaction.
Results CMV was isolated from both grafted corneal button and aqueous humor derived from his right eye and it was identified by direct immunoperoxidase technique with human monoclonal antibody against p65 antigen. Specimens derived from both eyes were also positive for CMV DNA.
Conclusion Our study suggested the CMV may be one of the causative agents of idiopathic corneal endotheliitis.

2434

ACANTHAMOEBA KERATITIS: DIAGNOSIS AND TREATMENT

MANGANELLI C., FOCOSI F., TURCO S., LOCARNO C.M., SCULLICA L.
Dept. Ophthalmology, Catholic University – Roma (Italy)

Purpose To review methods of diagnosis and effective treatment of Acanthamoeba keratitis, a condition that has become increasingly common since the 1980's.
Methods We report 5 consecutive cases of Acanthamoeba keratitis diagnosed at the Catholic University in Rome from mid 1996 through 1997. Patients were 3 males and 2 females (mean age 46, ranging from 32 to 62). Risk factors were represented by contact lens wear, agricultural trauma, steroid use and intensive care for cardiac surgery. Symptoms were present from 7 days to 8 weeks. Diagnosis was established by corneal scrapings (smears and culture on nonnutrient agar with overlaid Escherichia coli). Patients were treated by PHMB 0.02%, low dose steroids and tobramycin. In one case Amphotericin B and Itraconazole were also required for a mycotic co-infection.
Results Four patients recovered good vision with medical treatment, the case with mycotic co-infection required keratoplasty following descemetocele.
Conclusions. A high degree of suspicion is important for Acanthamoeba keratitis diagnosis and timely treatment with antiamebic drugs can cure the severe infection with a good visual outcome.

2435

EXPRESSION OF APOPTOTIC AND INFLAMMATORY MARKERS IN DRY EYE SYNDROME

Baudouin C[1], Goldschild M[1], Brignole F[2], Bourcier T[1], Goguel A[2] Depts of Ophthalmology[1] and Immunology[2], Ambroise Paré Hospital, University of Paris-V, France.

Purpose: To investigate by flow cytometry in normal and pathological conjunctival epithelium the expressions of Fas, Fas ligand, the apoptotic marker APO2.7, and of HLA DR, CD40 and its ligand, as inflammatory markers. **Methods:** Impression cytology specimens were collected in 90 patients: 20 normal, 50 with dry eyes, 20 with nonspecific chronic conjunctivitis. Cells were immediately fixed, then extracted and processed for flow cytometry. Percentages of positive cells were recorded and levels of fluorescence quantified by using a calibration curve established with fluorescent beads at standardized fluorescence intensities. **Methods:** Fas was found in all specimens, but quantitation of fluorescence showed a significantly higher expression in pathological eyes than in normal ones, without difference between the different pathologies. APO2.7 and Fas ligand and CD40 ligand were variably expressed by conjunctival cells, but in significantly higher percentages of cells in pathological eyes than in normal ones. In these eyes a strong expression of HLA DR and CD40 was also observed, whereas normal eyes showed lowest levels. Highly significant correlations were found between Fas, CD40, APO2.7 and HLA DR levels. **Discussion:** This study confirms that conjunctival epithelial cells normally express Fas, Fas ligand, and CD40, but these markers are significantly enhanced in dry eyes and correlated to HLA DR.

2441

EXPERIMENTAL VITREOUS REPLACEMENT WITH PERFLUORHEXYLOCTANE - MORPHOLOGICAL RESULTS

BECKER J, WOLF S, KUCKELKORN R, ZEANA D and KIRCHHOF B.
Dept. of Ophthalmology, Technical University Aaachen, Aachen, Germany

Perfluorocarbon liquids are established tools for hydrokinetic retinal manipulation. Their high specific gravity is likely to cause mechanical retinal damage, when applied as a long term vitreous substitute. Perfluorohexyloctane was developed as a long term vitreous substitute, due to its low specific gravity. The current study was performed to investigate retinal tolerance to perfluorohexyloctane as a long term vitreous substitute in the rabbit.
Methods: Vitrectomized eyes of 15 pigmented rabbits underwent intravitreal injection of 1.0-1.2 ml perfluorohexyloctane (n =10) or balanced salt solution (n =5). Additionally eyes received perfluorohexyloctane in the anterior chamber (n =5). After a period of 3 months the eyes were enucleated and processed for light and electron-microscopy.
Results: Results demonstrated a saved architecture of the retinal layers. Weak irregular distribution of photoreceptor nuclei and "drop out" into the photoreceptor layer were observed. Rods and cones seemed to be less compact in some eyes but showed normal aspects. In some cases phagocytes adjacent to the retina showed empty vacuoles, which may have contained perfluorohexyloctane before processing. The external limiting membrane remained intact.
Perfluorohexyloctane in the anterior chamber caused no inflammatory reactions in the corneal stroma. Histological alterations were found correspondingly in eyes filled with perfluorohexyloctane and balanced salt solution.
Conclusions: These findings suggests perfluorohexyloctane as a suitable long-term vitreous subsitute, but further investigations on the quality of the tamponade are needed

2442

FIRST EXPERIENCES WITH PERFLUOROHEXYL-OCTANE (F6H8) AS INTRAOPERATIVE TOOL

ZEANA D, WOLF S, KIRCHHOF B.
Universitätsaugenklinik der RWTH Aachen (Germany)

Purpose: A semifluorinated alkane - F6H8 - was tested as intraoperative tool for flattening the retina and as wash-out fluid during silicone oil removal.
Methods: We applied F6H8 in 20 eyes during vitrectomy. In 10 eyes with proliferative vitreoretinopathy retinal detachment F6H8 was used to flatten the retina. At the end of the surgery F6H8 was exchanged in 7 eyes with silicone oil and in 3 eyes with SF6 20%. In 10 eyes F6H8 was only used as wash-out fluid for silicone oil removal.
Results: In 7 eyes the retina could be easily flattened with F6H8. In 3 eyes areas of residual retinal traction initially prevented total flattening of the retina. The relatively low specific gravity ($1.35 g/cm^3$) as compared with perfluorocarbon liquids helped to identify these residual tractions. F6H8 as irrigation fluid was able to dissolve emulgated silicone oil only in 50% of the cases.
Conclusions: F6H8 was shown to be a useful tool to flatten the retina intraoperatively. Moreover, F6H8 facilitates removal of silicone oil, which seems to be especially helpful in eyes with silicone intraocular lenses.

2443

VITREORETINAL SURGERY AND LIQUID PERFLUOROCARBONS IN THE MANAGEMENT OF MASSIVE SUPRACHOROIDAL HEMORRHAGE

GARCÍA-ARUMÍ J. CALATAYUD M. CORCOSTEGUI B.
Dept.Ophthalmology, Barcelona University, Barcelona (Spain)

Purpose: Massive suprachoroidal hemorrhage (MSH) is a devastating complication of anterior segment and vitreoretinal surgery. Some eyes evolve to pthisis, PVR or neovascular glaucoma. Vitreoretinal surgery in the early postoperative period combined with the use of PFCL may obtain very good anatomic and functional results.
Methods: 15 patients with MSH (between 50% and 80% of vitreous cavity was occupied by the choroidal detachment measured by tridimensional ecography) were operated. In twelve patients the choroidal hemorrhage occurred during cataract extraction, in 2 eyes during trabeculectomy and in 1 eye during vitreoretinal surgery. In 10 cases, a retinal detachment accompanied the choroidal hemorrhage. Three patients had kissing MSH, 12 eyes had vitreous incarceration in the surgical wound, 2 eyes retinal incarceration and 7 eyes had vitreous hemorrhage. Preoperative visual acuity ranged from light perception to hand motion. Surgery was performed when adequate clot lysis was observed by ecography. A 23G infusion cannula was placed in the anterior chamber and a sclerotomy was performed in the quadrant with the highest choroidal detachment. After obtaining some degree of peripheral choroidal reattachment, a pars plana 6 mm long infusion cannula was placed in the quadrant with the least choroidal detachment. A vitrectomy was performed, and PFCL was injected in order to expel the choroidal hemorrhagic detachment from the posterior pole towards the peripheral sclerotomy, where it drained. Diode laser endophotocoagulation was employed in 5 cases with large peripheral retinal tears. A relaxing peripheral retinotomy was performed in one case. C3F8 or silicone oil was left in the vitreous cavity.
Results: Retinal and choroidal reattachment was obtained in every case. Some posterior choroidal folds persisted in 8 cases, RPE changes appeared in 6 cases, and epimacular membranes in 2 cases, being removed posteriorly. One eye required penetrating keratoplasty because of corneal decompensation. Final visual acuity ranged from counting fingers to 20/50, with a mean of 20/80.
Conclusions: Some massive suprachoroidal hemorrhages, if left untreated, will evolve poorly owing to kissing choroidal detachments, MSH associated to hemorrhagic retinal detachment and vitreous hemorrhage, retinal-vitreous incarceration in the surgical wound, retained lens fragments.... In our patients, adequate vitreoretinal surgery has shown to obtain very good anatomic results with few complications. Even in cases with secondary epimacular membranes that had to be removed, a considerably good visual acuity was obtained.

2444

rt-PA AND PNEUMATIC DISPLACEMENT IN THE MANAGEMENT OF SUBMACULAR HEMORRHAGE.

Ruiz Lapuente C, Martínez Palmer A, Martínez Giralt O, Castilla Céspedes M.
Dept. Ophthalmology, Hospital de la Esperanza y H. del Mar, Barcelona (Spain)

Purpose: To study the efficacy and safety of a combined treatment with intravitreal tissue plasminogen activator and pneumatic displacement of submacular hemorrhage.

Methods: Nine eyes of nine patients undergoing a variety of diseases with the common feature of submacular hemorrhage with less than 8 days of evolution were treated . Eyes underwent intravitreal injection of a solution containing 20 to 40 μg of rt-PA in 0,1 ml. of diluent. The diluent varied from 100% of the manufacturers diluent to 25% diluted in 75% BSS.A filtered air buble was injected intravitreally to displace lysed blood.

Results: Six out of nine eyes improved their V.A. ≥2 Snellen lines by 7 days or less. Three out of nine remained estable with no improvement of V.A. Four cases showed some extent of retinal toxicity.

Conclusions: The combined treatment of intravitreal rt-PA with pneumatic displacement of submacular hemorrhage is effective in the treatment of submacular blood. Visual prognosis depends on underlaying disease. Retinal toxicity is likely to occur when injection of rt-PA exceeds 33 μg.

2445

MACULAR STATUS IN EYES WITH RETINOPATHY OF PREMATURITY TREATED BY CRYOTHERAPY

OROS A, BEDOV T, GRKOVIC D, ZIKIC Z, TANASIJEVIC-FILIPOV I

Clinical Center, University Eye Clinic, Novi Sad (Yugoslavia)

Purpose This study was designed to investigate macular status in eyes with ROP which had received cryotherapy.
Methods Cryotherapy was performed in 22 infants, on 44 eyes with stage 3+ ROP. Four eyes of two infants had developed stage 5 and were excluded from the study. Fourty eyes with successfully performed cryotherapy were examined for regression of disease and macular alterations.
Results Seven eyes out of 40 developed macular changes.These changes were in the form of hyperpigmentation or hypopigmentation, with or without subretinal or epiretinal prolipheration.Before treatment there was no evidence of similar alterations in the macular region of those eyes.Eyes with macular changes had received more extensive cryotherapy because of a greater presence of posterior disease.
Conclusion.Eyes with a more posterior location of ROP had received a greater amount of cryotherapy, and were more liable to develop macular changes.Examination of visual acuity on the same study group in the future, should determine the significance of thiose changes for macular function.

2447

Perioperative prevalence of epiretinal membranes (EM) in senile cataract

C.E. Jahn, V. Minich, S. Moldaschel

Praxis Dr. Jahn, Kempten, FRG

Purpose: Evaluation of the prevalence of epiretinal membranes in patients undergoing surgery for senile cataract (CE). This is important since EM may cause lower postoperative visual acuity. It is also unclear whether EM can be induced by apparently uncomplicated CE.

Patients and Methods: Within 2 weeks prior and 2 weeks after uncomplicated phacoemulsification and implantation of an IOL the macula of 400 consecutive eyes was examined with a Volk 78 D lens. EM were classified into cellophan-like membranes (EM-C) and Macular Pucker (EM-P).

Results: Mean age of the patients was 75 (50 - 97) years. Preoperatively we found EM in 22 of 400 eyes (6%, $CI_{95\%}$ 5-9%). 17 of 22 were EM-C and 5 of 22 were EM-P. Postoperatively we saw EM in 50 of 400 eyes (11%, $CI_{95\%}$ 9-16 %). Of these 42 of 50 were EM-C and 8 of 50 were EM-P.

Conclusions: EM-C were more prevalent than EM-P. Frequently EM-C and sometimes EM-P could only be detected after cataract surgery. Any statement about the induction of EM by CE would need to take as baseline prevalence the one observed immediatedly after CE. Results from this cohort can also serve as crude estimate for the prevalence of EM in the general population.

2446

CHANGES IN DIABETIC MACULOPATHY AFTER PARS PLANA-VITRECTOMY A LONG TIME FOLLOW-UP

PÖSTGENS H, HÖRLE S, KROLL P.
Dept. of Ophthalmology, Philipps-University, Marburg (Germany)

Purpose: In diabetic maculopathy, one of the leading causes of blindness, there is no therapy generally approved except lasercoagulation in clinically significant macular edema. We investigated the effect of pars plana-vitrectomy in diabetic maculopathy.
Methods: Eyes, that underwent pars plana-vitrectomy for diabetic vitreous hemorrhage and were documented with fundus photo and fluorescein angiography in 6 months before and after vitrectomy, were included. In a retrospectiv study fundus pictures and photos of fluorescein angiographies were examined by a new grading system. 13 funduscopic and angiographic characteristics were classified before and in different time intervalls after the operation.
Results: In the first 10 eyes of 10 patients this quantitative grading enables an easy control of the course of diabetic maculopathy during this therapy. After vitrectomy there seems to be an improvement in the number of microaneurysms and exudates and in the extent of edema. But there is no positive influence on the extent of ischemia or cystic changes demonstrable.
Conclusion: The new grading system of diabetic maculopathy is an useful tool for demonstration of treatment efficacy. Vitrectomy has a therapeutic influence in this entity.

3211

ISCHAEMIA, GLUTAMATE AND NEUROPROTECTION: RELEVANCE TO GLAUCOMA

OSBORNE N.N, UGARTE M, NASH M.S, CHIDLOW G and WOOD J.P.M
Nuffield Laboaratory of Ophthalmology, Oxford University, Oxford, UK

Purpose
Elevated extracellular glutamate as occurs in ischaemia is known to cause death to neurones containing NMDA receptors. Ischaemia is thought to play a part in some forms of glaucoma. Support for this comes from the finding that glutamate is elevated in the vitreous humour of glaucomatous eyes and ganglion cells possess NMDA receptors. Substances that blunt the ischaemia-induced cell death in animal studies may therefore potentially protect against ganglion cell death in glaucoma.
Methods
Ischaemia was induced to the rat retina by raising the intraocular pressure. The effect of ischaemia/reperfusion of the retina was determined by analysing the ERG, the morphology of the retina and the localisation and content of defined antigens in the retina.
Results
Ischaemia/reperfusion caused measurable changes to the retina and these were partially reversed by pre-treatment of the animal with either betaxolol (β_1-blocker), memantine (NMDA antagonist) or flupirtine (acts on redox potential of NMDA receptor).
Conclusions
Betaxolol, memantine and flupirtine are all drugs that have a history of use in humans. The present findings suggest that they can be applied to protect against ganglion cell death in glaucoma.

3212

ADULT MAMMALIAN RETINAL GANGLION CELL CULTURE AS MODELS TO STUDY NEUROPROTECTION

HICKS D, HEIDINGER V, PICAUD S, DREYFUS H, SAHEL J.
Lab. de Physiopathologie Rétinienne, Clin. Ophtalmol., CHRU Strasbourg, France

Purpose To examine neurotoxic mechanisms in adult retinal ganglion cells (RGC).
Methods Retinas from adult pig eyes were dissected, dissociated carefully and the dispersed cells placed in routine culture. Under such conditions, many neurons survived and regenerated neurites for long periods *in vitro*. After one week, cultures were treated with the following substances for 24 hr: 1-5mM glutamate, kainate, NMDA, potassium cyanide. Cultures were fixed and immunocytochemistry (anti-200 kDa neurofilament) was used to identify and count RGC. Using enriched RGC cultures prepared from isolated RGC layers, whole cell patch-clamp recordings of RGC were also made.
Results RGC were reliably identified as neurofilament-immuno-positive neurons with long neurites. In control cultures they represented <1% total neurons, but ~10% estimated original RGC. RGC viability was not affected by any excitotoxic treatment tested (numbers varying from control levels by <5%). In contrast, potassium cyanide treatment (or delaying the post-mortem time to culture) decreased significantly RGC survival (20-80%). Patch clamp recording showed the presence of both NMDA and non-NMDA receptors in cultured RGC.
Conclusions Neurons from fully adult mammalian retinas survive and regenerate neurites in standard monolayer tissue culture conditions. Immunocytochemically identified RGC are not affected adversely by excessive concentrations of excitatory amino acids, thought to be involved in retinal pathologies such as ischemia and glaucoma. Their surivival is however compromised by hypoxic and hypoglycemic insults.

3213

EFFECT OF NITRIC OXIDE ON IOP, OCULAR BLOOD FLOW, AND NEUROTOXICITY: RELEVANCE TO GLAUCOMA

HAEFLIGER I.O.
Laboratory of Ocular Pharmacology and Physiology, University Eye Clinic Basel, Basel (Switzerland)

Purpose
Glaucoma is an optic nerve head neuropathy. In this neuropathy there is a loss of retinal ganglion cells. Glaucoma is associated with risk factors such as a high intraocular pressure and/or blood flow dysregulation. Nitric oxide (NO) is a cellular mediator involved in the regulation of different ocular functions which are of importance in glaucoma.
Methods
With a myograph system to measure isometric forces the effect of NO on the contractile tone of isolated ciliary arteries and trabeculum meshwork was studied. Using cultured retinal neurons the effect of NO on cell survival was investigated.
Results
NO evokes relaxation of ciliary arteries and trabeculum meshwork. NO can lead to death of retinal neurons by apoptosis.
Conclusions
NO appears to be involved in fundamental aspects of the pathogenesis of glaucoma, in particular in the regulation of intraocular pressure, the modulation of blood flow, and the death of retinal neuronal cells.

3214

STIMULATING REGROWTH OF RETINAL GANGLION CELL AXONS IN RATS: RELEVANCE FOR GLAUCOMA

SCHWARTZ M, SPIEGLER O AND YOLES E.
Dept. Neurobiology, The Weizmann Institute of Science, Rehovot (Israel)

Purpose
Glaucoma is now viewed as an optic nerve disease in which some neurons have already degenerated, others are degenerating but still have viable retinal ganglion cells, and yet others are still functioning. We have suggested that treatment, in addition to reducing intraocular pressure, should aim to protect still-functioning neurons from further degeneration and to promote the regeneration of axons whose cell bodies are still viable. Here we describe discuss the control of dialogue between injured axons and immune cells as a way to promote optic nerve regeneration in rats.
Methods
Rat macrophages, prestimulated *ex vivo* by incubation with regenerating peripheral nerve segments, were implanted into completely transected rat optic nerves.
Results
Rat macrophage-treated optic nerves exhibited behaviour reminiscent of the peripheral nerve response to injury in terms of Wallerian degeneration and axonal regrowth.
Conclusions
Regeneration failure in CNS axons (including those damaged by glaucomatous neuropathy) may be related to the unique nature of the dialogue between the CNS (an immune-privileged site) and the immune system. The relationship of the immune system to retinal and repair will be discussed.

3221

FUNDUS AUTOFLUORESCENCE CHANGES IN PATIENTS WITH CENTRAL SEROUS CHORIODOPATHY

A.W.A. WEINBERGER, B.E. MAZINANI, H. KNABBEN, S. WOLF
Universitätsaugenklinik der RWTH Aachen (Germany)

Purpose: Fundus autofluorescence (AF) can be detected with a confocal scanning laser ophthalmoscope (SLO). In this study we investigated changes in fundus AF in patients with central serous choroidopathy (CSC).
Methods: In 23 patients with CSC AF images were obtained with a confocal SLO (HRA, Heidelberg Engineering, Germany). Increases or decreases in fundus AF were correlated to fluorescein angiographic and funduscopic findings and analyzed in regard of sympthom duration.
Results: 83 % of patients with CSC showed changes in fundus AF. Fresh lesions with serous retinal detachment showed rather decreased AF in the area of the edema whereas lesions with clinical sympthoms of 4 weeks or more tended to show increased AF in the area of CSC.
Conclusions: In this study we could show that fundus AF is decreased in early CSC lesions and increases with longer observation time. We speculate that the initial decrease in AF is due to a blockage phenomenon of the retinal edema. In later stages, the observed increase could be due to RPE stress following a higher photoreceptor outer segment turn over and / or due to oxidative stress.

3222

INDOCYANINE GREEN ANGIOGRAPHY IN DOMINANT DRUSEN

BANERJEE S[1], DUVALL-YOUNG J[1] and YONEYA S[2]
1. Dept of Ophthalmology, Wycombe General Hospital, UK
2. Dept of Ophthalmology, Saitama Medical School, Japan.

Purpose: To investigate the role of the choroidal vasculature in the pathogenesis of dominant drusen.

Methods: 6 patients with dominant drusen from families with known pedigree had ICG angiograms. They were studied over 30 minutes from the time of dye injection.

Results: The patients' ages ranged from 47 to 77 years and the visual acuity from 6/5 to counting fingers. We examined the ICG angiographic characteristics of the drusen. In some cases the choroidal filling was delayed and not uniform with an exaggerated sectorial pattern. In the late images a number of different patterns of hypofluroscence were seen. In one patient who had a choroidal rupture there were no drusen on that side and the choroidal filling was grossly abnormal.

Conclusions: The appearances of dominant drusen are heterogeneous. Choroidal circulation is related to the deposition of and the disturbances of the choriocapillaris filling appear to have a role in development. The absence of any drusen in the eye of the patient with choroidal rupture strongly suggests that the choroidal circulation plays a part in the development of drusen.

3223

CHARACTERISTICS OF DRUSEN AND BRUCH'S MEMBRANE IN POST-MORTEM EYES WITH AGE-RELATED MACULAR DEGENERATION

SPRAUL CW[1], LANG GE[1], GROSSNIKLAUS HE[2] AND LANG GK.[1]
1. Dept. Ophthalmology, University Eye Clinic, Ulm (Germany)
2. Dept. Ophthalmology, Emory University, Atlanta, GA (USA)

Purpose: We performed a histopathologic study to compare eyes with different stages of AMD to age-matched eyes in order to identify characteristics associated with exudative versus non-exudative AMD. Methods: We analyzed 51 eye bank eyes from 40 donors with different stages of AMD and compared them with 40 age-matched controls. The eyes were processed for light microscopy and the degree of calcification of Bruch's membrane, fragmentation of Bruch's membrane, number of different types of drusen, and basal laminar deposit (BLD) were assessed in the macular and extramacular regions. Results: In the macular area, there was a statistically significant difference observed in the degree of calcification and fragmentation of Bruch's membrane in eyes with exudative (1.6 and 5/eye) as compared to eyes with non-exudative AMD (0.8 and 1/eye) and controls (0.8 and 0/eye). Eyes with AMD displayed significantly more soft, confluent and large drusen and BLD in the macular area as compared to controls. Conclusion: Calcification and fragmentation of Bruch's membrane, soft, confluent and large drusen and BLD but not hard drusen strongly correlate with the histologic presence of AMD. Calcification and fragmentation of Bruch's membrane may be an important factor in the transition between the non-exudative and exudative form of AMD.

3224

CORRELATION OF LIPIDS AND ADHESIVE MOLECULES IN BRUCH´S MEMBRANE

D. PAULEIKHOFF (1), M. PEUSER (2), D. MÜLLER (3), S. WOJTECKI (2), A. HEILIGENHAUS (2)
(1) Augenabt. St. Franziskus Hospital, Münster (Germany)
(2) Universitätsaugenklnik Essen (Germany)
(3) Inst. für Mikrobiologie, Essen (Germany)

Purpose: In the pathogenesis of pigment epithelial detach-ments (PED) the developement of a hydrophobic barriere in Bruch´s Membrane (BM) is proposed correlating with increased lipids in BM. But because in PED a detachment of the RPE from the outer layers of BM is visible, an additional regression of adhesive molecules like laminin, fibronectin and collagen IV in BM may be necessary. The purpose of the present study was to investigate the presence of adhesive molecules in BM with age in correlation to the lipid deposition and composition in BM.
Methods: Lipids deposited in BM of 50 macular specimes (20-97y) were examined by histochemistry and chromatography. The results were correlated with immunohistechemical analysis for adhesive molecules in BM (collagen IV, fibronectin, laminin).
Results:For collagen IV, laminin and fibronectin an intensive staining in BM was visible in the group <40 y. in the basement membranes of the RPE and endothelium cells of the chor. capillaries. In the group 40-70 y. a decrease in staining intensity especially in the basement membrane of the RPE was visible and in donors >70 y. most often no staining was visible in the basement membrane of the RPE and a reduced intensity at the level of the endothelium cells. This change in the staining for adhesive molecules in BM was correlated with an increase of the staining intensity and the amount of extracted lipids from BM in the different age groups.
Conclusions: The increase of lipids in BM is consistent with the concept of the development of a hydrophobic barriere. This finding correlated with an decreased presence of adhesive molecules especially in the basement membrane of the RPE which may promote a detachment of the RPE like in PED.
Supported by the DFG (DFG HE1877/91)

3225

AGE-RELATED MACULOPATHY AND OPTIC DISC MORPHOLOGY

BUDDE WM, JONAS JB, SCHÖNHERR U

Department of Ophthalmology, Friedrich-Alexander Universität Erlangen-Nürnberg, Erlangen (Germany)

Purpose To assess a relationship between age-related maculopathy and appearance of the optic disc.
Methods By morphometric evaluation of wide-angle color fundus photographs, 143 patients with age-related maculopathy were compared with 33 normal subjects and with 83 diabetic patients.
Results Size and shape of the optic disc, and size of parapapillary atrophy did not vary significantly (P>0.12) between the study groups.
Conclusions Age-related maculopathy is not associated with special features in the appearance of the optic disc. Parapapillary atrophy, large or small optic disc, and abnormal disc shape are neither risk factors nor protective factors of age-related maculopathy.

3226

CHANGES IN FOVEAL THRESHOLD AFTER RADIO-THERAPY FOR AGE-RELATED MACULAR DEGENERATION

ETER N[1], SCHÜLLER H[2], SPITZNAS M[1], KLEIN W[1]
[1]University Eye Hospital, [2]Dept. of Radiology, University of Bonn, Germany

Purpose: To evaluate the change in foveal threshold in patients with subfoveal choroidal neovascularization after external beam radiotherapy
Methods: Using a confocal scanning laser ophthalmoscope (Rodenstock) foveal threshold was determined in 16 patients with subfoveal choroidal neovascularization before as well as 6 months after radiotherapy with a total dose of 20 Gy in10 fractions.
A helium-neon laser served as light source for background illumination and for generating the stimulus. Fundus imaging was achieved by an infrared diode laser scanning synchronously with the helium-neon laser. Stimulus size was 279x250 arc minutes, placed on the fovea (not necessarily on the fixation point) . Light sensitivity was measured in dB between 0 and 36 dB. Results were correlated with the change in visual acuity obtained at the same appointments.
Results: Mean foveal threshold decreased slightly from 17.37 dB (± 8.7dB) before radiotherapy to 17.12 dB (± 9.9dB) 6 months after treatment. Mean visual acuity decreased from 0.16 (± 0.11) before radiation to 0.1 (± 0.08) 6 months after therapy. Mean foveal threshold showed no statistically significant changes, whereas there was a mean loss in visual acuity of 27 % (p = 0.007). No correlation between changes in visual acuity and foveal threshold was found.
Conclusions: 1.There were no changes in foveal threshold 6 months after radiotherapy for age-related macular degeneration. 2.Changes in visual acuity did not affect foveal threshold.

3227

OCULAR STRATEGIES OF NORMAL EYES ASSESSED WITH CONFOCAL S.L.O.

FONTANAY S.[1], BENCHABOUNE M. [1], MAZOYER V.[2], KNOBLAUCH K. [2,3], VITAL-DURAND F. [2], KOENIG F[1].
1. Hôpital de BELLEVUE, Saint-Etienne, France
2. Unité INSERM 371, Bron, France
3. Université Jean Monnet, Saint-Etienne, France

Purpose To assess ocular mechanisms of visual perception for symbols, letter recognition and line-drawing identification.
Methods A confocal scanning laser ophthalmoscope (Zeiss Inc) was used in blue light (488nm) in order to project objects on the fundus in 10 normal sujects (shadow-technique). Recognition of geometric symbols placed on a variable sized square, letters of decreasing sizes and Snodgrass line-drawings were explored. Recorded ocular displacements and central fixation (visible xanthophyll pigment) were analysed using a computerized system.
Results For pictures and symbols, number, accuracy, amplitude, delay of saccades and eye movements depend on size, excentricity, global orientation, inductor elements and semantic content of the stimuli. For separate letters, identification is achieved through accurate fixation and quick displacement from one letter to the other.
Conclusion Visual function is a complex task in which global recognition appears more rapidly than central fixation. This technique could help to assess the visual performance of macular disabled patients.

3228

METAMORPHOPSIA AND FIXATION BY SCANNING LASER OPHTHALMOSCOPY

Salle M, Debruyne P, Defoort S, Hache JC, Arndt CF.
Expl. Fonctionnelle de la Vision, CHR&U Lille, France

Purpose: To confront fixation and metamorphopsia with macular lesions.
Methods: A grid of 256 squares with an angular size of 1 degree each were projected by a scanning laser ophthalmoscope on the retina. The subject was instructed to fixate the center of the grid and to indicate every time he perceived a deformed or abnormal squares. The results of metamorphopsia and fixation were represented on a graph superimposed on an infrared fundus image. 15 eyes of 15 patients with metamorphopsias were evaluated by this method. The test-retest reliability was evaluated in repeating the test between 2 hours and 7 days after the first test.
Results: In 12 eyes, a reliable response was obtained, the results of the first tests were compared to those of the second. The mean difference between the 2 tests was less than 4 (1.3, p > 0.1) when considering the total amount of squares.
Conclusions: As the test-retest reliability has been determined in the present study, further prospective work is necessary to test this technique in macular surgery.

3229

IMPLANTATION OF SUBRETINAL MICRO-PHOTODIODES IN RABBIT AND MINIPIG. AB INTERNO ACCESS

SACHS HG[1] KOBUCH K[1] ZRENNER E[2] GABEL V-P[1]
1. University Eye Clinic, Regensburg (Germany)
2. University Eye Clinic, Tübingen (Germany)

Purpose. The development of visual prothesis for blind or highly visually handicapped persons requires the development of surgical strategies to implant these devices. We investigated the ab interno access of the subretinal space for microphotodiode array implantation in rabbit and minipig. Methods. Pars plana vitrectomy was carried out in both rabbits and micropig. Access to the subretinal space was achieved via a retinotomy. The inner retina was carefully seperated from the retinal pigment epithelium using viscoelastic fluid and different chips were implanted. To regain complete reattachment of the partial elevated retina gas tamponade with SF 6 gas was performed. Results. In the follow up period of 1 year the implants are well tolerated. No inflammatory reaction has been observed. Intraoperative complications decreased when using smaller microphotodiode arrays. Atrophy of the retina covering the chip was discovered in rabbits with unperforated chips. Conclusions. Observation of retinal atrophy in rabbit led to the use of perforated chips in rabbit. In addition various implants in the minipig eye with its different retinal supply are under investigation. Further modification of the implant is required to meet surgical and functional demands.

3231

AN OVERVIEW OF THE ETHANOL-INDUCED CHANGES IN THE DEVELOPING OPTIC NERVE

Pinazo-Durán, MD[1], Guerri C[1], Hellström A[2] and Strömland K[2]
1) Instituto de Investigaciones Citológicas Valencia (Spain)
2) Dept. Pediatric Ophthalmology, Univ. of Göteborg (Sweden)

Purpose: Children born to chronic alcoholic mothers display craniofacial anomalies, delay in growth and central nervous system dysfunction, the signs of fetal alcohol syndrome (FAS). We collected ophthalmological data from a group of these children (FASG) and their matched controls (CG), in order to compare with the results obtained from a rat experimental model of FAS. Our main goal was to investigate whether prenatal ethanol may alter the axonal outgrowth and the oligodendrocyte and myelin sheath development in the optic nerve (ON), at a level that it may irremediably contribute to the visual impairment.
Methods: The visual acuity was tested and the retinal fundus photographs were morphometrically analysed to classify the 60th children's optic discs. Two groups of rats were used: 1) ethanol-fed animals (ETG), which were given 35% ethanol 5% w/v, as daily total calories and 2) isocaloric pair-fed animals (IPG), which were considered as the nutritional controls. The ON were processed for morphological, morphometrical and immunological assays, using antibodies anti-galactocerebroside (GLC), -myelin basic protein (MBP) and -neural cell adhesion molecules (NCAM, L_1), to be examined in light and electron tr microscopes. SDS polyacrilamide gel electrophoresis and immunoblotting assays were performed in the ON from both groups, during development.
Results: When compared with the CG, the FASG displayed significantly reduced vision ($p \leq 0.001$). Ranging from mild to severe forms, the optic nerve hypoplasia (ONH) was detected in all FASG but not in the CG. A significant decrease in the ON cross-sectional area, oligodendrocyte and axon densities and myelin content was noted in the ETG of rats as compared to the IPG. A delayed expression and significantly lower values of the GLC and MBP was observed in the ETG-ON than in the IPG ($p \leq 0.001$). NCAM and L_1 immunostaining patterns were altered in the developing ON as a result of alcohol's action.
Conclusions: The present work highlights the teratogenic effects of ethanol in the development of vision, suggesting that the altered glial/axonal/myelin relationship may be causing widespread anomalies in the nerve impulse conduction which consequently contribute to the visual disturbances observed in children with FAS.

3232

PLATELET-DERIVED GROWTH FACTOR - A MULTIFUNCTIONAL STIMULATORY CYTOKINE FOR HUMAN TENON'S CAPSULE FIBROBLASTS.

KNORR M[1], DENK PO[1], ROTH S[2], GRESSNER AM[2]
1. University Eye Clinic Tübingen
2. University of Marburg, Dept. of Clinical Chemestry

Purpose: To evaluate the potential role of platelet-derived growth factor (PDGF) in the wound healing response after glaucoma filtration surgery, the stimulatory effect of PDGF-AA and -BB isoforms on different cellular activities (growth rates, cytokine secretion, synthesis of extracellular matrix components) of cultured human Tenon's capsule fibroblasts (HTF) was investigated. Methods: HTF, cultured under serum-free culture conditions, were stimulated with PDGF-AA, and -BB isoforms in concentrations ranging from 0.01-100ng/ml. Growth rates (expressed as PD/d=population doublings/day), secretion of TGF-ß1, synthesis of hyaluronate and fibronectin were determined after an incubation period of 5 days. Results: Stimulation of HTF with PDGF-AA and -BB led to an dose-dependent rise in growth rates. Maximum response (0.148±0.67 PD/d; mean±SD, n=4) was obtained with PDGF-AA (control:-0.017+0.005 PD/d). Additionally, PDGF-AA and -BB caused a significant increase in the synthesis of the ECM components hyaluronate and fibronectin, and an increased secretion of TGF-ß1 (approx. 6 fold over baseline levels). Conclusion: Our results indicate that PDGF-isoforms are multifunctional stimulatory factors for HTF in-vitro, supporting the idea that PDGF modulates the wound healing response after glaucoma filtration surgery by different mechanisms.

3233

EXPRESSION OF TGF-ß- AND PDGF-RECEPTORS ON HUMAN TENON'S CAPSULE FIBROBLASTS

DENK PO, RIEDINGER C, KNORR M
University Eye Clinic, Tübingen (Germany)

Purpose. To evaluate the expression of TGF-ß- and PDGF receptors on human Tenon's capsule fibroblasts.
Methods. Human Tenon's capsule fibroblasts (1st passage) were cultivated using WM/F12 medium with 10% FCS and seeded on coverslides, which were subsequently processed for immunocytochemistry. After fixation, cells were incubated for 1h at room temperature with monoclonal antibodies against PDGFR-α and PDGFR-ß and polyclonal antibodies against TGF-ß-RI, -II and -III. After washing with TBS, cells were incubated for 30min with the corresponding FITC-conjugated secondary antibodies. Immunostaining was evaluated under a fluorescence microscope.
Results. Significant immunostaining was observed for all receptors tested, except TGF-ß-RIII. Staining was most intense for PDGFR-ß, less intense for TGF-ß-RI, and faint for TGF-ß-RII and PDGFR-α. The cellular distribution of immunostaining was homogeneous except for TGF-ß-RII, which revealed a strong perinuclear staining.
Conclusions. Our results indicate, that PDGF- and TGF-ß-receptors are widely expressed on human Tenon's capsule fibroblasts, except TGF-ß-RIII. Specific inhibition of receptor expression may be a future pharmacological tool to modulate wound healing after glaucoma filtering surgery.

3234

MORPHOLOGY OF THE ANTERIOR EYE SEGMENT IN THE ABYSSINIAN CAT WITH PROGRESSIVE RETINAL ATROPHY

MAY CA, NARFSTRÖM K, LÜTJEN-DRECOLL E.
Dept. Anatomy II, University Erlangen-Nuernberg (Germany)
Dept. Small Animal Clinical Sciences, Uppsala (Sweden)

Purpose In the abyssinian cat blood flow is decreased not only in the retina but also significantly in the iris (Narfström et al., 1997). To explain these physiological data we studied the morphological changes in iris and ciliary body vasculature and innervation in different stages of retinal atrophy. Methods The left eyes of 8 dystrophic and 6 age-matched control cats were fixed either in Ito's solution or in 4% paraformaldehyde. Morphology of the vasculature was studied electronmicroscopically and with antibodies against smooth muscle actin. Changes in innervation were investigated using antibodies against PGP 9.5, tyrosin hydroxylase, substance P, and nitric oxide synthase. In addition, sections of the anterior eye segment were critical point dryed and investigated with a scanning electron microscope. Results The iris arteries and arterioles showed loss of smooth muscle cells, elastic tissue, and synaptic endings; the lumina of the capillaries were narrowed. The ciliary processes appeared shortened. At places in the anterior part of the ciliary processes the epithelial cells contained numerous vacuoles. Free cells were found between the two epithelial layers in this region. Conclusions Retinal degeneration in abyssinian cats is accompanied by vascular and neuronal changes in the iris.

3235

INNERVATION OF SCLERAL SPUR AND TRABECULAR MESHWORK IN MONKEY EYES

SELBACH JM, WITTMANN M, LÜTJEN-DRECOLL E
Dept. of Anatomy II, University of Erlangen (Germany)

Purpose: To investigate the innervation of the scleral spur and the different portions of the trabecular meshwork (TM), which presumably serve different functions. Methods: Serial tangential sections of the anterior segments of 6 cynomolgus monkey eyes were investigated immunohistochemically using antibodies against neurofilament (NF), synaptophysin (Syn), SP, CGRP, ChAT (Choline Acetyltransferase), VIP, NPY, TH, GABA and smooth muscle a-actin (SMA). The NADPH-diaphorase reaction served to show the presence of nitric oxide synthase. Results: The trabecular meshwork and scleral spur cells stained for SMA and numerous terminals staining for ChAT, NADPH-diaphorase and CGRP were found in all parts of the meshwork and in the scleral spur. GABA- and SP-IR was present mainly in the spur and anterior non filtering portion of the TM whereas only single VIP-IR and no TH- or NPY-IR nerve fibers were found in the anterior region. Staining for NF and Syn was mainly present in the spur region. Conclusions: We assume that part of the transmitters released from the terminals in the meshwork and scleral spur might be related to contractility. However, the distribution indicates that some of the neuropeptides serve other functions. Scleral spur endings staining for NF and Syn show similarities to the terminals discussed as mechanoreceptors in human eyes.

3236

FINE STRUCTURE OF HIGH ENDOTHELIAL VENULES IN THE HUMAN CONJUNCTIVA

KNOP E and KNOP N
Lab. for Cell Biology, Medical School Hannover (FRG)

Purpose: High endothelial venules (HEV) are an important component of the conjunctiva associated lymphoid tissue as entry site for lymphocytes during their recirculation. The fine structure of HEV in the human conjunctiva is unknown.
Methods: Complete human conjunctival sacs obtained from cadaver eyes at the anatomical department were investigated by light and transmission electron microscopy.
Results: HEV were regularly associated with the organised follicular form of lymphoid tissue and the diffuse lymphoid layer type. In transmission electron microscopy the high endothelial cells showed a prominent cubical cytoplasm bulging into the vessel lumen. The roundish nuclei were electron lucent with a small heterochromatic rim and frequently a large nucleolus. Inside the cytoplasm cell organelles as mitochondria and Golgi apparatus were plenty compared to normal endothelial cells and oriented towards the apical zone; Weibel-Palade bodies were numerous. A prominent feature was a perinuclear accumulation of intermediate filaments. The cells were mainly interconnected by desmosomes, distinct tight junctions were rare. Occasionally intense interdigitations were seen. The endothelial cells were encircled by one or more layers of pericyte cell extensions.
Conclusions: The HEV of the human conjunctiva are distinctly different from the normal endothelial cells and resemble those in other lymphoid tissues.

3237

APICAL MYOTENDINOUS NERVE TERMINALS OF EXTRAOCULAR MUSCLES IN CYNOMOLGUS MONKEYS

RUSKELL G,[1] and KJELLEVOLD-HAUGEN I-B.[2]
1. Dept. Optometry & Visual Science, City University, London, U.K.
2. Institute of Optometry, Buskerud College, Kongberg, Norway

Purpose To describe apical myotendinous nerve endings and to identify their source
Methods Unilateral intracranial oculomotor and/or trochlear neurotomies were performed on 3 of 8 monkeys; 5 were unoperated or used in other experiments unrelated to the orbit. Animals were fixed by perfusion - experimental animals 3,6 & 12 days after surgery. Muscle origins of the superior rectus and levator and a selection of other extraocular muscles were examined by LM and EM.
Results Nerve terminals, similar to myotendinous cylinders of distal myotendon were present. Their density varied between animals and were associated only with Felderstruktur muscle fibres, and none were present in the levator. No Golgi tendon organs were found. Terminals were degenerated following the neurotomies.
Conclusions Terminals are described for the first time in the apical myotendinous region of primate extraocular muscles. They issue from ocular motor nerves and are therefore likely to represent a detail of the compound motor innervation of Felderstruktur fibres, rather than serving proprioception.

3238

NEURONS OF THE MOTOR FACIAL NUCLEUS RELATED TO BLINKING; *A retrograde tracing study in the monkey.*

F. VanderWerf[1], M. Aramideh[2], J.A. Otto[1], B.W. Ongerboer de Visser[2].
1. Dept. Medical Physics University of Amsterdam and The Netherlands Ophthalmic Research Institute, Amsterdam(NL).
2. Dept. Clinical Neurophysiology, Academic Medical Center, Amsterdam (NL)

Purpose To investigate the distribution and organization of pretarsal motoneurons involved during blinking within the intermediate subnucleus of the motor facial nucleus (NVII).
Methods WGA/HRP was implanted in the pretarsal portions of the upper and lower orbicularis oculi (OO) muscle in the rhesus monkey and visualized with the DAB-Nickel method.
Results All WGA/HRP-labelled motoneurons were located in the ipsilateral intermediate subnucleus of NVII. The upper pretarsal motoneurons were located in the dorsal half of the intermediate subnucleus forming a dome-like structure. The lower pretarsal motoneurons were mainly located ventrally to these upper pretarsal ones and are less numerous.
Conclusions Motoneurons subserving the OO muscle are all located in the intermediate subnucleus of NVII. It appears that the upper pretarsal portion of the OO muscle is most densely innervated and about one third of all intermediate motoneurons subserve the pretarsal myofibers. The absence of multiple innervation of the relatively short pretarsal myofibers and the presence of numerous upper pretarsal motoneurons indicate that the upper pretarsal portion is innervated by small motor units.

3311

METHYLENE-H4-FOLATE REDUCTASE TT677 GENOTYPE IN A YOUNGSTER WITH CRVO

LEROY BP[1], MESSIAEN LM[2], MESTDAGH C[1], KESTELYN Ph[1], DE LAEY JJ[1], BAELE G[3]
[1] Dept. Ophthalmology, [2]Dep. Med. Genetics and [3]Coag. Laboratory, University Hospital, Ghent (Belgium)

Purpose : To illustrate a Central Retinal Vein Occlusion (CRVO) attributed to an inherited disorder of folate transport responsible for hyperhomocysteinemia, in a youngster.
Methods : We clinically examined a 22-year old young male with sudden loss of vision in his LE due to a CRVO three months earlier. He also underwent an electrophysiological evaluation. Molecular analysis of the gene encoding the enzyme methylene-tetra-hydrofolate reductase (MTHFR) was performed. A search for mutations in other genes known to cause thrombophilia was also carried out.
Results : VA in the LE was CF. Fundoscopy and FA showed chronic OD oedema, haemorrhages, hard exudates and retinal oedema, but no ischemia. ERG findings proved the absence of the latter. The RE was normal. One year later, VA in the LE remains poor, due to macular RPE changes and subretinal fibrosis. Gross retinal function is normal on ERG. Systemically, only an elevated plasma homocysteine level could be demonstrated. Molecular analysis of the MTHFR gene showed homozygosity for the mutation C677T. This results in a thermolabile MTHFR causing hyperhomocystinemia. The latter is considered to be a risk factor for thrombogenesis. Homocysteine levels normalized after treatment with pyridoxine and folate.
Conclusions : Homozygosity for the C677T mutation in the MTHFR gene is most probably a risk factor for CRVO.

3312

INTRAVITREAL rTPA IN THE MANAGEMENT OF BRANCH RETINAL VEIN OCCLUSSION.

AUTHORS: Martínez V, García Arumí J., Rodríguez Infante R., Freixes S., Alforja S., Puig J.
Dept. Ophtalmology, Vall d'Hebron Hospital. Barcelona (Spain).

Purpose: Branch Retinal Vein Occlussion (BRVO) is a common patology. Two major forms have been described so far: ischemic and non-ischemic ones. The use of intravi treous rTPA may act over the pathologic mechanisms of this entity.

Methods: 4 patients with BRVO were operated. 2 of them had had the occlussion 8 weeks before, 1 more than 8 weeks and 1 less than 8 weeks. Surgery was performed under local anesthesia. A pars plana vitrectomy with hyaloid dissection and application of intravitreous rTPA over the thrombus was performed in every case. In three cases adventicial diseccion was performed in arteriovenous crossing. An experimental model of retinal branch vein occlusion was developed in the pig in order to know the retinotoxicity of 25 microgrames of rTPA in a filled- air vitreous cavity. Founding no retinotoxicity of rTPA this model was clinically applied.

Results: . Clinical and angiographic edema and intrarretinal hemorrages diminished significantly after surgery.No toxic effect of rTPA was shown to happen. No complications during surgery and in the postoperative period appeared. Our minimal follow-up period was of 4 months
All patients showed improvement of their visual acuity as well as the quality of vision.

Conclusions: The use of rTPA as a treatment in the BRVO appears to be a promising therapeutic approach. Further evaluation is required.

3313

ACTIVITY OF CORE 2 GlcNAc-T IS INCREASED IN LEUKOCYTES FROM DIABETIC PATIENTS WITH RETINOPATHY: A NOVEL MECHANISM FOR CAPILLARY OCCLUSION.

BEN-MAHMUD BM, ,CHIBBER R, BELGORE FM, COPPINI D, CHRIST E, KOHNER EM.
Division of Medicine, UMDS, St Thomas's Hospital, UK.

Purpose Capillary occlusion by leukocytes is an early feature of diabetic retinopathy. The aim of the study was to test the hypothesis that the activity of glycosylating enzyme, core 2 GlcNAc-T, is responsible for increased leukocyte-endothelial cell adhesion in diabetes.
Methods Leukocytes were isolated by density centrifugation and lysed in 0.9% Triton x-100. The activity core 2 GlcNAc-T was measured in the presence and absence of the acceptor Galβ1-3GalNAcαPNP.
Results The mean enzyme activity (pmol/h/mg protein) in leukocytes was higher in IDDM patients compared to age-matched controls [1378 ± 272 (n = 37) vs 161 ± 31 (n = 23), P = 0.0001]. There was a significant difference between IDDM patients with and without retinopathy [1913 ± 417 (n = 21) vs 671 ± 216 (n = 16), P = 0.013]. There was also a strong correlation between enzyme activity and leukocyte-endothelial cell adhesion
Conclusions On the basis that branched O-linked oligosacchrides formed by the action of core 2 GlcNAc-T participates in leukocyte adhesion, the present data suggest the involvement of this enzyme in capillary occlusion in diabetic retinopathy.

3314

DOES VISUAL ACUITY MEASUREMENT IDENTIFY UNCOVERED CASES WHEN SCREENING FOR SIGHT-THREATENING DIABETIC RETINOPATHY?

PRASAD S[1], JONES K[2], KAMATH GG[1], PHILLIPS RP[1].
1.Dept. Ophthalmology, Arrowe Park Hospital, Wirral,(UK)
2.Diabetes Register Manager, Wirral, (UK)

Purpose: To assess if measurement of visual acuity (VA) identified additional cases of sight threatening retinopathy (STR) when screening for diabetic retinopathy.
Methods: All diabetics referred with STR in accordance with local guidelines and those having VA ≤ 6/12 in either eye were examined by an ophthalmologist as part of the Wirral Diabetic Retinopathy Surveillance Scheme. This scheme uses specially trained "high-street" optometrists using slit lamp biomicroscopy.
Results: 3450 diabetics were screened in this scheme from June 1997 to May 1998. 110 patients were reported to have a VA ≤ 6/12 in either eye and no known pre-existing pathology to account for their poor vision. On examination 15/110 patients had STR. 95/110 had other pathology to account for poor vision but no sight threatening retinopathy. 219 other diabetics with vision ≥ 6/12 were also examined, including patients referred with STR and subthreshold patients. 36/219 in this group had STR. All cases of STR in both groups would have been picked up on the basis of the referral grading even if the visual acuity were disregarded.
Conclusion: VA measurements do not reveal additional cases STR in screening for diabetic retinopathy. They may however, help identify other pathology.

3315

RETINAL THICKNESS AND FLUORESCEIN LEAKAGE IN DIABETIC RETINOPATHY

Cunha-Vaz JG, Lobo C, Oliveiros B, Bernardes R.
Center of Ophthalmology, Biomedical Institute for Research in Light and Image, Coimbra, Portugal

Purpose: Examine correlations between localised changes in fluorescein leakage and retinal thickness in the human diabetic retina in the earliest stages of the disease.
Methods: Localised retinal leakage was mapped using a Retinal Leakage Analyser, developed from a Zeiss cSLO. Localised changes in retinal thickness were mapped using the Retinal Thickness Analyser (RTA).
Results: Localised areas of increased retinal fluorescein leakage and increased retinal thickness were detected in the diabetic retina even before the development of ophthalmoscopically visible lesions. Increased retinal thickness (N +2SD) is seen not only in areas where there is also a marked breakdown of the BRB ($<2.7 \times 10^{-6}$ cm/sec), but also in areas where the permeability of the BRB remains within normal limits.
Conclusions: Both types of retinal edema, cytotoxic (intracellular) and vasogenic (extracellular) occur, side by side, in the earlier stages of diabetic retinopathy.

3316

CHANGE IN FIXATION STABLITY AFTER RETINAL PHOTOCOAGULATION FOR DIABETIC MACULOPATHY

F.Møller[1, 2] and T.Bek[1]

[1]Department of Ophthalmology, Århus University Hospital
DK-8000 Århus C, DENMARK

[2]Department of Ophthalmology, Odense University
DK-5000 Odense C, DENMARK

Purpose: To study the change in fixation stability after retinal photocoagulation for diabetic maculopathy.
Material: Twenty patients with diabetic maculopathy and VA ranging between 0.05-0.77 were studied at baseline and 1, 3, 6, and 12 months after retinal photocoagulation. Fixational eye movements were quantified from video recordings of the ocular fundus obtained with the Rodenstock scanning laser ophthalmoscope.
Results: No relation was found between the change in amplitude and direction of fixational eye movements and the change in visual acuity (VA) 12 months after retinal photocoagulation. However, for patients with VA < 0.70 a positive correlation was found between the change in the retinal area of fixation and the VA at the 12 month follow-up examination ($p<0.006$). Furthermore, independent of VA a negative correlation was found between the change in the retinal area of fixation 12 months after laser treatment and the retinal area of fixation at baseline ($p<0.005$).
Conclusion: Changes in fixation stability after retinal photocoagulation are complex. It can be hypothesized that restoration of VA after macular laser treatment is related to an increase in the retinal area of fixation.

3317

FULL PANRETINAL PHOTOCOAGULATION AND EARLY VITRECTOMY IMPROVE PROGNOSIS OF EALES' DISEASSE

AL-KHARASHI SA AND ABU EL-ASRAR AM
Dept. of Ophthalmology, College of Medicine, King Saud University, Riyadh (Saudi Arabia)

Purpose: Eales' disease is an uncommon vasoproliferative retinal disease affecting otherwise healthy young men that is characterized by obliterative retinal periphlebitis. This study was undertaken to determine whether visual prognosis of Eales' disease can be improved by appropriate photocoagulation and surgical management.
Method: The authors retrospectively studied 21 patients (31 eyes) who were treated in KAUH from 1992 to 1997. Recorded date included patient age, sex, race, medical history, medications, results of the ophthalmologic examination, results of diagnostic laboratory evaluation, and details of systemic and surgical treatments. The mean follow-up was 10.8 months.
Results: Fifteen patients who presented with active periphlebitis received systemic steroids and antituberculous therapy. Extensive full panretinal photocoagulation was performed in 14 eyes that presented with new vessel formation and peripheral capillary closure with or without vitreous hemorrhage. Vitrectomy and endolaser panretinal photocoagulation was necessary in 10 eyes. Complete regression of the disease was achieved in all eyes. Vitrectomy resulted in a significant visual improvement with 9 of the 10 eyes (90%) achieving ≥ 20/200 visual acuity.
Conclusion: These results suggest that aggressive treatment of Eales' disease with full panretinal photocoagulation and early vitrectomy, when necessary, may result in improving the visual outcome.

3318

FIBRINOLYTIC ACTIVITY IN RETINAL VEIN OCCLUSION

ABU EL-ASRAR AM[1] ; ABDEL GADER AM[2] ; AL-AMRO S[1]; AL-MOMEN A[3]
1. Dept. of Ophthalmology; 2. Coagulation Research Lab.; and 3. Dept. of Medicine (Div. Of Hematology), King Saud University, Riyadh (Saudi Arabia).

Purpose: Impaired fibrinolytic function is a common finding in patients with thrombotic disease. The present study was initiated to evaluate the fibrinolytic response to a venous occlusion test (VOT) in patients with retinal vein occlusion.
Methods: Euglobulin clot lysis time (ECLT), tissue plasminogen activator (t-PA) activity, and plasminogen activator inhibitor (PAI) activity were measured before and after VOT in a group of 26 consecutive patients presenting with retinal vein occlusion and in 15 healthy age and sex matched controls.
Results: Before VOT (baseline) higher proportion of patients (54%) had ECLT more than 5 hours compared with controls (6.7%) ($p = 0.0027$) indicating decreased overall fibrinolytic activity. Patients had non-significantly lower t-PA and higher PAI activities compared with controls. After VOT a higher proportion of patients (34.6%) had ECLT more than 5 hours compared with controls (6.7%) ($p = 0.05$). Patients had significantly lower t-PA activity ($p = 0.0232$) and significantly higher PAI activity ($p = 0.0292$). Subgroup analysis revealed that patients with ECLT more than 5 hours had significantly higher levels of PAI activity at baseline ($p = 0.0326$) and after VOT ($p = 0.0184$) compared with patients with ECLT less than 5 hours. However, t-PA activity was significantly higher ($p = 0.0153$) at baseline, and non-significantly higher after VOT in patients with ECLT more than 5 hours when compared with patients with ECLT less than 5 hours.
Conclusions: These findings suggest that impaired fibrinolysis due to increased PAI activity may play role in the pathogenesis of retinal vein occlusion.

3321

ASSOCIATION OF CATARACT WITH RISK FACTORS OF ISCHEMIC HEART DISEASE (IHD)

VAICAITIENE R[1], PAUNKSNIS A[2], CERNIAUSKIENE L[1], DOMARKIENE S[3].

1.Lab. of Clinical Biochemistry, Institute of Cardiology
2.Lab. Ophthalmology, Institute for Biomed.Research
3.Lab. of Population Investigations, Institute of Cardiology, Kaunas Medical Academy (Lithuania)

Purpose. The aim of the work - to determine the association of cataract with some risk factors of IHD.
Methods. Kaunas city elder habitants, 358 males (M) and 214 females (F), aged 66-82 years, were investigated for cataract, using the slit lamp (LOCS III) and interviewed.
Results and conclusions. Lens opacities in one or both eyes were determined in 63.9 percents of M and in 71 percents of F. An early cortical cataract was most frequent type of cataract. The risk of cataract was associated with age ($p<0.001$), with gender - the rate of cataract in both eyes was significantly higher in F than in M ($p<0.01$). The development of cataract was slightly associated with smoking in M, with arterial hypertension in F, with intake of antioxidantic vitamins and some dietary habits in both M and F.

3322

THE INFLUENCE OF VITAMIN LEVELS AND BASE-LINE VARIABLES ON THE PROGRESSION OF CATARACT IN THE ROCHE EUROPEAN AMERICAN CATARACT TRIAL (REACT)

Köpcke W[1], Schalch W[2], Chylack LT Jr[3], Phelps-Brown N[4], Thien U[5], Mitchell S[6], Bron A[4], Hurst M[6], and the REACT-Group
1. Univ. Münster (Germany), 2. F. Hoffman-LaRoche Ltd. (Basel, Switzerland), 3. Brigham and Women's Hospital (Boston, USA), 4. Univ. of Oxford (UK), 5. Biometrisches Zentrum (München, Germany), 6. Univ. of. Bradford (UK)

Purpose: To define possible prognostic factors for cataract progression in the REACT-study by correlating the difference in % pixels opaque with the status of baseline variables as well as with the data on cumulative serum levels of vitamins and carotenoids measured quarterly.
Methods: In addition to simple univariate tests the method of classification and regression trees (CART) was used to model the relationship between the % pixels opaque and potential influencing factors.
Results: Univariate analyses comparing patients with low (≤ 1. tertile) serum levels of vitamins C, E and ß-carotene against those with high (≥ 2. tertile) levels showed that patients with low levels had an increase in % pixel opaque which were 1.5 to 4.0 time higher than in high level patients. The CART analysis based on the AUC serum values detected Vitamin E as the variable with the highest impact.
Conclusion: Vitamin E seems to reduce the risk of cataract progression.

3323

THE ROLE OF ANTIOXIDANT AS RADIOPRTOTECTOR IN RADIATION CATARACT .

GAMAL M [1] , TALATT E [2] , MOEMEN L [3] .

1- Biophysics Dept., Research Institute of Ophthalmology, Giza, Egypt.
2- Radiotherapy Dept., Research Institute of Ophthalmology, Giza, Egypt
3- Biochemistry Dept., Research Institute of Ophthalmology, Giza, Egypt

Purpose : This study aimed to test the effectiveness of vitamin C as natural radioprotector in inhibiting radiation cataractogenesis.

Methods : Twenty eight newzealand rabbits were used. Four rabbits were served as control. The remaining 24 rabbits were classified into 3 groups which further subdivided into 2 subgroups. All the rabbits were received 30, 50 and 100 Gy β- radiation to their right eyes with and without receiving a daily dose of vitamin C respectively. After 2 months, all groups were decapitated. The lens and aqueous humour proteins were fractionated by gel chromatography, the refractive index was measured and the dielectric constant of each protein was calculated. Also, the level of glutathione peroxidase and reductase were measured.

Results : Vitamin C has protective effect to lens and aqueous humour proteins and to the level of glutathione peroxidase and reductase enzymes. This protective effect is dose dependent .

Conclusion : Antioxidant has proven to be effective in preventing oxidative damage and protein cross linking in lens and aqueous humour.

3324

Angular change of back scattering of light in human lens with cataract

QIAN W, CHEN E, SÖDERBERG P & PHILIPSON B.
St. Eriks Eye Hospital, Karolinska Institute, Stockholm, Sweden.

Purpose: To determine the angular change of back scattering of light in front plane of the human lens with Scheimpflug photography.

Method: Totally 10 eyes from ten persons with cataract lens were photographed by Nidek EAS-1000 system. For each eye, the back scattering from two angles (0° and 90°) were recorded, and two photos were taken for each angle. A common lens nuclear area was employed for evaluation of the intensity of the back scattering light. The data was analyzed statistically.

Results: The precision of the measurement is 2%. It is found that there is a significant difference of back scattering light between the images taken at 0° and that at 90° ($p=0.006$). Furthermore, the difference is independent with the amount of lens opacity ($p=0.015$).

Conclusions: To characterize nuclear cataract, at least two angles in the front plane of the lens nucleus should be evaluatied.

3325

INCREASED PUNCTATE CALCIUM STAINING AT THE EQUATORIAL REGION IN MODEL PRECATARACTOUS DIABETIC RAT LENSES

J. Trevithick[1], V. Bantseev[2] and J. Sivak[2]
1.Faculty of Medicine, Department of Biochemistry, The University of Western Ontario, London, Ontario, Canada N6A 5C1;
2.School of Optometry, University of Waterloo, Waterloo, Ontario, Canada N2L 3G1.

Purpose: To localize intracellular free Ca^{2+} in serial optical sections of rat lenses in 55.6 mM glucose *ex vivo* **Methods**: Selected 1 month old rat eyes were incubated for 2 days in 1) 55.6 mM glucose-containing medium to simulate diabetes or 2) controls. Equatorial regions of lenses were stained with Calcium Green-2 AM ester and immobilized in 1% agarose. Optical sections were obtained using a Zeiss inverted confocal laser scanning microscope with a 40X water immersion objective **Results:** After 2 days, in 55.6 mM glucose, significantly increased cytoplasmic intracellular calcium staining was punctate in appearance, and sometimes associated with early appearance of vacuoles at the equatorial region. **Conclusions:** The punctate appearance of free calcium staining may be associated with some intracellular structural component which does not bind calcium as tightly as the Calcium Green does. Increased intracellular calcium may activate calpain, initiating cortical cataractogenesis. **Support:** NSERC,. DREO, Henkel and Eastman Fine Chemicals.

3326

ANTERIOR LENS CAPSULE AS SUPPORT FOR TRANSPLANTATION OF RETINAL PIGMENT EPITHELIUM (RPE) AND IRIS PIGMENT EPITHELIUM (IPE)

HARTMANN U, STEINHORST UH, KUSTER S, WINTER R.
Dept. Ophthalmology, Medical School Hannover (Germany)

Purpose To establish a method for transplantation of cultured monolayers of RPE and IPE, lens capsule was evaluated for its suitability to serve as growth support. Methods Twenty-four anterior lens capsules were obtained from porcine and human eyes. Six capsules of each species were stored at -80°C before being transfered to dishes coated with typeI collagen. Another 6 capsules were treated accordingly except for cryo-treatment. A last set of capsules was exposed to 0.05% trypsin. To each well, suspended RPE and IPE were added (5x 10^4cells/ml). Cultures were maintained in a water-saturated atmosphere at 37°C in 5% CO_2. Density and morphology of RPE and IPE were determined after 10 days. Results Storage at -80°C and incubation in trypsin resulted in a significant reduction of lens epithelium. The capsules remained transparent. Confluent monolayers of RPE and IPE with epitheloid morphology were obtained when lens capsules which had undergone cryo-or trypsin-treatment served as support. The cell layers were firmly attached to the capsules. Untreated capsules were still covered with lens epithelium. Only few pigmented cells had attached to these capsules forming mixed cultures. Cell growth and morphology of RPE and IPE was similar on human and porcine lens capsules. Conclusions The present study indicates that lens capsule might be suitable for supporting monolayers of RPE or IPE. Organic carriers may offer the option to manipulate coherent cell plaques for subretinal transplantation without inflicting mechanical damage.

3331

THE USE OF ANTERIOR SEGMENT ANGIOGRAPHY IN THE DIFFERENTIATION OF MOOREN'S ULCERS

WATSON, P.G.

Honorary Consultant
1. Addenbrooke's Hospital, Cambridge, England
2. Moorfields Eye Hospital, London, England

Purpose
To differentiate between the various types of Mooren's ulcer.

Method
Anterior segment fluorescein angiography can be performed by using still photographs at one second intervals or by video angiography. This technique reveals areas of vascular closure, abnormalities in the vascular architecture and sites of vascular leakage. The normal appearances, changes with age and disease, are now well recognised.

Results and Conclusions

The clinical presentation of patients with Mooren's ulcer and the pattern of vascular changes revealed by angiography suggest that there are three forms of this condition; a unilateral destructive disease (commonly found in elderly caucasians), a bilateral aggressive disease relatively common in Asian, Indian and African populations and a bilateral indolent form so far only noted in patients of Indian origin.

3332

HLA SUSCEPTIBILITY TO MOOREN'S ULCERATION

TAYLOR CJ[1], SMITH SI[1], MORGAN CH[1], STEPHENSON SF[1] and WATSON PG[2]. [1]Tissue Typing Laboratory, [2]Hon Consultant Ophthalmologist. Addenbrooke's NHS Trust, Cambridge, UK.

Purpose The aetiology of Mooren's Ulceration (MU) is unclear although auto-immune mechanisms are almost certainly involved. Its predominance in certain racial groups and their second generation migrants world-wide indicates a genetic as well as geographic predisposition. Human Leukocyte Antigens (HLA) present self and foreign peptides to T lymphocytes and confers genetic susceptibility to several autoimmune disorders. We have investigated a possible link between MU and HLA genotype.
Methods Patients (N=16) with corneal ulceration were HLA typed (class I and II) by PCR using sequence specific primers. Differential diagnosis confirmed MU in seven patients and other degenerative inflammatory disorders in nine (controls). The MU patients were from varied ethnic backgrounds with 3 Indian, 1 Black African and 3 European Caucasian (from Denmark, Poland and United Kingdom).
Results Of the seven patients with MU, five (71%) were HLA-DR17 positive compared to one of nine (11%) controls (P=0.01). In addition, six patients with MU (86%) were HLA-DQ2 positive compared to 3 (33%) controls (P=0.04).
Conclusion These results indicate a possible association between HLA genotype and susceptibility to MU. The association with HLA-DR17 and DQ2 is interesting as this constitutes a haplotype known to confer susceptibility to several auto-immune disorders. However, the number of patients studied is small and this association is therefore tenuous. We are now attempting to verify these findings in a larger patient cohort.

3333

EPIDEMIOLOGY OF MOOREN'S ULCER IN SOUTH INDIA.

Cunningham ET Jr,[1] Srinivasan M,[2] Zegans M,[1] Santhi CB,[2] Whitcher JP,[1] Margolis TM,[1] and Leitman T.[1]
1. The Francis I. Proctor Foundation, San Francisco, California (USA).
2. Aravind Eye Hospital, Madurai, (India).
Purpose: To describe the clinical characteristics at presentation of a large cohort of patients with Mooren's ulcer in South India.
Methods: The medical records of patients with Mooren's ucler examined in the cornea clinic at Aravind Eye Hospital between May, 1985, and February, 1996, were reviewed retrospectively.
Results: 167 patients with Mooren's ulcer were identified. Men outnumber woman by a ratio of 4.8:1. The median age at presentation was 65, with a range of 13 to 95. One eye was involved in 54% of patients. Visual acuity in the affected eye ranged from 20/20 to light perception. 35 of 243 (14%) affected eyes had vision of 20/40 or better, 168 (69%) had vision between 20/40 and 20/400, and 39 (16%) had vision worse than 20/400. Partial peripheral corneal ulceration was observed in 223 of 243 affected eyes (92%), complete peripheral corneal ulceration was observed in 15 (6%), and total corneal ulceration was observed in 5 (2%). For those eyes with partial peripheral ulceration, 152 (68%) showed temporal involvement, 129 (58%) showed nasal involvement, 30 (13%) showed superior involvement, and 116 (52%) showed inferior involvement. Perforation was observed in 14 eyes with partial peripheral ulceration, 11 with complete peripheral ulceration, and 1 with total corneal involvement. Risk factors included prior corneal surgery (22%),trauma (17%),and infection (2%)
Conclusions: Mooren's ulcer is a rare eye condition observed commonly at Aravind Eye Hospital. Men are affected more frequently than woman, and may present with either unilateral or bilateral disease. Perforation is observed in about one in ten eyes at first visit. The occurrence of prior surgery, trauma, or infection in over one-third of patients supports theories of corneal antigen exposure in the pathogenesis of this disorder.

3334

Conjunctival Expression of Co-stimulatory and Adhesion Molecules in Mooren's Ulcer

Sangwan VS[1], Zafirakis P[2], Rojas B[2], Livir-Rallatos C[2], Baltatzis S[2], Dorfman DM[3] and Foster CS[2].

1. L.V.Prasad Eye Institute, Hyderabad (INDIA)
2. Massachusetts Eye & Ear Infirmary, Boston (USA)
3. Department of Pathology, Brigham and Women's Hospital, Boston (USA)

Purpose : To determine the pattern of costimulatory and adhesion molecules expression in the conjunctiva from patients with Mooren's Ulcer. **Methods :** Expression of the adhesion molecules (VCAM-1, VLA-4, ICAM-1, LFA-1, and E-selection) and costimulatory molecules (CD28, CD80, CD86) was determined by immuno-histochemistry on frozen sections of human conjunctiva using monoclonal antibodies. Conjunctival biopsy specimens were obtain from six patients with Mooren's Ulcer and control specimens undergoing cataract surgery or PUK patients. **Results :** There was significantly increased expression of CD28, CD80, and CD86 on inflammatory cells around blood vessels and along the basement membrane zone in patients with Mooren's Ulcer. VCAM-1 and LFA-1 expression was significantly higher on conjunctival epithelium from patients with Mooren's Ulcer than in patients with PUK. Additionally, VCAM-1 and ICAM-1 expression on the vascular endothelium was significantly higher in Mooren's Ulcer than in PUK. **Conclusions :** This simultaneous expression of CD80 and CD28 positive cells in the Mooren's Ulcer conjunctiva suggest that their interaction potentially contributes to the sustained immune mediated destruction of tissue utilizing specialized adhesion molecules.

3335

THE SIGNIFICANCE OF CORNEA SPECIFIC ANTIGENS IN MOOREN'S ULCERATION

GOTTSCH J, LIU S.H.
Wilmer Ophthalmological Institute, Baltimore, MD, USA

Purpose A cornea associated antigen (CO-Ag) has been found to be identical to calgranulin C (CaGC), a neutrophil-derived protein. CaGC has been isolated on the surface of onchoceracal worms and has been implicated in the pathogenesis of Mooren's ulcer, a peripheral ulcerative keratitis that has been associated with helminthic infections. We sought to establish that CaGC is expressed in the human cornea and in corneal keratocytes after cytokine stimulation and we wanted to determine if recombinant human CaGC has biologic activity against filarial parasites.

Methods *In situ* hybridization and immunohistochemistry were used to localize CaGC mRNA and protein in normal and diseased human corneas including a specimen with Mooren's ulcer. Cultured bovine keratocytes were stimulated with IL-1α or TNF-α. Reverse transcription polymerase chain reaction (RT-PCR) was performed to amplify CaGC cDNA from cytokine stimulated keratocytes and unstimulated controls. Southern blots were used to verify the specificity of RT-PCR amplification products. *Brugia malayi* microfilariae were harvested from the peritoneal cavity of a chronically infected gerbil. Larvae were transferred to the wells of a 96-well plate containing 0.2 ml of DMEM. Recombinant CaGC was added at 5, 2.5, 1.88, 1.25. or 0.63 μg/well. The parasites were observed and graded for motility at 5, 15, 30, 60, 180 minutes and at 18 hours of culture.

Results Human CaGC mRNA was detected in the stroma by *in situ* hybridization of post-infectious corneas and in a Mooren's ulcer. In cultured bovine keratocytes, maximal levels of CaGC mRNA was reached at 6 hr post-stimulation with IL-1α or TNF. Southern blots with oligonucleotide probe specifically designed for CaGC detected the RT-PCR products of expected sizes (273 bp) and provided confirmation that the amplified CO-Ag sequence was identical to CaGC. At the three highest concentrations of CaGC, the microfilariae remained immobile signifying that they had been killed by CaGC treatment. However, at lower CaGC concentrations, the larvae demonstrated a partial recovery of motility that was dose dependent. Thus, at lower concentrations, CaGC affects larval motility.

Conclusions Human corneal stromal cells are capable of producing CaGC (CO-Ag) and levels of CaGC are upregulated in corneas with inflammation and with Mooren's ulcer. CaGC binds to worms and may enable the host to kill or immobilize helminthic parasites. A host-parasite interaction may cause autoimmunity to CaGC in the cornea resulting in a Mooren's ulcer.

3341

HELPING READING WITH COLOURED FILTERS

WILKINS AJ
Visual Perception Unit, University of Essex (UK)

We review the use of colour to help with reading. We have developed a system of coloured plastic sheets that can be laid upon text when reading (known as overlays). The overlays sample CIE 1976 UCS chromaticity systematically, comprehensively and efficiently. We have shown that about 20% of normal children read more quickly when the text is coloured in this way, provided that colour is selected to suit the individual child. The increase in speed is accompanied by an increase in accuracy and cannot be attributed simply to placebo effects. In 5% of children the speed increase exceeds 25%. There is little relationship between the benefit from coloured filters and conventional orthoptic abnormalities. However, children who benefit from coloured overlays tend to have migraine in the family. The colour optimal for use in overlays (a surface colour) differs from that optimal for use in lenses (which have an effect similar to that of coloured light). We have developed a system for ophthalmic tinting that enables individuals to select a therapeutic tint for spectacles whilst the eyes are colour adapted. Precision tints selected using this system have been shown to reduce symptoms of asthenopia in a double-masked placebo-controlled cross-over study. In this study two tints were compared, each with similar colour, but one selected using the tinting system. The findings indicate that the tint needs to be selected with precision for optimal effect.

3342

OFF-AXIS ASTIGMATISM OF THE CORNEAL MODEL WITHOUT THE ROTATIONAL SYMMETRY

KASPRZAK H.

Inst. of Physics, Wrocław Univ. of Technology (Poland)

Purpose The majority of corneas have on-axis astigmatism due to the nonrotational symmetry of the cornea. Since the geometrical axis of the eye differs from the visual one, it is important to know whether lack of rotational symmetry of the cornea can reduce its off-axis astigmatism.

Methods A model of the nonrotational cornea was approximated by four different analytical formulas of the $z=f(x,y)$ type. The computer program has calculated spot diagrams in the focal region of the cornea of light rays illuminating the cornea. Falling rays were inclined to the geometrical axis of the cornea with the angle of 2, 4 and 6 degrees.

Results Calculations have shown that the size of spot diagrams (concentration of the light energy) depends very much on approximation of the corneal surface, angle of inclination and position of the plane in the focal region of the cornea, where the spot diagram was calculated.

Conclusions Some results of calculation show that nonrotational cornea causes reduction of off-axis astigmatism in comparison to the axial one. This can be one of potential explanation why the visual axis of the eye is inclined to the optical one.

3343

DISCRIMINANT ANALYSIS OF THE ACTIVITY OF RETINAL GANGLION CELL POPULATIONS.

AMMERMÜLLER J[1], NORMANN RA[2], FERRANDEZ JM[3], BOLEA JA[3], and FERNANDEZ E[3].
1. Dept. Biology, Universität Oldenburg, Oldenburg, (Germany). 2. The John Moran Laboratories, University of Utah, Salt Lake City, (USA). 3. Inst. Bioeng. Universidad Miguel Hernandez, Alicante, (Spain).

Purpose: To study how visual stimulus features are represented by networks of retinal ganglion cells.
Methods: The Utah intracortical multielectrode array with 100 fine tipped, isolated silicon electrodes was used to simultaneously record light responses from many ganglion cell in the isolated retina of *Pseudemys scripta* turtles. Multidimensional discriminant analysis was used to identify those spike parameters that allow a better discrimination of the stimulus features.
Results: Individual ganglion cells are poor specifiers of intensity, color and form. On the other hand even small populations of neurons improved specification capability. Correct classification was almost 100% using the spike data from 15 randomly selected cells. Number and timing of spikes were the most important parameters. Coding of intensity, form and color was redundant.
Conclusion: We conclude that in spite of the variability of individual ganglion cell responses, even relatively small populations of ganglion cells can be used to unambiguously represent visual stimuli.

Supported by DFG - SFB 517

3344

SPATIAL SUMMATION OF BLUE-ON-YELLOW LIGHT INCREMENTS AND DECREMENTS IN HUMAN VISION

VASSILEV A[1], ZLATKOVA M[1], MANAHILOV V[1], KRUMOV A[2], SCHAUMBERGER M[3], LACHENMAYR B.[3]

1. Institute of Physiology, Academy of Sciences, Sofia, (Bulgaria)
2. Central Solar-Terrestrial Influences Laboratory, Academy of Sciences, Sofia (Bulgaria)
3. University Eye Hospital, Munich (Germany)

Purpose. To obtain comparative data on the areas of spatial summation of light increments and decrements upon selective stimulation of the S-cones in man.
Methods. A 3 cd/m^2 blue light was superimposed on a 300 cd/m^2 yellow background and the test stimulus consisted in an increment (I) or a decrement (D) from this steady level over a circular area of variable size centred at 12^0 retinal eccentricity. Stimulus duration was 100 ms. Within the test-stimulus spectral band, sensitivity was that of Stiles' π_1 mechanism. In a control experiment, red-on-red stimuli were used.
Results. Ricco's area of complete spatial summation was about 0.8 deg in dia for blue light-I, 1.2-1.6 deg for blue light-D and 0.2 deg for both red light-I and -D.
Conclusions. A correlation of extent of spatial summation with the paucity of ganglion cells receiving an on- or off-input from the S-cones is suggested.
Supported by Volkswagen Stiftung (Project I/69966/1994).

3345

VISUAL FUNCTION TESTING IN PATIENTS AND HEALTHY VOLUNTEERS RECEIVING VIAGRA™

LATIES A,[1] ELLIS P,[2] KOPPIKER N,[2] PATAT A[3] and STUCKEY B.[4]
[1]Dept. Ophthalmology, Univ. of Pennsylvania, Phila. (USA); [2]Pfizer Ltd., Sandwich (UK); [3]Biotrial, Rennes (France); [4]The Keogh Institute for Medical Research (Australia)

Purpose: To study the effects of VIAGRA™ (sildenafil citrate), a potent inhibitor of phosphodiesterase (PDE) type 5 with low affinity for retinal PDE6, on visual function in men. *Methods*: In two clinical trials, acute and long-term effects of VIAGRA on a range of visual function tests were studied. *Results*: A single supratherapeutic dose (200 mg) of VIAGRA produced no clinically significant effects on visual field, visual acuity, photostress test, intraocular pressure, and electroretinograms. A small, transient increase in error score on the FM-100 hue test (blue-green) was evident 1-2 hours post-dose, but resolved within 5 hours of dosing. In patients receiving VIAGRA 50-200 mg *prn* (12-week, placebo-controlled) followed by 25-100 mg *prn* (40-week, open-label), no clinically significant changes were seen in visual acuity, contrast sensitivity, FM-100 hue test, photostress test, and slit-lamp examination. No serious visual adverse events (AEs) or discontinuations due to visual AEs occurred. *Conclusion:* VIAGRA can cause modest, transient, reversible effects on discrimination in the blue-green colour range but has no effect on this or any other visual function test following long-term administration.

3347

INFLUENCE OF THE TYPE OF INTRA-OCULAR LENSES AND IN PATIENT QUALITY OF LIFE

LEITE E, PEDRUCO A, OLIVEIROS B, GONÇALVES C.
Centre of Ophthalmology Biomedical Institute for Light and Image Research, Coimbra, Portugal

Methods Fifty-four patients undergoing cataract surgery with different types of (IOL) implantation were assessed to determine (1) influences of the IOL on functional status/mental status, (2) influences of the IOL on quality of life, (3) relationships among age, professional activities, hobbies and physical status. Four groups were evaluated: group M1-19 patients (mono IOL/1 eye); group M2-14 patients (mono IOL/2 eyes); group D1-9 patients (diffra IOL/1 eye); group D2-12 patients (IOL/2 eyes). Subjects completed the SCL-90-R, Rand Vision, EORTC-QLQ-C30 and VF-14. The *Mann-Whitney test, Wilcoxon* and *Kendall τ correlation* were performed.
Results Significant improvements were found in all four groups. The profile of the improved group (M2/D2) showed significantly higher scores on physical functioning ($p<0.005$), emotional functioning ($p<0.002$), role functioning ($p<0.04$), quality of life ($p<0.007$), social functioning ($p<0.04$), general well-being ($p<0.002$), direct visual acuity ($p<0.0009$) and mobility limitation ($p<0.0009$) among other specific variables. Comparisons intra and inter-groups (D1 vs D2 and M1 vs M2) were made.
Conclusions Higher improvement of quality of life was obtained with diffractive IOLs. These two trends show apparently that patients profile should be characterized and IOL implanted accordingly.

3346

THE EFFICIENCY OF ELECTROPUNCTURAL REFLEXOTHERAPY IN PATIENTS WITH THE SPASM OF ACCOMODATION

GLUSCHAK H.V., RESHETNYAK W. B., PONOMARCHUK V.S.
The Filatov's Institute Of Eye Diseases And Tissue Therapy (Ukraine)

Reflexotherapy is one of the basic methods of therapeutic influence in different pathological diseases of neurous system, sensor systems and, in particular, the visual analyzer and neuro-muscular apparatus of eye. The aim of the research: study of the influence of electropunctural reflexotherapy, being done according to F.G. Portnov's methods, on visual function and the work of accommodation apparatus of the eye in patients with accommodation spasm. 70 patients (140 eyes) with the spasm aged from 7 to 15 have been examined. The method includes the irritation of points of local and general influence on accommodation apparatus. The search of accupunctual points and influence of halvanic currents on them is done with the help of apparatus «Elita-4». The course of treatment consists of 6. Results: 100% patients improved their far sight from 0,37±0,08 up to 0,54±0,09 on the right eye and from 0,45±0,08 up to 0,61±0,08 on the left eye ($p<0,05$). The strength of corrective glasses was eliminated in 22,4% on the right eye ($p<0,01$).The reserves of accommodation were increased sufficiently from 2,5±0,4D up to 6,0±0,6D ($p<0,05$) on the right eye and from 2,7±0,4D up to 6,3±0,6D ($p<0,05$) on the left eye. The accommodation zone for close sight was increased from 4,45±0,3D up to 5,70±0,25D. Thus, reflexotherapy leads to increase of functional activity of accommodative-convergent system in patients with accommodation spasm and also to the increase of reserve adaptive abilities of the sight analyzer.

3411

QUADRANT ANALYSIS OF PERIPHERAL COLOUR CONTRAST THRESHOLDS PREDICTS GLAUCOMATOUS VISUAL FIELD LOSS. POURJAVAN S, DEVOS M, VAN MALDEREN L, GOETHALS M, SPILEERS W. Dept. of Ophthalmology, UZ Leuven, Belgium.

Purpose: Peripheral colour contrast thresholds were investigated in early glaucoma patients and glaucoma suspects, and correlated with changes in the visual field.
Methods: Colour contrast thresholds were investigated in 4 visual field quadrants of 47 early glaucoma patients and 45 glaucoma suspects. Visual field examinations (HC30-2) were performed at the same day, and repeated on consecutive visits. For glaucoma patients analysis of the visual field changes were performed after a mean follow-up of 6.8 months, and after 1.5 year. For glaucoma suspects preliminary data were obtained after 1.5 year. Visual fields were analysed by the regional parameters of each quadrant using the Peridata-program 6.2.
Results: For glaucoma patients, the regional mean of 46% of the quadrants with only minor alterations on perimetry but abnormal colour contrast thresholds showed a decrease of at least 2 dB after 6.8 months. Results were confirmed at the follow-up analysis of 1.5 year. For glaucoma suspects 27% of the quadrants with abnormal colour contrast thresholds showed a decrease in regional mean of 2 dB or more after 1.5 year.
Conclusions: Quadrant analysis of peripheral colour contrast thresholds can predict the development of glaucomatous visual field loss.

3412

CORRELATION BETWEEN STANDARD THRESHOLD PERIMETRY INDICES, OPTIC DISC PARAMETERS AND HIGH PASS RESOLUTION RELATIVE DISPERSION ANALYSIS.

IESTER M, TRAVERSO CE, ALTIERI M, CAPRIS P, ZINGIRIAN M
Department of Ophthalmology, University of Genoa, Genoa (Italy)

Purpose: To evaluate the correlation of the Humphrey perimeter indices and optic disc parameters with relative dispersion analysis (RDA), which provides a new High Pass Resolution Perimetry (HRP) index, able to capture a novel aspect of visual field abnormality[1].
Methods: Twenty-two patients with glaucoma (high intraocular pressure, abnormal visual field and/or optic disc) and 22 glaucoma suspect subjects (high intraocular pressure, normal visual field, not evident optic disc defect) were randomly recruited. Only one eye for each subject was randomly chosen. All the subjects were examined with Humphrey Perimeter, program 30-2, and HRP. All the HRP data were also analyzed by relative dispersion analysis program. Each patients had a computerized optic nerve head analysis by Image-net X Rev-3.51b, Topcon Europe. Findings were assessed by Pearson's correlation.
Results: A significant ($0.05<p<0.001$) Pearson's correlation was found between RDA index and mean deviation ($r = -0.46$), corrected pattern standard deviation ($r = 0.6$), pattern standard deviation ($r = 0.6$) and short-term fluctuation ($r = 0.35$). No correlation was found between optic nerve head parameters and RDA.
Conclusions: Although good correlations were found between the new HRP index and standard threshold perimetry indices, no correlation was found with optic disc parameters. More data will be necessary to evaluate this new technique.

1) Frisen L, Rossitti S. Relative dispersion analysis enhances perimetric sensitivity. Vis Research 1995;36:491-7

3413

IMPROVEMENT OF SPATIAL CONTRAST SENSITIVITY AFTER TRABECULECTOMY IN UNILATERAL HIGH-TENSION GLAUCOMA

GANDOLFI SA and CIMINO L
Glaucoma Service, University Eye Clinic, Parma (Italy)

Purpose: to measure the spatial contrast sensitivity before and after surgery in eyes bearing a high IOP and showing no visual field defect on achromatic static perimetry.
Methods: prospective clinical trial, 10 consecutive subjects with IOP > 30 mmHg (without treatment) in one eye and IOP < 18 mmHg in the fellow eye, normal Octopus G1 in OU, best corrected v.a. ≥ 20/20 in OU; standard trabeculectomy per= formed in the eye showing high IOP, the fellow eye kept un= treated as internal control. Spatial contrast sensitivity measured (CSV1000, Vecto Vision, OH) upon recruitment and at every follow up visit. IOP (diurnal curve) measured con= currently. Power = 90%, alpha probability = 10%.
Results: contrast sensitivity improved at 3, 6 and 12 cyc/ deg in each operated eye. The improvement was significantly correlated with the amount of IOP drop observed after sur= gery. The improvement levelled after 9 months post-op and remained stable up to 24 months post-op. No change in con= trast sensitivity was observed in the normal untreated fel= low eyes.
Conclusions: an improvement of central visual function, as measured by spatial contrast sensitivity, can occur in human eyes showing a high IOP and undergoing a filtration procedure.

3414

SLITLAMP BASED OPTICAL COHERENCE TOMOGRAPHY IN THE ANTERIOR SEGMENT OF THE EYE

H. HOERAUF [1], C. SCHOLZ [2], R. ENGELHARDT [2], P. KOCH [2], R. BIRNGRUBER [2], H. LAQUA [1]
[1] Eye Hospital, University Lübeck (Germany)
[2] Medical Laser-Center-Lübeck (Germany)

Purpose: To evaluate the diagnostic potential of a slitlamp-adapted OCT-system for the anterior segment. We present OCT-generated images of different anterior segment pathologies in vivo.
Methods: Patients were examined by a slitlamp-adapted OCT prototype (Fa.Schwind, D-Kleinostheim), which allows examination of the anterior and posterior segment using 100-200 axial scans, 50Hz scan frequency and a scan length of 7.5mm
Results: Corneal structures and changes can be demonstrated very precisely, the chamber angle can be visualized and measured reproducably. Morphologic changes of the iris, lens and secondary cataract formation can be well observed. Incident light is attenuated by the iris pigment epithelium, completely shadowing structures which are located posteriorely to it like the ciliary region or the pars plana.
Conclusion: Slitlamp based OCT is a useful diagnostic tool in the anterior segment and may be helpful in pre- and postoperative chamber angle evaluations in glaucoma patients.

3415

HAEMODYNAMIC IN OPEN-ANGLE GLAUCOMA

BORISOVA S., SHAMSHINOVA A., NIKITIN Y.
Moscow Helmholtz Research Institute of Eye Diseases
Institute of the Neurology, RAMS, Russia

Purpose: To research disturbance of the hemodynamic in glaucoma and determine her role in genesis optic nerve atrophy.
Methods: We used Color Doppler imaging. The blood supply of the orbital vessels was measured with the US-Dopscan by the probes 2, 4, 8 MHz. We introduced the new «Borisova's Index eye's Perfusion» (IP) - the following ratio:

IP= Vm a.ophth.- Vm a.supratr./ Vm a.ophth.,

where Vm a.ophth.- mean flow velocity in ophthalmic artery; Vm a.supratr.- mean flow velocity in ipsilateral supratrochlear artery. Were examine 60 normal patients and 60 patients with primary open angle glaucoma(from early to terminal stages) before and after surgery.
Results: In normal subjects the IP were 0,56+0,04; the patients with glaucoma showed reduction the statistically significant of the Borisova's index (0,46±0,06 in early and 0,28±0,07 in terminal glaucoma). This data were correlated with definition of activity of the cone's system, spatial contrast sensitivity and visual field changes. This Index was increased after surgery in some of the patients .
Conclusions: So, Doppler studies showed decrease of the blood flow in the orbital vessels during evolution of glaucoma's process and possibility using of the new Index for determine of haemodynamical changes and its significance in genesis visual dysfunction in glaucoma.

3416

RETINAL BLOOD FLOW IN MYOPIC PATIENTS WITH OR WITHOUT GLAUCOMA

MUZYKA M[1], KAGEMANN L[2], ZAJAC-PYTRUS H[1], NIZANKOWSKA M[1], A.HARRIS[2].
1. Dept. Ophthalmology, Wrocław University School of Medicine (Poland)
2. Glaucoma Research & Diagnostic Center, Indianapolis (USA)

Purpose. Early diagnosis of glaucoma in myopic patients is often difficult. The aim of our study was to evaluate retinal blood flow in myopic patients with or without glaucoma and in emmetropic patients with glaucoma.
Methods. Heidelberg Retinal Flowmeter (HRF) was used to measure retinal perfusion in 72 patients (22 with myopia without glaucoma, 16 with myopia and glaucoma,17 with glaucoma without myopia and 17 control subjects). We have examined both eyes in 4 peripapillary areas. HRF images were analysed with pointwise method (described previously in ARVO 1997 and BJO 1998)
Results. We found significant differences in number of zero flow pixels (avascular areas) between myops with glaucona and myops without glaucoma in superior temporal peripapillary area (p.= 0,03)
Conclusions. Consideration of superior temporal peripapillary area perfusion parameters may provide useful additional information in the diagnosis of glaucoma in myopic patients.

3417

EFFECT OF LUMINANCE FLICKER ON JUXTAPAPILLARY RETINAL BLOOD FLOW IN GLAUCOMA PATIENTS

A.Patzelt, G.Michelson, J.Welzenbach, J.Harazny
Dept. of Ophthalmology, University Erlangen-Nuernberg, Schwabachanlage 6, D-91054 Erlangen, Germany

Purpose: To compare normal subjects with patients suffering from glaucoma (OAG, NTG) in respect to the changes of juxtapapillary retinal blood flow resulting from diffuse flicker illuminating the retina.
Methods and Patients: The blood flow of superficial retinal capillaries was measured by Scanning Laser Doppler Flowmetry (Heidelberg Engineering, HRF), evaluating well-focused capillary areas of 200x200 μm^2. The measurement was triggered by ECG. The flicker light (8 Hz, 5.5 cd/cm^2) was guided by an optical fiber (bundle diameter 5 mm) to the eye to be examined. After taking a baseline perfusion-image, flicker was applied to illuminate the retina for 30 seconds. A second perfusion-image was taken while still flickering. For statistical analysis the t-test for paired samples and the Mann- Whitney U Wilcoxon-test were performed. We examined 27 eyes of 27 normal subjects and 12 eyes of 12 patients suffering from advanced glaucomatous optic neuropathy.
Results: In glaucomatous eyes the juxtapapillary retinal blood flow showed no increase during flickering in contrast to control eyes. In normal eyes we found a significant increase of 46±19%.
Conclusions In contrast to normal eyes eyes with advanced glaucoma showed no increase in juxtapapillary retinal blood flow in response to diffuse flickering. Measuring the capacity of vascular regulation in respect to flickering may play a major role in the diagnosis of glaucma in future.

3425

RETINAL PIGMENT EPITHELIAL MONOLAYERS CULTURED ON BIOMATERIALS FOR IMPLANTATION

MCLAUGHLIN BJ,[1] SINGH S,[1] HADLOCK T,[2] VACANTI JP,[3] BARR C[1]; [1]Dept. Of Ophthalmology & Visual Sciences, University of Louisville (USA), [2]Dept. Of Surgery, Children's Hospital (USA) [3]Harvard Medical School & Children's Hospital (USA)

Purpose To culture retinal pigment epithelial (RPE) monolayers on biodegradable substrates for future use in monolayer transplantation in the eye.

Method The biodegradable polymers poly-L-lactic acid (PLLA) and poly-DL-lactic-co-glycolic acid (85:15) (PLGA) (both 105 kDa) were the biomaterials used. Biomaterials were seeded with pig/human retinal pigment epithelial cells and were maintained in tissue culture conditions.

Results All cell types attached to the polymers within 24 hours and were grown to confluent epitheloid monolayers between 7-14 days. Trypan blue exclusion assays of monolayers demonstrated 86-90% viability and an average cell density of 2500 cells/mm^2. Immunostaining with ZO_1 indicated intact cell junctions and rhodamine-phalloidin demonstrated normal actin distribution. Implantation into pig eyes of PLLA resulted in an inflammatory response or subretinal fibrosis at 2 weeks postoperative.

Conclusions Because PLLA films do not appear to be tolerated well, experiments are underway to implant RPE monolayers grown on hydrogel lenses which are well tolerated in the eye.

Supported by Baptist Memorial Research Foundation, Memphis, Tennessee, NIH EY02853, and an anonymous donor.

3441

THE USE OF MRI FOR PREOPERATIVE ASSESSMENT OF ORBITAL SHOT GUN INJURIES

HESS U[1], HARMS J[2], LANZL I[3].
1. Dept. of Nuclear Medicine, 2. Dept. of Surgery and 3. Dept. of Ophthalmology, Technical University, Munich (Germany)

Purpose: MRI is rarely used for preoperative assessment of shotgun injuries due to concerns of displacing the possibly ferromagnetic foreign body within the surrounding tissue.
Methods: 50 different projectiles underwent testing with a commercially available 1.5 T-MRI-scan (ACS II, Philips, Germany) either in vitro or in pig cadavers. Image quality was compared to CT scans.
Results: Projectiles with ferromagnetic properties can easily be distinguished from non ferromagnetic ones by pretesting the motion of an identical projectile within the MRI coil. When ferromagnetic projectiles were excluded, MRI yielded the more precise images, compared to other imaging techniques. Projectile localization and associated soft tissue injuries were visualized without artifacts in all cases.
Conclusions: When ferromagnetic foreign bodies are excluded from MRI by "pretesting" their properties within the MRI with an identical projectile, MRI is an excellent imaging procedure for detailed planing of surgical removal of intraorbital bullets.

3442

CALVARIUM BONE SPLIT GRAFT AS A TREATMENT MODALITY OF MOTILITY DISORDERS AFTER ORBITAL FRACTURES

GOCKELN R,[1] DAMMS CH,[1] HÜLSSNER O,[1] SCHIERLE HP,[2] WINTER R.[1]
1. Dept. Ophthalmology, Medizinische Hochschule, Hannover, (Germany)
2. Dept. Orofacial Surg., Medizinische Hochschule, Hannover, (Germany)

Prupose To reconstruct the orbita, besides using Hydroxyapetite granules and PDS (Vicryl) sheets the method of implanting autologous calvarium bone splits is becoming more popular. We evaluated the ocular motility disorders after reconstruction of orbital fractures using this method.
Methods Thirty subjects suffering from different types of orbital fractures underwent orbital reconstruction using autologous calvarium splits. We assesed the postoperative monocular and binocular motility, the extent of enophthalmus and depression of the globe as well as the stereopsis.
Results In 43% of cases an active deficiency of elevation and depression was evident. Fiftyseven percent of these subjects claimed about diplopia by vertical deviation. Patients with complex fractures (20%) showed additionally horizontal heterotropia. In spite of these motility disorders 70% of the subjects had at least a rough stereopsis. In 33% of cases we could measure an enophthalmus.
Conclusions The recurrence of symptoms was present to a lesser degree in subjects treated with calvarium splits compared to those treated with other implants.

3443

THE RESULTS OF THE OPTIC NERVE ATROPHY SURGICAL TREATMENT IN GLAUCOMA WITH THE USE OF THE ALLOPLANT BIOMATERIALS

MULDASHEV E., KARUSHINN O., KORNILAEVA G., KIIKO J.
Russian Eye and Plastic Surgery Center, Ufa (Russia)

Purpose Activization of the functional state of the optic disk fibers by the improvement of the peripapillary choroid blood supply.

Methods Optic nerve revascularization surgery was performed with the use of the Alloplant biomaterials. 178 patients were operated on diagnosed as the optic nerve atrophy in compensated glaucoma.

Results Long-term results were valued in 95 patients. The age ranged from 31 to 86, with 65 males and 30 females. The analysis of the state of the visual functions in the long-term follow-up (6 to 72 months) showed that there was an improvement in 64-75% of the operated on patients with no changes in 23.0-32.2% and became worse in 3.5-7.7%.

Conclusions The obtained data with the above mentioned surgeries allow to make the following conclusions:
-stabilization and improvement of a number of visual functions in the long-term follow-up are observed in most of the operated-on patients;
- there is a direct relationship between the effect of the given surgery and seriousness of the visual system affection;
- there is observed a direct dependence of the outcome of the surgery upon the time it was performed. The earlier it is performed the better is the prognosis for the favourable results.

3444

BILATERAL ANTERIOR ISCHAEMIC OPTIC NEUROPATHY DUE TO BURIED OPTIC DISC DRUSEN: A DIAGNOSIS MADE IN RETROSPECT

KAMATH GG, PRASAD S and PHILLIPS RP
Dept. Ophthalmology, Arrowe Park Hospital, Wirral, (UK)

Case Report: A 64 year old man presented with swollen optic discs and features suggestive of anterior ischaemic optic neuropathy (AION) in both eyes at two separate episodes 11 months apart. Detailed ocular examination at presentation and systemic investigations did not reveal an underlying cause for the AION. At a later follow-up examination optic disc drusen were noted in both eyes as partial optic atrophy had set in, this was confirmed by a ultrasound B`scan and demonstration of autofluorescence.
Discussion: Non arteritic AION is a common cause of significant visual loss in the elderly. Whilst systemic associations are common, an underlying ocular cause like disc drusen is rarely found. Optic disc drusen can lead to retinal and optic nerve head vascular problems. Buried drusen are not easily detectable on fundus examination, especially when the presentation is with a swollen hyperaemic disc. In our patient axonal degeneration following AION made visualisation of the drusen easier.
Conclusion: In patients presenting with AION or retinal vascular occlusions uncommon underlying causes must be considered. Routine ultrasound B scan at presentation can easily establish or exclude optic disc drusen as an underlying cause.

3445

THE EFFECT OF CAROTID ENDARTERECTOMY ON PULSATILE OCULAR BLOOD FLOW

O'TOOLE L[1], SAIDLEAR C[1], EARLY A[1], FLITCROFT I[1], CORRIGAN T[2], O'MALLEY K[2] and EUSTACE P[1]
1. Institute of Ophthalmology, University College Dublin, Mater Misericordiae Hospital (MMH), (Ireland)
2. Department of Vascular Surgery (MMH), (Ireland)

Purpose: We set out to determine the effect of carotid endarterectomy on pulsatile ocular blood flow (POBF).

Methods: Patients with carotid occlusive disease diagnosed by triplex ultrasound were identified pre carotid endarterectomy. An ophthalmic examination was performed on each patient and the POBF recorded from each eye using a non-invasive ocular blood flow tonograph. POBF was then rerecorded immediately post surgery and at outpatient review.

Results: 23 patients underwent 23 carotid endarterectomies. There was a rise in the immediate postoperative POBF in the ipsilateral and contralateral eye to the carotid endarterectomy ($p<0.005$, <0.05 respectively, Wilcoxon matched pairs test). 11 patients were seen at followup, there was no statistically significant sustained elevation of POBF ($p>0.5$).

Conclusion: There is a rise in pulsatile ocular blood flow immediately post carotid endarterectomy.

3446

VISUAL HALLUCINATIONS IN TEMPORAL ARTERITIS

NESHER R [1], NESHER G [2], ROZENMAN Y [2], SONNENBLICK M [2]
1. Dept. Ophthalmology, Sapir Medical Center, Kfar-Saba,
2. Depts. Rheumatology Ophthalmology and Geriatrics, Shaare-Zedek Medical Center, Jerusalem (Israel).

Purpose: Evaluation of the prevalence, clinical significance and outcome of visual hallucinations (VH) in patients with temporal arteritis (TA).
Methods: All patients diagnosed by the authors as having TA between 1992-97 were evaluated prospectively. Data on clinical symptoms, including ophthalmic manifestations and questioning the possible occurrence of VH were collected.
Results: TA was diagnosed in 25 patients. 5 presented with visual loss (VL): anterior ischemic optic neuropathy in 4 and central retinal artery occlusion in 1. In 4 of these cases VL was preceded by 1-10 days of VH, in forms specific for each case: flowers, a carriage and horses, cats chasing mice, and colorful rays. VH were not the reason for seeking medical advice, and the patients were quite reluctant initially to describe their VH, fearing the labeling of "psychotic reaction". There were 3 women and 1 man, all were biopsy-positive and none had a psychiatric disorder. VH did not occur in any patient without VL. VH disappeared within 10 days of starting steroid therapy.
Conclusion: VH is not rare in TA, occuring in 16% of the patients in this group. Its occurrence in cases suspected as TA should alert us to the possible development of VL.

3447

CENTRAL RETINAL ARTERY BLOOD FLOW VELOCITY REDUCTION AFTER SUCCESSFUL SCLERAL BUCKLING

ROLDAN-PALLARES M[1], OSSAMA IA[1], CONTRERAS E[2], HERNANDEZ J[2], GANADO T[2] and BRAVO C[3].

1. Dept.Ophthal.,Hosp.S.Carlos.Madrid (Spain)
2. Dept.Radiology,Hosp.S.Carlos.Madrid (Spain)
3. Dept.Statistics,C.Cálculo UC.Madrid (Spain)

Purpose. To analyze ocular blood flow velocity changes after scleral buckling surgery (SB) for retinal detachment (RD).
Methods. 36 patients with unilateral rhegmatogenous RD were selected. Color Doppler Ultrasound was used to measure blood flow velocities in Ophthalmic Artery (OA), Central Retinal Artery (CRA) and Vein (CRV) and Posterior Ciliary Arteries (PCA) of both eyes of each RD patient, before and after (1 week; 1, 3, 7 months) surgery. Intraocular pressure (IOP) was measured prior to each ultrasound study. Matched T was used for statistical analysis.
Results. In eyes with RD, Peak Systolic (PS) velocity of OA was decreased ($p = 0.04$) also was it the Pulsatility Index of CRA ($p = 0.05$). One week after surgery a statistically significant reduction in both PS ($p = 0.02$) and End-Diastolic (ED) ($p = 0.05$) velocities of CRA was found. No other significant changes between blood flow velocities or indices were found.
Conclusions. Short-term (1 week) blood flow velocity reduction has been detected in CRA after SB surgery but no long-term changes have been found.

Supported by FIS 98/0718

3448

FUNCTIONAL OUTCOME OF RETINAL DETACHMENT SURGERY IN EYES WITH AND WITHOUT Nd:YAG LASER CAPSULOTOMY

RANTA P, KIVELÄ T
Department of Ophthalmology, Helsinki University Central Hospital, (Finland)

Purpose: To compare the functional outcome of retinal detachment (RD) surgery in pseudophakic eyes with and without Nd:YAG laser posterior capsulotomy (LCT).
Methods: 100 patients with strictly uncomplicated cataract exctraction, followed by rhegmatogenous RD in 1990-96, fell into two groups; 51 with an intact posterior capsule and 49 with a LCT at the time of RD. The best corrected VA, visual fields, IOP, and retinal status were determined. The patients answered 26 questions about visual performance.
Results: The baseline data of the two groups did not differ. The median number of RD operations (1 vs 1) or VA before (-logMAR 1.0 vs 1.23; equivalent to 0.1 vs 0.06) and after surgery (-logMAR 0.40 both; 0.4) were comparable between control and LCT eyes. Retina remained detached in 9 eyes (6 vs 3, p=NS). The median horizontal diameter of the visual field tended to be smaller in the LCT group (100 vs 90, $p=0.05$). Visual performance in everyday life was similar between the two groups.
Conclusions: The functional outcome of pseudophakic RD was similar regardless of presence of prior Nd:YAG capsulotomy.

The 1997 Abstract book (Ophthalm. Res. vol. 29 suppl. 1) had two abstracts inadvertendly truncated while printing.
Here follows the correct version:

139

VISUAL PROGNOSIS IN CHILDREN WITH JUVENILE CHRONIC ARTHRITIS

NGHIEM M-H[1], BODAGHI B[1], CASSOUX N[1], GUEX-CROSIER Y[1], FARDEAU C[1], PRIEUR AM[2], LEHOANG P[1].
1- Service d'Ophtalmologie, Hôp. Pitié-Salpêtrière, Paris (France)
2- Unité d'Immunologie et d'Hématologie Pédiatriques, Hôp. Necker Enfants Malades, Paris (France)

Purpose : To evaluate the clinical features and complications of juvenile chronic arthritis (JCA) associated-uveitis.
Methods : Data from 25 patients (40 eyes) presenting with JCA associated-uveitis and referred to the Ophthalmology Dept. from 1989 to 1995 were retrospectively analyzed.
Results : The average age at onset of arthritis was 6 years (range, 3 to 13 years). Sex ratio (F/M) was 17/7. Pauciarticular onset was noted in 18 cases (72%), polyarticular onset in 6 cases (25%) and systemic onset in 1 case (4%). Antinuclear antibodies were present in 16 cases (64%). All patients were seronegative for IgM rheumatoid factor. Uveitis was bilateral in 21 cases (84%). A systemic steroid regimen was administered in 17 cases (68%). Cataract extraction was performed in 7 cases (28%). Glaucoma was medically controlled in 3 cases (12%). Four patients developed epiretinal membrane (16%). Cryopexy and scleral buckling were performed in 1 case of retinal detachment (4%). The mean follow-up was 33 months (range, 5 to 85 months). Final visual acuity was < 20/100 in 5 eyes (12.5%), between 20/100 and 40/100 in 11 eyes (27.5%) and ≥ 50/100 in 24 eyes (60%).
Conclusions : Acceptance of universal guidelines for ophthalmological screening and early management of children with JCA should reduce severe visual complications.

231

DIABETIC ISCHAEMIC MACULOPATY AND TREATMENT WITH TICLOPIDINE. FIBRINOGEN RELATION

Cilveti A. Lapeira M. Garcia Campos JM.
Servicio de Oftalmología Hospital Universitario Virgen de la Victoria de Málaga. Unidad docente de Oftalmología Universidad de Málaga.

Purpose. This study was designed to determine the influence of the Ticlopidin on the macular ischaemia evolution, we are based on that Ticlopidin is an anti-aggregate to the platelet which acts on the plasmatic Fibrinogen level and its addition to the platelet.
Method. We used a control group of 15 diabetic patients with ages ranged from 27 to 76 years old. They were followed up for 1 year period. The experimental group was of 14 diabetic patients with ages ragend from 34 to 69 years old. All of them had a variable grade in the split of the perifoveal arcus showed by AFG. We applied on them the same follow up protocol as we did on the control group, but they were treated with 500 mg. of Chlorhidrate of Ticlopidine per day. When we finished the study we carried out a statistical study that compared the initial and final AV on each eye of each patient in both groups. It was compared the previous and post treatment Fibrinogen levels.
Results.The AV previous and post treatment of the patients treated with Ticlopidine for 1 year period got better in a statistically significant way when they were analyzed compared as pair cases. In the diabetics type I the statistical significance of the diference between the AV is p<0,05. In those of type II is p<0,01. The rate of plasmatic Fibrinogen decreses from 10 to 19% on those patients treated, and the decrease is bigger on the diabetics type II. In the control group the AV is stable or tends to a slight decrease after a year of evolution.
Conclusions. The treatment with an anti-aggregate to the platelet that acts on Fibrinogen levels can have influence on the AV of the patients with several grades of ischaemia in the macular area, this visual improvement could have some relations with the Plasmatic Fibrinogen Rate.

Author Index

All authors of abstracts are listed alphabetically by last name.

Three-digit numbers refer to posters, reproduced on pages 13 to 101

Four-digit numbers refer to oral presentations printed on pages 103 to 181

An asterisk(*) preceding the number indicates an abstract
for which the author is the first author.

AUTHOR INDEX